INTRODUCTION
TO MATHCAD
FOR SCIENTISTS
AND ENGINEERS

Also Available from McGraw-Hill

Schaum's Outline Series in Computers

Most outlines include basic theory, definitions, and hundreds of solved problems
and supplementary problems with answers.

Titles on the Current List Include:

Advanced Structured Cobol

Boolean Algebra

Computer Graphics

Computer Science

Computers and Business

Computers and Programming

Data Processing

Data Structures

Digital Principles, 2d edition

Discrete Mathematics

Essential Computer Mathematics

Linear Algebra, 2d edition

Mathematical Handbook of Formulas & Tables

Matrix Operations

Microprocessor Fundamentals, 2d edition

Programming with Advanced Structured Cobol

Programming with Assembly Language

Programming with Basic, 3d edition

Programming with C

Programming with Fortran

Programming with Pascal

Programming with Structured Cobol

Schaum's Solved Problems Books

Each title in this series is a complete and expert source of solved problems containing
thousands of problems with worked out solutions.

Related Titles on the Current List Include:

3000 Solved Problems in Calculus

2500 Solved Problems in Differential Equations

2000 Solved Problems in Discrete Mathematics

3000 Solved Problems in Linear Algebra

2000 Solved Problems in Numerical Analysis

Available at your College Bookstore. A complete list of Schaum titles
may be obtained by writing to: Schaum Division

McGraw-Hill, Inc.

Princeton Road, S-1

Hightstown, NJ 08520

INTRODUCTION TO MATHCAD FOR SCIENTISTS AND ENGINEERS

Sol Wieder

Fairleigh Dickinson University

McGraw-Hill, Inc.

New York   St. Louis   San Francisco   Auckland   Bogotá
Caracas   Lisbon   London   Madrid   Mexico   Milan   Montreal
New Delhi   Paris   San Juan   Singapore   Sydney   Tokyo   Toronto

This book was set in Times Roman by Electronic Technical Publishing Services.
The editors were Eric M. Munson and John M. Morriss.
The cover was designed by Carol Couch.
Project supervision was done by Electronic Technical Publishing Services.
R. R. Donnelley & Sons Company was printer and binder.

INTRODUCTION TO MATHCAD FOR SCIENTISTS AND ENGINEERS

3 4 5 6 7 8 9 0   DOC DOC   9 0 9 8 7 6 5 4 3

P/N 070108-3

Library of Congress Cataloging-in-Publication Data

Wieder, Sol.
    Introduction to MathCAD for scientists and engineers / Wieder,
Sol.
      p.   cm.
    Includes index.
    ISBN 0-07-911306-0. — ISBN 0-07-832513-7. — ISBN 0-07-832516-1
    1. MathCAD.   2. Mathematics—Data processing.   I. Title.
  QA76.95.W54   1992
  510'.285'5369—dc20   91-41214

ABOUT THE AUTHOR

Sol Wieder received his Ph.D. in physics from New York University and taught there before joining the faculty of Fairleigh Dickinson University in 1967. He has also taught at the City College of New York and served as a Member of the Technical Staff at Bell Telephone Laboratories. He has authored two other texts, *The Foundations of Quantum Theory* and *An Introduction to Solar Energy for Scientists and Engineers*. Professor Wieder has worked as a researcher in solid state physics, atomic physics, atmospheric science, and energy systems and serves as a consultant to business and industry on the topic of computers. His current academic interests include the application of microcomputers to teaching mathematics and science. He is a member of the Association for the Advancement of Computers in Education (AACE).

May the Lord make thee as Ephraim and as Manasseh.

To my sons:
Stephen Ari
Alan Jonah
Kenneth Jeremy

CONTENTS

Preface   xiii

Notation and the Data Diskette   xv

1   Fundamentals of MathCAD   1

1.   Getting started, a first worksheet, saving the worksheet, printing
     and loading worksheets into the workspace.   1
2.   MathCAD operations, constants and functions, graphs.   6
3.   Tables, numerical formats, MathCAD functions and symbols.   11
4.   Derivatives and integrals.   15
5.   Text entry.   16

2   Basic Operations I   20

1.   Solving equations, root function, solve block.   20
2.   MathCAD vectors, subscripted variables, vectorization of formulas.   24
3.   Units and dimensional analysis.   32

3   Basic Operations II   38

1.   MathCAD's elementary built-in functions—trigonometric, logarithmic,
     exponential, and hyperbolic.   38
2.   Special functions—floor, ceil, if, mod, rnd, Heaviside function.   39
3.   Evaluating derivatives and integrals.   44
4.   Sequences, series, sums, products, factorials.   53
5.   Vectors   57

4   Applications to General Calculus   63

1.   Graphing elementary functions, first and second derivatives, maxima
     and minima, points of inflection, regions of rise and fall, concavity.   63
2.   Applications of derivatives to related-rate and maxima-minima
     problems.   66
3.   Antiderivatives, applications of integrals to area problems.   69

ix

4. Sequences and series, recursion, convergence of geometric series.   72

5. Conic sections, parametric equations, polar coordinates. Polar plots, area calculations, arc length integrals.   77

6. Solve blocks and inverse functions.   82

7. Multiple integrals. Calculation of areas and volumes.   84

8. Multivariable calculus. Functions of more than one variable. Partial derivatives, the gradient, Green's theorem.   89

5   Applications to General Physics   98

1. Units, dimensions, vectors, and scalars.   98

2. Newton's laws, projectile motion, collisions.   106

3. Vibrations, waves, beats, interference.   110

4. Calorimetry, heat transfer.   117

5. Electric fields, Coulomb's law, Gauss' law.   123

6. DC circuits.   127

7. AC circuits.   128

8. Nuclear decay.   133

6   Differential Equations and Special Functions   140

1. First-order differential equations, numerical methods, the Euler-Heun method.   140

2. Second-order differential equations, numerical methods, the Runge-Kutta-Nyström method.   143

3. Linear differential equations, equations with constant coefficients, homogeneous equation, damped motion.   147

4. Nonhomogeneous equation, forced motion, Laplace transforms, response to an impulse.   150

5. Fourier representation of periodic functions, steady state analysis.   157

6. The vibrating string and the boundary value problem.   162

7. Bessel's function, Gaussian error function, gamma function, cumulative normalization function.   164

7   Matrices and Complex Variables   171

1. Matrix structure, algebra of matrices, inverse, transpose, determinant, trace.   171

2. Solutions of linear systems and circuits.   180

3. Eigenvalues and eigenvectors, coupled modes of vibration.   182

4. Complex variables, analytic functions, contour mapping.   191

5. Contour integrals. Cauchy's integral formula, and residues.   197

8   Special Topics in Engineering   204

1. Mean value, standard deviation, and variance of a data set.   204

2. Statistics and histograms.   209

3. Curve fitting, linear regression, linear interpolation, cubic splines.   210

4. Fast Fourier transforms, discrete sampling, waveform filters.   215

5. Convolutions, subscript operations.   223

6. Boolean logic, gate circuits.   226

9 Advanced Topics in MathCAD   233

1. Enhancements of Version 2.5: Data sorts, surface plots and sketches.   233
2. Reading (importing) and writing (exporting) data files with MathCAD.   241
3. Split windows, cursor control and scrolling.   247
4. Text editing and printing finished reports. Appending worksheets.   250
5. Special configurations and commands.   252
6. DOS shell, command lines and abbreviated commands.   252

Appendix A Summary of Commands and Functions   255

Appendix B Error Messages   275

Appendix C Installation Procedures   283

Index   287

PREFACE

Many academic institutions are turning to computer-assisted instruction. This is especially true in science and engineering where courses are being introduced to teach students how to use computers as tools of the trade. MathCAD's potential as a computational tool has already been recognized by a number of institutions.

MathCAD is an extremely valuable problem-solving tool for students of mathematics, science, and engineering. While the learning curve is somewhat steep, the effort of learning MathCAD is well worth it. MathCAD turns a computer display into a note pad or scratch sheet. It utilizes screen and printer graphics to express formulas and equations using the conventional symbolism and notation of mathematics. Developing MathCAD worksheets requires an approach not unlike structured programming. A worksheet is composed of individual building blocks, which we call "objects." Each object contains equations or operations and each follows logically from the ones preceding it. Calculated results can be displayed in tabular or graphical form.

One of MathCAD's strongest features is that it allows the user to answer the "what if" question. If a worksheet is properly designed, the user can change appropriate parameters and see the results change on the display—in many cases almost immediately. Students not only learn decision making in a mathematical setting, but they also learn to translate their thoughts into well-structured reports.

This text is designed to teach how to apply MathCAD to problems in science and engineering. While the book reviews the fundamentals of MathCAD in the first three chapters, its main focus is in the remaining chapters where a variety of applications to mathematics, science, and engineering is presented. The book is not intended as a basic text on the various subjects of mathematical science and engineering, but rather as supplementary material. It is assumed that the student is using a standard text as a primary learning tool on the subject matter.

The order of the material suggests that the student of science and engineering could start with the book while he or she begins his or her studies with general calculus and physics and continue with it through the more advanced courses of the undergraduate curriculum, such as differential equations, linear algebra, complex variables, and engineering analysis. The material covers the topics in essentially the same order as standard texts. The worksheets are designed not only to illustrate applications of MathCAD but also to demonstrate the power of the "what-if" approach in the learning process. The worksheets are provided on diskette for the student's convenience as are the solutions to the problems given at the end of each chapter.

I wish to express my special gratitude to Prof. Howard Silver of the Department of Electrical Engineering of Fairleigh Dickinson University not only for proofreading the material, but also for making a number of significant suggestions and contributions, especially to the subject matter of Chapter 8. The following reviewers also provided many helpful comments and suggestions: Carol Freeman, Nebraska Wesleyan University; Leendert Kersten, University of Nebraska–Lincoln; Steve Margolis, SUNY—Buffalo; and John Sheffield, University of Missouri–Rolla. Thanks also to my three sons Ari, Jonah, and Jeremy to whom this book is dedicated. Finally, I wish to thank my wife Suzanne who painstakingly proofread the manuscript. She has been my true partner in life and a source of inspiration for this work.

Sol Wieder

NOTATION AND THE DATA DISKETTE

NOTATION

Special compound keystrokes are enclosed in curly brackets { }. The brackets themselves are not MATHCAD keystrokes and are *not* to be typed. The control and alternate keys are designated as **<Ctrl>** and **<Alt>**. Examples are:

Notation	Keystroke
{Enter}	Type the enter key.
{Esc}	Type the escape key.
{Tab}	Type the tab key.
{F10}	Type the F10 function key.
{<Ctrl>R}	Depress the control key and type the R key.
{<Alt>P}	Depress the alternate key and type the P key.

MathCAD keystroke sequences are shaded to distinguish them from ordinary text and punctuation. Examples are:

(a) "To assign the range variable n, type: **n:1,3;11**, followed by **{Enter}**."

(b) "To display the matrices A, B, and C, type: **A=**, **{Enter}**, **B=**, **{Enter}**, and **C=**, **{Enter}**."

THE DATA DISKETTE

The enclosed diskette contains all the worksheets and problems presented in the text. The worksheet files are labeled WKSn_m.MCD where n refers to the chapter and m to the number. For example, WKS4.3.MCD and WKS5_B.MCD refer to Worksheets 4.3 and 5.11 respectively. There are no worksheet files for Chapters 1–3. The solutions to the problems at the end of each chapter are in disk files labeled PROBn_m.MCD. Thus PROB6_1.MCD refers to Problem 1 at the end of Chapter 6.

You should make a backup copy of the worksheets and problems. You will then be free to experiment with the files. If you load a worksheet, modify it, and then save it under a new name, the original disk file will not be altered.

If the version of the book you have purchased includes MathCAD Version 2.5, Student Edition, the data files are combined with the MathCAD programs. In the 5-1/4″ format, two diskettes are provided; in the 3-1/2″ format, only one disk is required. The procedure for setting up your hard disk and installing the files is explained in Appendix C.

INTRODUCTION TO MATHCAD FOR SCIENTISTS AND ENGINEERS

1

FUNDAMENTALS OF MATHCAD

WHAT IS MATHCAD?

MathCAD (developed by MathSoft, Inc.) is an electronic scratchpad that allows mathematical calculations to be performed on a computer screen in a format similar to the way it would be done manually with paper and pencil. While MATHCAD employs the usual mathematical symbols $(+, -, \cdot, /, =)$ for algebraic operations, it also uses the conventional symbols of calculus for differentiation and integration

$$\frac{d}{dx}y(x) \qquad \text{and} \qquad \int_0^2 y(x)\,dx$$

to perform these operations. It preserves the conventional symbolic form for subscripting, special mathematical functions, series operations, and matrix algebra. We shall see that, when expository text is added, MathCAD's symbolic format leads to reports that are easily understood by others. Data can be presented in both tabular and graphical forms.

MathCAD can also be used to answer the "what-if" question in science and engineering problems the way spreadsheet software answers that question in business and financial applications. With a well-designed worksheet (also called a document), parameters can be changed and the results viewed almost immediately on the computer display.

MathCAD works mainly in the computer's memory (RAM) and only on occasion will it access the disk drives.[1] In fact while a hard disk is very convenient and highly

---

[1] MathCAD version 2.5 uses overlays and will access the disk more frequently than previous versions.

1

recommended, it is not absolutely essential for operation. A far more important factor is the computational power of the computer's microprocessor. For an IBM PC compatible system, a system with an 80286 microprocessor or better is recommended. A math coprocessor is also highly recommended. Waiting for lengthy calculations to be performed can be irritating.

MathCAD requires either a monochrome graphics (Hercules compatible) or a color (CGA, EGA, or VGA) display adaptor. It supports a number of graphics printers and plotters.

Two editions of MathCAD exist for the IBM PC compatible family. There is the professional edition whose latest DOS version at this writing is 2.5. There is also a more-affordable student edition. In the student version, a worksheet is limited to two pages, each eighty characters per line. Also the size of certain mathematical structures (e.g., matrices) is limited.

GETTING STARTED

Installing and invoking MathCAD is a simple task. We will assume that the user has a hard disk (drive C:). A subdirectory `C:\MCAD` should be created and all the MathCAD *programs* (i.e., those with extensions *other* than `.MCD` and `.PRN`) be copied to that subdirectory. Next, it is suggested that a subdirectory `C:\MCAD\MCFILES` be created. MathCAD worksheets stored as disk files have the extension `.MCD`. All such files as well as those with the extension `.PRN` should be copied into the `C:\MCAD\MCFILES` subdirectory. To invoke MathCAD, we create the following batch file which we name `MC.BAT`:

```
REM MC.BAT
CLS
C:
CD C:\MCAD\MCFILES
C:\MCAD\MCAD
CD C:\
```

This batch file may be placed in any directory referenced in the DOS `PATH` command. `PATH` is a command that should reside in the `AUTOEXEC.BAT` file. For example, if you already have a subdirectory `C:\DOS`, then place `MC.BAT` in that subdirectory and make sure that the path `C:\DOS` is included in the `PATH` statement in your `AUTOEXEC.BAT` file. (Consult your DOS manual for details.)

You should also add the following command to your `AUTOEXEC.BAT` file:

```
SET MCADDIR = C:\MCAD
```

To start MathCAD simply type `MC`. The batch file `MC.BAT` will first log you into the worksheet subdirectory and then invoke the MathCAD program `MCAD.EXE`. You are now ready to use MathCAD.

The Blank Worksheet

When MathCAD is first invoked you will see the MathSoft logo and some copyright information which disappear as soon as you touch any key. Press the backspace key. What remains is a blank screen except for a header or *message* line at the top which looks something like:

```
┌─────────────────────────────────────────────────────────────┐
│ no file                                    .   0   0    auto  │
└─────────────────────────────────────────────────────────────┘
```

The word `no file` means that no file has been loaded and that the current worksheet has not yet been named. You will see a flashing cursor (underscore) in the upper left corner. You are now ready to create a worksheet. The numbers toward the right of the message line indicate the current row and position of the cursor. Actually the uppermost left position for entry in the worksheet is always at row 0 and column 1. The word `auto` indicates that MathCAD is in the automatic recalculation mode. (We will explain the recalculation modes later.)

It is suggested, that for the next few examples, you convert to the "draw box" mode. Do so by holding the control key down and typing a **V** (denoted by ^V or **{<Ctrl>V}**). When you become proficient, you will likely choose to work without boxes to give the worksheet a cleaner appearance.

A First Worksheet

We begin with an elementary case in which we will add two numbers and display the result. With the cursor in the upper left (coordinates 0,1), type an upper case **A** and then a colon, i.e., **A:**. You should see the following: A := ■. Note that MathCAD places an equal sign after the colon and sets a block called a *placeholder*. The := is an *assignment* statement. Note that cursor is flashing on the placeholder and that it has taken the shape of a hook-to-the-left form (⌐). This "reverse-L" cursor is the *append* cursor. MathCAD is waiting for you to fill the marker. Do so by typing the number 4. Now with the right arrow key move the cursor to column 12. After it has moved, a box appears around the equation (a result of the **{<Ctrl>V}** invoked above) and the cursor changes back to the underscore. The worksheet should show,

```
┌─────────┐
│ A := 4  │
└─────────┘
```

Note: If you make a mistake use the **{Del}** key or **{BkSpc}** to erase the entry or type **{F3}** to erase the entire equation. With the cursor in column 13, type **B:3**. Move the cursor to column 24. You should see,

```
┌─────────┐        ┌─────────┐
│ A := 4  │        │ B := 3  │
└─────────┘        └─────────┘
```

Type **C:A+B** and move to column 40 and the display should show:

```
┌─────────┐        ┌─────────┐        ┌───────────────┐
│ A := 4  │        │ B := 3  │        │ C := A + B    │
└─────────┘        └─────────┘        └───────────────┘
```

With the cursor in column 40, type **C=**. Move the cursor to column 53 and type **{<Ctrl>R}** (Screen Redraw). You should see:

$$A := 4 \qquad B := 3 \qquad C := A + B \qquad C = 7$$

We have our first worksheet. We have added 4 and 3 and demonstrated that the result is 7. We have done so by assigning 4 to a variable A, 3 to a variable B, $A + B$ to a variable C, and finally displaying the contents of the variable C. To see the "what if" capability of MathCAD, move the cursor directly over the 4 in the A assignment box. Press the backspace once; the 4 disappears and the placeholder reappears. Type **8** and use the right or down arrow key (or the **{Enter}** key) to leave the box. Note that the moment we leave the box, the new assignment to A is made and the value of C changes to 11.

Names of variables (such as A, B, and C) must begin with letters but can contain numbers. MathCAD is *case sensitive*, that is, "Horse" is treated as a different variable name from "HORSE". It is often convenient to use a *literal* or *notational* subscript to clarify a variable. To add such a subscript, follow the variable name with a period and continue with the subscript. Thus if we type **HORSE.Big:1** we see:

$$HORSE_{Big} := 1$$

Literal subscripts, as opposed to mathematical subscripts, introduced in Chapter 2, are words and are used for descriptive purposes only. As we shall later see, mathematical subscripts are integers which are used in calculations with arrays, vectors, and series sums. Blank spaces cannot be entered into variable names. To use a multi-word variable name, use the *underscore* as a separator as in:

$$Horse\_Big := 1$$

While the addition example presented here is a trivial one, it nevertheless illustrates some fundamental features of MathCAD. First note that the *colon* (which displays as $:=$) is used for assignment whereas the *equal* sign is used to display the contents of a variable or the results of a calculation. Second, observe that MathCAD is composed of units which we will call *objects*. Each object resides in its own boxed region. Objects must be entered into a worksheet in a logical sequence. The object sequence is from left to right and downward in a manner similar to that of a written report. An object must follow (i.e., be to the right of or below) those objects upon which it depends for its definition. In addition to mathematical objects, such as those presented in our addition example, we can also create text objects. Text may be placed in any blank region in the worksheet. We discuss text objects later in this chapter.

Having seen how box outlines look, we can now erase these object boundaries by typing **{<Ctrl>V}**. The command **{<Ctrl>V}** can be used at any time to toggle the boxes on and off. Even without the boxes, you can tell if you are inside or outside of an object region by the shape of the cursor. A hooked cursor means that you are inside, whereas an underscore means that you are outside. In text regions, however, the cursor is always an underscore. In the remainder of the book, we will work in the "no-box" mode. Note that sometimes, as a result of editing or turning boxes on and off, the screen appears to either retain residual "junk" or acquire partially erased (incomplete) regions. To restore a proper screen, type **{<Ctrl>R}** (redraw) at any time.

Before continuing, restore the value of A=4 in the worksheet. If you have erased the boxes, you should see:

```
A := 4          B := 3        C := A + B        C = 7
```

Saving the Worksheet

To save the worksheet as a MathCAD file (document), type the **{F10}** (menu) key and bring up the main menu on the message line. Type **F** (file) and get the File pull-down menu. Type **S** (save) to save the file. (Note: You can accomplish the same thing by typing the **{F6}** (Save) key.) Supply a valid DOS filename containing up to eight characters (without an extension) and type the **{Enter}** (or Carriage Return) key. The worksheet will be saved on the disk in the current subdirectory C:\MCAD\MCFILES. MathCAD adds the extension .MCD to your file name. Since this worksheet is so elementary, we do not recommend saving it on disk.

Clearing the Worksheet

If you wish to clear the workspace and start a new worksheet, type **{F10}** (menu). You will see the main menu on the message line. Type **F** (file), **C** (clear). If the current worksheet has been altered but not saved, the prompt Changes not saved. OK to discard ? will appear. If you respond with a **y {Enter}**, the workspace will be cleared. (Do *not* clear the above worksheet yet. Answer with **n {Enter}** or type **{Esc}**.)

Printing the Worksheet

MathCAD supports a number of graphics printers and plotters. To select a particular printer, type **{F10}** (menu), **S** (system), **S** (select Printer) and select the printer of your choice. To store this choice permanently in MathCAD, type **{F10}** (menu), **S** (system), **C** (config Save), **{Enter}**. To print the worksheet, type **{F10}** (menu), then type **S** (system), **P** (print), **{Enter}**, **{Enter}**. You may also type **{<Ctrl>O}**, **{Enter}**, **{Enter}**. The entire worksheet will be sent to the printer. We shall see in Chapter 9 how to print only a portion of the worksheet.

Loading a New File into the Workspace

To load a MathCAD file into the workspace, type the **{F10}** (menu) key and bring up the main menu on the message line. Type **F** (file) and get the File pull-down menu.

Type **L** (load) to load the file. (Note: You can load a file by typing the **{F5}** (Load) key.) Supply a valid DOS filename containing up to eight characters (without an extension) and type the **{Enter}** key. The worksheet will be loaded into the workspace. If the file does not exist, the message `File not found` appears on the message line. If you do not supply a name and just type **{Enter}**, MathCAD will display a listing of the files in the current directory, in our case, the `C:\MCAD\MCFILES` subdirectory. Move the color bar to the desired file and type **{Enter}**.

Errors in the Worksheet

Let us return to the above worksheet and erase the first object. To do this easily, move the cursor into the first object region, i.e., into the one assigning the value of *A*. (Note the change in the shape of the cursor.) Press the **{F3}** (cut) key. This erases the box and stores it in a temporary buffer or *clipboard*. You should see the following:

```
B := 3        C := A + B        C = ■ ■
                   |                 |
              ┌───────────┐     ┌───────────┐
              │ undefined │     │ undefined │
              └───────────┘     └───────────┘
```

MathCAD is telling us that since the variable *A* has not been assigned a value, any object which uses it cannot be executed. Even if we make the assignment afterward, any object using the variable *A* beforehand would be undefined. To verify this, move the cursor down to row 5, column 2 and type the **{F4}** (paste) key. This takes the object that was stored in the temporary clipboard by the **{F3}** (cut) key and locates it at the current cursor position. The worksheet appears as,

```
B := 3        C := A + B        C = ■ ■
A := 4             |                 |
              ┌───────────┐     ┌───────────┐
              │ undefined │     │ undefined │
              └───────────┘     └───────────┘
```

To eliminate the error, type the **{F3}** (cut) key to cut the *A* assignment object, move back to the coordinates (0,1), and type **{F4}** (paste). The *A* assignment object returns to its original position and the error indicators disappear. A list of error messages and their meanings is given in Appendix B.

Constants and Functions

To examine the other algebraic operations, move to position (6,1); type **Difference:A-B**; move to (6,20) and type **Product:A∗B**; move to (6,50) and type **Quotient:A/B**. Next move to (10,1) and type **Difference=**; move to (10,25) and type **Product=**; move to (10,50) type **Quotient=**; move to (15,1) type **Power:A^ 2**; move to (16,10) and type **Power=**; move to (19,1) type **SqRoot:\A**; move to (19,10) type **SqRoot=**. Finally, move the cursor to any blank area. The worksheet will appear as:

```
    A := 4            B := 3          C := A + B         C = 7

    Difference := A - B      Product := A·B      Quotient := A
                                                            ─
                                                            B

    Difference = 1              Product = 12         Quotient = 1.333

    Power := A²              Power = 16

    SqRoot := √A            SqRoot = 2
```

Note that the square root operation is generated by the backslash (\) key. Assignment objects use colons to make assignments to variables and functions. Display objects use equal signs to display the contents of a quantity.

We may use assignment objects to store constants shown earlier or to assign *user-defined* functions. A user-defined function may be assigned for example using the object **y(x):x^ 2+3*x-2** which displays as:

$$y(x) := x^2 + 3 \cdot x - 2$$

In general, to define a function f of variables (x, y, z), we use the form $f(x, y, z)$. For example, we may make the assignment:

$$f(x, y, z) := x^2 + y^2 + z^2.$$

MathCAD evaluates a function at the time of display (e.g., as a graph or a table) and *not* at the time of definition. Therefore the arguments (independent variables) of a function need not be assigned prior to defining the function itself. However, the values of the arguments must be assigned before the function can be evaluated and displayed.

MathCAD has built-in functions for the sine, cosine, tangent, and the logarithm. We will examine these functions here and in the next chapter. As we introduce other subject matter, we will encounter more of MathCAD's built-in functions.

DISPLAYING DATA WITH MATHCAD

Graphing Functions

Let us graph the sine function and study its behavior. If you wish to save the above worksheet, do it now; otherwise clear the workspace by typing the **{F10}** (menu) key, and then typing: **F** (file), **C** (clear), **Y** (yes). You should have a clear workspace.

At (0,1) type **A:1**; move to (0,20) type **w:1**; move to (0,40) type **p:0**; move to (4,0) type **y(x):A*sin(w*x+p)**; move to (4,30) and type **x:0,.5;7**. You should see:

```
    A := 1                        w := 1                p := 0
    y(x) := A·sin(w·x + p)        x := 0, .5 ..7
```

The first three objects define the amplitude A, angular frequency w, and phase p of the waveform. The fourth object defines the sine function as the waveform, using y as the function name. Its independent variable is x. The parameters A, w, and p are constants and must be defined *before* the function is assigned.

The fifth object defines x as a *range* variable. When MathCAD evaluates the function $y(x)$ in tabular or graphical form, it does so at the points defined by the range variable x. In this case, x is defined at the points $0, .5, 1, 1.5, \ldots, 7$ (a total of $14 + 1 = 15$ points), The first number on the right-hand side of the range assignment represents the beginning of the range, the second determines the increment, and the last fixes the end of the range. The increment is determined by the difference between the first two numbers in the range definition (in this case $\{0.5 - 0\}$). (Note that in defining a range variable, the semicolon character ; generates the double dot "$..$" in the range definition.) Thus a range variable must be defined to tell MathCAD which values to plot or tabulate.

We now display $y(x)$ as a graph. Move the cursor to (8,23) and type **@**. The screen should look like Fig. 1.1.

Place the cursor over the middle placeholder on the horizontal axis and type **x**. Move to the middle marker on the vertical axis and type **y(x)**. (To move the cursor, use either the arrow keys or the **{Tab}** key.) Move out of this object by typing the **{Enter}** key. Your screen should look like Fig. 1.2.

Note that to graph a function we type the **@** key. This key generates a plot *template* with six placeholders, three on each axis. The central ones on each axis tell MathCAD what is to be plotted. The outer two indicate the range limits or the scale to be plotted. If the range markers are left blank, MathCAD automatically sets the scale. Note the little hooks under the scale numbers. These indicate that MathCAD has automatically set the scale. (These hooks appear only on the screen and not in the printed report.) To override an auto-scale value, move to the appropriate scale marker with the arrow keys or the **{Tab}** key. Erase the auto-scale value with the backspace key, and enter the desired manual scale value. Move the cursor out of the object region and the graph will be redrawn with the manually set scale. Values set manually do not have hooks under them. To return to an auto-scale value, erase the manually-set value. You will see an empty placeholder. Leave the object (type

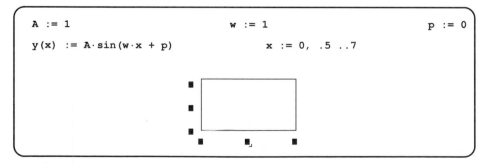

FIGURE 1.1

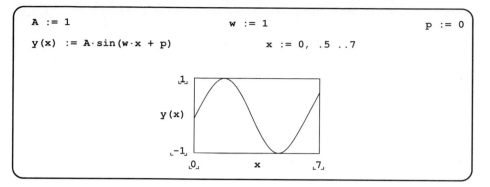

FIGURE 1.2

{Enter}) and the auto-scale is restored. From Fig. 1.2, we see that MathCAD assumes the argument of trigonometric functions to be in radians.

Finally, let us examine a "what-if" situation. Move the cursor to the first object which assigns the value of A (amplitude). Place the cursor over the 1. Delete it using the backspace or delete key and fill the placeholder by typing 2. Leave the object region by typing **{Enter}**. Notice how the graph immediately changes to reflect the new amplitude. Now move to the second object defining the frequency. Place the cursor over the 1 and replace it with 2 and type **{Enter}**. Note the new frequency. Finally, change the value of p (phase) to 1.57 and leave the region. Note how the waveform shifts. You may have noticed that the curve now looks more jagged than before. This is because the higher frequency results in a more rapid variation. The curve is generated from the range variable x whose values are defined over only 15 points. Let us move to the object which defines the x range and change the .5 to .1. Place the cursor over the 5, type the **{BkSpc}** or **{Del}** key once (removing the 5) and then type 1. Press **{Enter}** and observe the change. Note that the graph is plotted using 71 points and is now much smoother. However the trade-off is that it takes much longer to plot the graph. While MathCAD is recalculating the worksheet, it flashes a period (.) after the word WAIT on the right-hand side of the message line. When it is finished, the word auto reappears.

Auto vs. Manual Recalculate Mode

Some worksheets involve many calculations and take MathCAD a long time to compute. Every time we edit the worksheet, MathCAD displays WAIT. on the right-hand side of the message line. (To interrupt a lengthy computation, type **{<ctrl>Break}**. Respond to the Interrupt calculation? prompt by typing **{y}, {Enter}**.) To avoid unnecessary waiting, we can put MathCAD in its *manual* recalculate mode. Type **{F10}** (menu), then type **C** (compute), **M** (manual). You should see the word auto disappear in the right of the message line. You are now in the manual recalculate mode. When you edit an object, MathCAD does not immediately alter the rest of the worksheet. Instead the word calc F9 appears in the upper right of the message line. Press the **{F9}** (recalculate) key and all the objects from the beginning of the worksheet to the last one visible on the screen will be updated. In the manual mode, we make all the necessary changes first and then type **{F9}** (recalculate) to update the worksheet. To return to the auto mode, type **{F10}** (menu), **C** (compute), **A** (automatic). Even while in the auto recalculate mode, we may use the **{F9}** (recalculate) key to recalculate the worksheet without leaving the object being edited. Thus in the example above, when we change the value of the amplitude, we may remain inside the object and type **{F9}** (recalculate). The worksheet will be recalculated without leaving the object.

Formatting the Graph

Before proceeding, we reset the parameters of the sine curve to their original values, i.e., $A = 2$, $w = 1$ and $p = 0$. To change the appearance of the graph, place the cursor anywhere within the graph area and type the **f** key. In version 2.0 of MathCad, the message line will be overlaid with a graph format menu line as follows:

```
no file    logs=0,0 subdivs=1,1 size=5,15 type=1      9    10 auto
```

Move the cursor along the line to change the parameter values. Typing **{Enter}** puts the changes into effect. The **{Esc}** key cancels the changes.

In version 2.5 the local-plot-format pull-down menu has the following form:

```
Size=5,15
Trace Types = 1
Log Cycles = 0,0
Subdivisions = 1,1
Global Default
Revert
Done
```

Move the color bar to the desired option. Make the required changes and type **{Enter}**. Global default has the same effect as typing **d** in the plot area. Revert will undo all changes made. To leave the menu without making any changes type **{Esc}**. To leave the menu and put the changes into effect, move the cursor to Done and type **{Enter}**.

You may change from a linear to a logarithmic scale using logs (Log Cycles) and change the subdivisions on each axis using subdivs (Subdivisions). You may also change the size of the graph using size (Size), or change the marker scheme using type (Trace Types). For example, if we change the parameters of subdivs from (1,1) to (4,7) and those of *size* from (5,15) to (15,45), our graph would appear as shown in Fig. 1.3.

The *subdivs n,m* format option allows the user to subdivide the y-axis and x-axis into n and m subdivisions respectively. The *size n,m* format option allows the user to adjust the respective sizes of the y-axis and x-axis. The default *type* is a line graph (1). You may use instead the following (unconnected) markers: dots (d), exes (x),

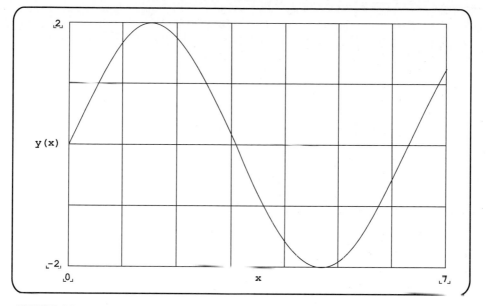

FIGURE 1.3

pluses (p), rectangles (o), or diamonds (v). Using upper case values (i.e., X, P, O, or V) will cause the markers to be connected with lines. Later in the book we will use the other marker schemes—bar chart (b), error bar (e), and step (s)—when we plot statistical information and histograms. You can return to the global plot format by placing the cursor anywhere in the graph area and typing the key **d**.

Note on color displays: You can often improve a poor contrast situation on a color display by changing the foreground/background color combination. This is accomplished by typing {**<Ctrl>D**}. Each time you press {**<Ctrl>D**}, the foreground/background is changed until you return to the original combination.

It is possible to plot more than one function on a graph. Consider the worksheet shown in Fig. 1.4.

Note: You may also plot two functions *f* and *g*, each of which is a function of a *different* variable *x* and *t*, by entering **x,t** on the horizontal-axis placeholder and **f(x),g(t)** on the vertical-axis placeholder. The range assignments for both *x* and *t* must be made *before* the plot is performed.

Displaying Results in a Table

Place the cursor below the graph in the above worksheet and type the range **x:0;7**. Below that type **x=**. Move to the right and type **y(x)=**. You should see Fig. 1.5 (as a continuation of the worksheet shown in Fig. 1.4).

Note that we have redefined the range variable *x* to contain $7 + 1 = 8$ points. This assignment overrides the previous range assignment. Recall that the equal sign

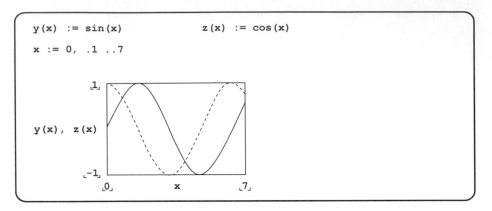

FIGURE 1.4

(=) displays the contents of functions and variables. Thus x and $y(x)$ are displayed in tabular form for the points of definition.

Formatting Numeric Data

If you wish to change the *local* format of displayed data, whether it is a single number or a table, place the cursor directly on any element of data and type the **f** key. In version 2.0 of MathCAD, the message line will be overlaid with a local-display-result menu line as follows:

```
no file    Local format   rd=d ct=10 et=3 pr=3          9    10 auto
```

Move the cursor along the line to change the parameter values. Typing **{Enter}** puts the changes into effect. The **{Esc}** key cancels the changes.

x := 0 ..7

x	y(x)
0	0
1	0.841
2	0.909
3	0.141
4	-0.757
5	-0.959
6	-0.279
7	0.657

FIGURE 1.5

In version 2.5 the local-result-format pull-down menu has the following form:

```
Radix = d
Precision Displayed = 3
Exponential Threshold = 3
Complex Tolerance = 10
Global Default
Revert
Done
```

Move the color bar to the desired option. Make the required changes and type **{Enter}**. Global default has the same effect as typing **d** in the plot area. Revert will undo all changes made. To leave the menu without making any changes type **{Esc}**. To leave the menu and put the changes into effect, move the cursor to Done and type **{Enter}**.

You can change the rd (radix) from decimal (d) to either hexadecimal (h) or octal (o). The default is decimal. The format parameter ct (complex tolerance) applies to complex numbers. We will introduce these in the next chapter.

The et (exponential tolerance) determines when numbers will be displayed in exponential (scientific) notation. Conversion occurs if the number is larger than e^{et} or smaller than e^{-et}. The maximum value is fifteen and the default is three. If you want to suppress exponential notation for those numbers larger than 10^3 or smaller than 10^{-3}, increase the value of et. To force the display into exponential notation, set et=0.

Finally, there is the pr (precision) setting. This determines the number of decimal places displayed. The maximum is fifteen and the default is three. If you set et=5 in the local format of a number such as $2.34 \cdot 10^{-4}$, the exponential notation will be suppressed and it will display as 0. Increase the local precision format to pr=6 and the number will appear as 0.000234.

When a local format has been set for displayed data, a small dot appears in the object indicating that fact. You can return to the global format by putting the cursor anywhere on the displayed data and typing **d**.

Global Formatting of Displayed Numbers and Plots

If you wish to change the format globally, (i.e., for the entire worksheet as opposed to for a single object), type **{Esc}**. The word command will appear on the message line. Type the word **FORM** (for format) and a global data format menu will appear. (To get this format menu, you may also type **{F10}** (menu), **C** (compute), **F** (format).) The global format menu line is essentially the same as that of the local format menu with the exception of the appearance of the options zt (zero tolerance) and im (imaginary unit). In version 2.5, the same menu appears as a pull-down menu. All numbers smaller than c^{-zt} will display as zero. The default is fifteen. The im (imaginary unit symbol) applies to complex numbers and will be discussed in the next chapter. Changing the format globally affects the entire worksheet except for the data whose format has been set locally.

Note: In version 2.5 the global-result-format pull-down menu has the following form:

```
Radix = d
Precision Displayed = 3
Exponential Threshold = 3
Imaginary Symbol = i
Zero Tolerance = 3
Complex Tolerance = 10
Overall Default
Revert
Done
```

Global formatting of graphs is accomplished by typing **{Esc}** and then typing the command **PL** (for plot format). In version 2.0 of MathCAD, the message line will be overlaid with a global plot menu line. In version 2.5, the same menu appears as a pull-down menu as follows:

```
Size = 5,15
Trace Types = 1
Log Cycles = 0,0
Subdivisions = 1,1
Overall Default
Revert
Done
```

Special Symbols

MathCAD allows special characters to be used in function and variable names. Greek letters may be entered by holding the Alternate key depressed while typing a regular letter. Below are the characters and how to generate them.

α=<Alt>A β=<Alt>B δ=<Alt>D ϵ=<Alt>E

ϕ=<Alt>F Γ=<Alt>G Φ=<Alt>H ∞=<Alt>I

λ=<Alt>L η=<Alt>N ρ=<Alt>R τ=<Alt>T

π=<Alt>P θ=<Alt>Q σ=<Alt>S Ω=<Alt>O

μ=<Alt>U ω=<Alt>W

The following four keyboard characters are assigned predefined values by Math-CAD and should not be reassigned by the user unless necessary:

π=   3.14159... (pi)   e= 2.71828...   (base of natural log)

∞= 10^{307} (Infinity for MathCAD)   % = 0.01   (Percent)

For example, to calculate the area of a circle of radius $R = 3$, create the following objects in sequence: **R:3**, **V:{<Alt>P}*R^2**, **V=** . Note that the character ^ produces exponentiation. You should see the following:

R := 3

$$V := \pi \cdot R^2 \qquad V = 28.274$$

In displaying the results, the character π is evaluated by the value of pi. (Note that when entering certain characters into an object, MathCAD repositions the entire object as necessary.) Similarly if we use the following objects: **y(x):e^ -x**, **y(1)=**, we would see:

$$y(x) := e^{-x} \qquad y(1) = 0.368$$

(The exponential function, $y(x) = e^x$, is a predefined function and may be entered as **y(x):exp(x)**. This form facilitates the typing of complicated arguments.)

DERIVATIVES AND INTEGRALS IN CALCULUS

Derivatives

We now consider two operations fundamental to calculus—differentiation and integration. Clear the workspace and setup the following worksheet: (1,1) **y(x):sin(x)**, (1,25) **y'(x):?**. You should see,

y(x) := sin(x)

$$y'(x) := \frac{d}{d\blacksquare}\blacksquare$$

Note that the question mark **?** is a special key that produces a derivative template. Note also that the *prime* symbol is generated by typing the *backquote* key ' and *not* the apostrophe key. The latter produces a pair of parentheses ( ). Locate the cursor over the appropriate placeholders and type **x** in the denominator and **y(x)** in the numerator and see,

y(x) := sin(x)

$$y'(x) := \frac{d}{dx}y(x)$$

You may move the cursor between the placeholders in the derivative template with the arrow keys or with the **{Tab}** key.

Next, set up a plot template by typing the **@** key. To obtain the graph shown in Fig. 1.6, fill the horizontal axis central placeholder with **x** and the vertical axis central marker with **y'(x),cos(x)**. Set the format size to (10,30) and the graph type to type=lo. The derivative function will be plotted using the line type and the cosine function using rectangles. Note that the graph confirms that the derivative of a sine is a cosine.

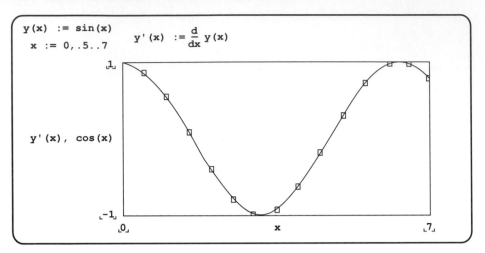

FIGURE 1.6

Integrals

To compute an integral, type **I:&** and see:

$$I := \int_{\blacksquare}^{\blacksquare} \blacksquare d\blacksquare$$

Fill the placeholders and display the result by typing **I=** , as in the following:

$$I := \int_0^\pi \sin(x)\ dx \qquad I = 2$$

Note that the ampersand key **&** generates the template for the integral. From the above worksheet, we have determined that the area under the sine curve between 0 and π is equal to 2.

The integral computed above has fixed limits and is called a *definite* integral. MathCAD also performs integrals with variable limits. We can define a function as:

$$I(x) := \int_0^x \cos(t)\ dt$$

By plotting the function, it can be verified that $I(x)$ is equivalent to the sine.

It is also possible to evaluate multiple derivative templates and multiple integral templates by typing respectively successive **?** and **&** keys. We shall use these templates in examples later in the book.

CONCLUDING REMARKS

Addition with Line Break (Equation Wrap)

Occasionally we will need to construct an object which involves the addition of a large number of terms. Such an object might not fit on one line. If this is a problem, either because you are using the student edition of MathCAD which limits the line width to 80 characters or because you want the printed reports to fit on ordinary $8\frac{1}{2} \times 11$ paper, you may use the *addition with line break* option. After any term of the sum, type **{<Ctrl>Enter}**. The equation will wrap and you will see something like:

```
Sum := a + b + c + d + e ...
       + ■
```

Continue with the equation. You may repeat this operation more than once in the object.

Entering Text in the Worksheet

A worksheet can be presented as a well-documented report by adding expository text in the appropriate places. Text can be entered as a MathCAD object by typing the double quote key ("). You will see a second double quote appear. Just type text as you would with a word processor and when finished use the arrow keys to leave the text region. When you leave the text region the set of double quotes disappears. Do not use the **{Enter}** key to leave a text region; otherwise a carriage return character will be embedded in the text. See Chapter 9 for the specifics of text entry and editing.

Cutting and Pasting with the Function Keys

As we have seen, MathCAD works with a sequence of objects. Some make assignments (:=), others display numeric results (=), while others display graphs (@) and text ("). Entering complicated equations can be confusing. Try to break up definitions into smaller objects. You should use appropriate parentheses (following the conventional rules of mathematics), where necessary, to define equations for Math-CAD. For example, the division of two polynomials requires the following sequence of parentheses: $(x-2)/(x-4)$. Except for text objects, MathCAD will not allow you to enter a blank space within an object; it automatically does so as needed.

Moving *entire* objects within the worksheet can be accomplished with the following three functions keys.

{F2} *Copy key.* Press this key with the cursor inside an object. The object will remain intact but the image will be copied into an invisible clipboard.

{F3} *Cut key.* Press this key with the cursor inside an object. The object will be erased from the worksheet but the image will be copied into the clipboard.

{F4} *Paste key.* Pressing this key with the cursor in any blank region will copy the current contents of the clipboard into the worksheet. (Try to avoid pasting objects into existing objects.)

To move an object intact, place the cursor in the object region and type the **{F3}** (cut). The object will disappear. Move to a new blank area and type **{F4}** (paste). The object reappears. To copy an object (without erasing it) into a blank region, use **{F2}** (copy) followed by **{F4}** (paste).

Moving component parts of objects in the worksheet can be accomplished with the following three "In-region" keys.

{<Ctrl>F2}	*InCopy key.* Press this key with the cursor inside an object region on any component of the object. The component will remain intact but an image will be copied into the clipboard.
{<Ctrl>F3}	*InCut key.* Press this key with the cursor inside an object region on any component of the object. The component will be erased from the object but its image will be copied into the clipboard.
{<Ctrl>F4}	*InPaste key.* Pressing this key with the cursor in any blank region or on any empty placeholder of another object will copy the component stored in the clipboard into the worksheet.

IMPORTANT NOTE. Sometimes when we enter or move an object carelessly, it may overlap and become entangled with another object. The two objects appear to be inseparable and cannot be edited. To effect separation, type the following key sequence: **{F10}** (menu), **E** (edit/move), **S** (separate). The entangled objects will be separated. To see if objects are overlapped, turn on the `draw box` mode **({<Ctrl>V})**.

Editing objects in a complicated equation can be a formidable task. If you delete a character, you may see the whole equation come apart. Don't panic! Simply type the **{F3}** (cut) key, erase the entire object, and reenter the equation from scratch. It is often easier to do this than to try to fix the equation. If, as a result of editing, the screen appears to have miscellaneous material or partially erased regions, type **{<Ctrl>R}** (redraw) to restore the screen.

The default mode of editing an object is "insert at right of cursor" or *append* cursor and is signified by a hook-to-left or a "reverse-L." Characters are inserted to the right of the cursor. To perform `insert at left of cursor`, press the **{<Insert>}** key once. The cursor will become an "L" shaped *insert* cursor and characters will be inserted to the left of the cursor. Pressing the **{<Insert>}** key toggles hook left and hook right. When you leave one object region and enter another, the cursor returns to the default (append) status. The **{F1}** (help) key provides on-line help and can be used any time during a MathCAD session. The **{Esc}** key returns the user from on-line help back to the worksheet.

Inserting and Deleting Blank Lines

A blank line in MathCAD is one that is free of objects. It is sometimes necessary to insert blank lines (to make room for objects) or to remove blank lines (to condense the worksheet). To insert blank lines at the cursor, type **{<Ctrl>F9}**. To remove blank lines at the cursor, type **{<Ctrl>F10}**.

The introductory material given in this chapter is intended to familiarize the reader with the basics of MathCAD. In the chapters that follow, we will learn by doing and we will introduce new concepts and procedures as needed.

PROBLEMS

1. Create a *trig table* with the following properties: The first MathCAD table should contain angles from zero to 360° in steps of 20 degrees. The second three tables to the right of the first should contain the values of the sine, cosine, and tangent respectively . What does MathCAD give for tan(90°)?

Hint: After setting up the range definition for the angle (x) in degrees, define a function rad(x) = $\pi \cdot x/180$ and express the sine function as sin(rad(x)). Express the other trig functions in a similar way.

2. On a single graph, make a plot of the sine, cosine and tangent from zero to $360°$. Since the tangent becomes large as the angle approaches $90°$ and $270°$, the autoscale feature produces too large a scale for the sine and cosine. Manually set the upper limit on the vertical axis to produce a meaningful plot.

3. Verify that the integral of a cosine is a sine by examining the following function:

$$I(x) \quad := \quad \int_0^x \cos(t) \; dt$$

Using the range $x = 0, \pi/10 \; ..2 \cdot \pi$, plot the functions sin(x) and $I(x)$ using lines and rectangles respectively. Display both functions in tabular form.

4. Verify that:

$$\frac{d^2}{dx^2} \sin(x) = -\sin(x)$$

Do so by having MathCAD compute $y''(x)$ and then plot $y''(x)$ and $-\sin(x)$ as in Problem 3.

5. Find the point of intersection for the curves $f(x) = x/2$ and $g(x) = \sin(x)$ on the interval $0 < x \leq \pi$. Hint: Obtain an estimate for x_0 by plotting the two functions on the interval. Construct the difference function: diff(x) = $f(x) - g(x)$. Beginning with this estimate use trial and error to determine the value x_0 that makes diff(x_0) ≈ 0. [Ans. $x_0 \approx 1.895$]

BASIC
OPERATIONS I

SOLVING EQUATIONS

MathCAD uses two methods to solve equations. The first, the *root* function method, can be used to find the zeros of a function, or equivalently, the intersection of the graphs of two functions. The second, the *solve block* method, is used to solve a more complicated set of equations with auxiliary conditions.

Using the Root Function

Suppose we wish to find the roots (zeros) of a cubic equation of the form:

$$a \cdot x^3 + b \cdot x^2 + c \cdot x + d$$

We enter the following objects in sequence:

a:1, b:1, c:1, d:1, y(x):a∗x^3+b∗x^2+c∗x+d, x:−2,−1.95;2

Next we generate a plot template by typing @. We fill the x-axis placeholder with **x** and the y-axis placeholder with **y(x)**. We also manually fill the upper-scale placeholder on the y-axis with a value of **10**. We invoke the local plot menu and set *subdivs=2,2*. (Recall, to invoke this menu, place the cursor in the plot region and type **f**.) This generates grid lines for $x = 0$ and $y = 0$.

We finish by entering the following objects:

x:1 , **x:root(y(x),x)** , **x=**

Figure 2.1 shows the objects in the worksheet. The first four objects assign the coefficients of the cubic equation while y(x) defines the equation itself. The coefficients could have been placed directly in the equation, but this form is more suitable for answering the *what if* question. The function is plotted using an assigned range for x. (Note that the upper scale value on the y-axis has been manually set to 10.) From the graph, we see that one root is in the vicinity of $x = -1$. Nevertheless, we intentionally make a poor guess, namely $x = 1$. The assignment x := 1 represents the *guess* for the root function. (Since the reassignment of x occurs after the plot template, it does not affect the graph.) The arguments of the root function are the function $y(x)$ whose zeros are being sought followed by the independent variable x whose value is being sought. The results of the **root** function are reassigned to the variable name x1 and displayed in the last object. Even with this poor guess, MathCAD was able to find the correct root, namely x1 = 1. In general, a good guess is essential for MathCAD to find the root. A graph of the function is always helpful in making the guess.

Since a cubic equation can have at most three distinct roots, we should see if there are other roots. Looking at the graph, we see that the function does not cross or touch the x-axis at any point other than $x = -1$. This means that if there are two other roots, they must constitute a complex conjugate pair. If we replace the original guess by typing **x:2i**, MathCAD produces the assignment object x := 2i. (There is no multiplication symbol between the 2 and the complex number i.) MathCAD assumes that ni, where n is any real number, represents n times the complex number i. You may also use j (by typing nj) to represent complex numbers. By default, MathCAD displays complex numbers using the letter i. If you wish the output expressed using j, use the global format option to change the im (imaginary unit symbol) parameter

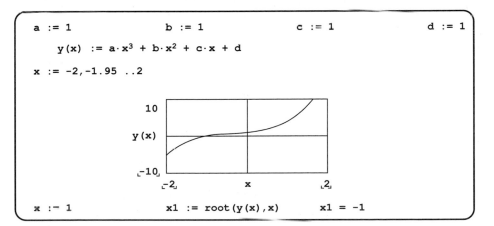

FIGURE 2.1

from i to j. With this guess, the root is displayed as $x = 2.29 \cdot 10^{-5} + i$. Note that the root is complex but that the real part is very small. The exact answer for the root happens to be $x = i$. MathCAD solves equations numerically to a predefined (default) tolerance of $TOL = 0.001$. Hence the solutions displayed are not always exact. This tolerance can be decreased (tightened) for greater accuracy using the SET command. Type **{Esc} SET** and change the value of TOL. You can also enter the tolerance directly into the worksheet using:

$$TOL := 0.0001$$

or, if you wish a *global* assignment, as:

$$TOL \equiv 0.0001 .$$

The global assignment $\equiv$ is made using the tilde key (`~`).

If you wish to suppress elements of complex numbers that are small, use the global format command (**{Esc} FORM**) and adjust the ct (complex tolerance) parameter. If the ratio of the imaginary part to the real part of a complex number is smaller than 10^{-ct}, the imaginary part will be suppressed. Similarly, if the ratio of the real part to the imaginary part is smaller than 10^{-ct}, the real part will be suppressed. In this example, setting ct=3 causes the answer to appear as $x = i$.

If we take as our guess $x := -2i$, MathCAD's root function determines the third root to be $x = -i$ (using ct=3). Thus the three roots to our cubic equation are found to be: $x = -1$, $x = -i$, and $x = +i$.

Using Solve Blocks

Assume we wish to solve a set of n simultaneous equations for n unknowns. Math-CAD performs this task using a *solve block*. Solve blocks begin with the word **Given** and end with the function **Find**. Consider an intersection point (x, y) of the two curves generated by plotting the equations $y = x$ and $x^2 + y^2 = 1$. These curves represent, respectively, a line passing through the origin (inclined at 45°) and a unit circle about the origin. To solve the two equations for the two unknowns x and y, we set up a worksheet with the following objects: **x:1**, **y:1**, **Given**, **x^2+y^2{<Alt>=}1**, **y{<Alt>=}x**, **R:Find(x,y)**, **R=**. You should see:

$x := 1 \qquad y := 1$

Given

$$x^2 + y^2 \approx 1 \qquad\qquad y \approx x \qquad\qquad R := Find(x, y)$$

$$R = \begin{bmatrix} 0.707 \\ 0.707 \end{bmatrix}$$

The first two objects assign guesses to the unknowns. After the **Given**, we have two objects each one representing a constraint. Equations inside a solve block are in the

form of constraints. One type of constraint,[1] the *relational equals*, is made using the
{<Alt>=} key (i.e., by holding the **<Alt>** key depressed while typing the "=" key). This
produces the symbol $\approx$. A solution, if found, is generated by the **Find** statement.
The results of a **Find** are stored in a vertical array structure known as a MathCAD
vector and, in this case, assigned to the vector R. The first (upper) value in the array
represents the solution to x and the second (lower) to y. The results are displayed by
typing **R=**.

   If we change the guess to x := −1 and y := −1, we find the other solution,
namely $x = -0.707$ and $y = -0.707$. If not enough information is given, or a
solution cannot be found, MathCAD will give a too few constraints error or a
solution not found error at the **Find** statement.

   MathCAD's ability to find a solution (if one exists) will, in general, depend
on the initial guess we make. Graphical methods or trial and error methods assist in
making a good guess. We illustrate this with the following problem. We wish to find
the points of intersection of the curves $y = x/12$ and $y = \sin(x)$. We first define a
range variable x, and graph both functions. The worksheet is shown in Fig. 2.2. Note
that the graphs intersect approximately at $x = \pm 3$, $x = \pm 7$, and $x = \pm 8.5$. They also
intersect exactly at $x = 0$. No other roots exist.

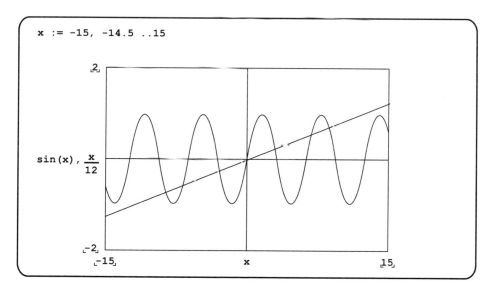

FIGURE 2.2

<hr/>

[1]It is also possible to use constraints in the form of relational inequalities. You may use $<$, $>$, $\geq$ (**{<Alt>)}**
key), $\leq$ (**{<Alt>(}** key), or $\neq$ (**{<Alt>#}** key). These relational operators are discussed in Chapter 3.

To find the exact values, we set up the following solve block:

```
x := 3      y := .5
Given       y ≈sin(x)
                            y ≈ x/12      R := Find(x,y)

      ⌈2.898⌉
R =   ⌊0.241⌋
```

By guessing the solution to be $x = 3$ and $y = .5$, we find one point of intersection to be (2.898, 0.241). If we change the guess to $x = 7$ and afterward to $x = 9$, MathCAD gives the following:

```
      ⌈6.895⌉               ⌈8.623⌉
R =   ⌊0.575⌋     and   R = ⌊0.719⌋
```

Thus, in addition to the point (0,0), we determine the other intersection points to be:

$$(\pm 2.898, \pm 0.241), \quad (\pm 6.895, \pm 0.575), \quad \text{and} \quad (\pm 8.623, \pm 0.719)$$

It is clear that the particular solution that MathCAD finds depends on the nature of the guess.

VECTORS, SUBSCRIPTS, AND VECTORIZATION

Extracting Components of Vectors

From the previous example, we see that the **Find** function stores its results in a vertical array. If the solve block contains n unknowns, the **Find** stores its results in a column with the n elements arrayed in the same order as the unknowns appear in the **Find** statement. A vertical array is called a "vector" by MathCAD. By default, MathCAD labels the first element as zero and the last element as $n - 1$.

Suppose a vector R contains two elements as follows,

```
      ⌈2.898⌉
R =   ⌊0.241⌋
```

We can extract the elements of the vector by using *mathematical* subscripts as opposed to notational (or literal) subscripts. A mathematical subscript can be any integer. To subscript a variable, we follow the variable name with the **[** key. If we type **R[** we observe:

R .

Note that the placeholder is positioned as a subscript. With the cursor on the placeholder, we type **0=** and observe:

$R_0 = 2.898.$

A similar operation gives:

$R_1 = 0.241.$

Using subscripting, it is possible to assign or display the components of vectors as simple scalar variables. If we try to display a third component, i.e., by typing **R₂ =,** MathCAD gives an `index out of bounds` error. This tells us that our vector has only two components—the first with a subscript of 0 and the second with a subscript of 1.

MathCAD subscripts must be integers. The lowest allowable subscript (called the origin or base) is by default equal to zero. This origin can be changed to any positive or negative integer using the `SET ORIGIN` option. For example, in certain situations, it is desirable to label the elements of an n component vector as going from 1 to n (instead of ranging from 0 to $n - 1$). MathCAD allows this globally if we use the `SET` command. Type **{Esc} SET** and choose the option `ORIGIN`. (Note that the default is zero.) Change the `ORIGIN` to 1. The components of the above vector are now displayed as $R_1 = 2.898$ and $R_2 = 0.241$. With this origin, trying to use zero as a subscript generates an `index out of bounds` error. You may also enter the `ORIGIN` command by entering it *directly* into the worksheet as follows:

```
ORIGIN := 1,
```

or, if you wish a *global* definition, as:

```
ORIGIN ≡ 1
```

The global assignment $\equiv$ is made using the tilde key (˜).

Subscripts can also be integer functions of other variables. Consider, for example, the following objects:

```
ORIGIN := -5          j := 2      k := 3
n(j,k) := j - k     a_n(j,k) := 2      a_-1 = 2
```

We have set the subscript origin to accommodate subscripts as low as -5. The values of j and k are assigned. A function, $n(j, k)$, is defined and used as a subscript for the variable a.

There are two ways of assigning the elements of a vector. One method is to use *subscript* assignment and the other *matrix* assignment. (We assume that the `SET ORIGIN` mode is at zero (the default) so that the n vector elements are referenced 0 to $n - 1$.)

Creating a Vector Using Subscripts

EXPLICIT ASSIGNMENT. Make the assignments **x[1:2** and **x[5:3** and display the value of x as a vector by typing **x=**. You should see:

$$
\text{ORIGIN} := 0 \qquad x_1 := 2 \qquad x_5 := 3
$$

$$
x = \begin{bmatrix} 0 \\ 2 \\ 0 \\ 0 \\ 0 \\ 3 \end{bmatrix}
$$

Because the highest subscript being assigned is 5, MathCAD makes the vector representation of x a six-component vector (0–5). (Note that a vector is composed of subscripted quantities and conversely that subscripted quantities constitute a vector.) Since the elements labeled $0, 2, 3, 4$ have not been assigned, each is assigned the value of zero in the vector. However, it is advisable to explicitly assign a value of zero to these subscripted variables.

FUNCTIONAL ASSIGNMENT. We can also assign subscripted variables using a more general technique. For example let us consider the following worksheet:

$$
\text{ORIGIN} := 0 \qquad n := 0 \, ..5 \qquad x_n := n^2 \,\text{(Functional assignment)}
$$

$$
x_0 = 0 \qquad x_1 = 1 \qquad x_2 = 4
$$

(Individually subscripted display)

$$
x_3 = 9 \qquad x_4 = 16 \qquad x_5 = 25
$$

x_n
0
1
4
9
16
25

(Tabular display)

$$
x = \begin{bmatrix} 0 \\ 1 \\ 4 \\ 9 \\ 16 \\ 25 \end{bmatrix}
$$

(Vector display)

We begin by assigning a range to the index (or subscript) variable n. Note that if no increment is implied in the range, MathCAD assumes integer increments. The second object assigns the value to the subscripted variable x_n using the function n^2. MathCAD performs this computation for all the values of n specified in the range. The contents of the variable may be displayed either as separate subscripted objects, as a *data table* (by typing **x[n=**), or as a *vector* (by typing **x=**). As a data table, the data is listed below the variable; as a vector it appears to the right of the variable.

TABULAR ASSIGNMENT. After assigning the range for the index variable n, as previously, we type **x[n:0,** and observe the following:

n := 0 ..5 x_n :=

0
■

Note that the *comma* creates a table with a placeholder below the first data element 0. We are able to fill the table with a total of six elements because of the previous range definition of n. If we continue by typing a **1** followed by a comma, we see,

n := 0 ..5 x_n :=

0
1
■

Using commas as separators, we extend and fill the data table. After the last data element is entered, we type the **{Enter}** key or use the arrow keys to exit the object. After displaying the data, our complete worksheet looks like:

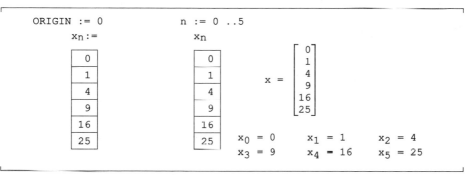

The first object (after the ORIGIN and range assignments) assigns the data table for the variable x. It is created using the following keystrokes: **x[n:0,1,4,9,16,25 {Enter}**. The second object is a display of the data table and is produced by typing **x[n=**. The third object displays the results as a vector by typing **x=**. Finally the subscripted components are displayed individually.

Warning: If you extend the entries beyond the assigned values of the subscript, MathCAD does not indicate an error. However, only those subscripted values for which the subscript is defined are actually stored. In this example, if we reduce the subscript range to n:=0 ..3, both the table and the vector will actually contain only the first four data elements (n=0,1,2,3). Typing **x[4=** or **x[5=** gives an index out of bounds error. *Avoid entering data into a table beyond the assigned subscript range.*

Creating a Vector Using Matrices

MathCAD allows entry of data directly into a vector using matrix entry. A matrix is a set of numbers arrayed in a grid of rows and columns. An $n \times m$ matrix T has n

rows and m columns. If T contains more than one row and more than one column, an element of the matrix is a doubly subscripted variable T_{ij}; otherwise it is singly subscripted. For example, the element in the second row and third column is labeled as T_{23}. To define a 2×3 matrix with MathCAD, we type the following: **T:{<Alt>M}**. A message line prompt appears which requests the dimensions of the matrix. (You can also reach this menu by typing: **{F10}** (menu), **C** (compute), **G** (generate matrix) instead of **{<Alt>M}**.) We type **2** followed by a space followed by **3** and type the **{Enter}** key. (The first number represents the rows and the second the columns.) The matrix name T was chosen arbitrarily; any legal variable name could have been used. We should see the following worksheet:

We place the cursor over each placeholder and enter the elements. We may move the cursor between placeholders using either the arrow keys or the **[Tab]** key. Once all the data has been entered, we use the **{Enter}** key (or the arrow keys) to leave the object. In Chapter 7 we will use the key stroke **{<Alt>M}** frequently to create $n \times m$ matrices. At this point, we consider only vectors (column matrices).

An n-dimensional MathCAD vector is a special matrix which has n rows but only one column. A single subscript is used to specify the row containing the element in question. To create a six-component vector, use the method outlined previously and type **R:{<Alt>M}**. When the matrix message line appears, type the single digit **6** and then **{Enter}**. (You may also enter the digits **6** and **1** separated by a space.) You should see:

$$x = \begin{bmatrix} \blacksquare \\ \blacksquare \\ \blacksquare \\ \blacksquare \\ \blacksquare \\ \blacksquare \end{bmatrix}$$

Fill the markers according to the following worksheet:

ORIGIN := 0   n := 0 ..5

$$x := \begin{bmatrix} 0 \\ 1 \\ 4 \\ 9 \\ 16 \\ 25 \end{bmatrix} \qquad x = \begin{bmatrix} 0 \\ 1 \\ 4 \\ 9 \\ 16 \\ 25 \end{bmatrix}$$

x_n
0
1
4
9
16
25

$x_0 = 0$ $x_1 = 1$ $x_2 = 4$
$x_3 = 9$ $x_4 = 16$ $x_5 = 25$

In this worksheet data is entered directly into a vector. The data is then displayed as a table, as a vector, and as individual subscripted quantities. The subscript range

(n= 0 ..5) is required only if we intend to display the data as a table or as subscripted quantities.

Note that to display a single element of the vector, let us say the second, we must use,

$$x_1 = 1 \qquad\qquad \text{or} \qquad\qquad x_2 = 1$$

according to whether the parameter of the SET ORIGIN command is set to zero (the default) or to one.

Vectorization of Equations

Suppose we have two tables of data, each containing five elements. Our objective is to perform operations with the corresponding elements of the two tables using a specified formula and then to store the results in the corresponding elements of a third table. We start by creating two data tables in the form of vectors A and B as follows:

$$A := \begin{bmatrix} 2 \\ 4 \\ 6 \\ 8 \\ 10 \\ 12 \end{bmatrix} \qquad\qquad B := \begin{bmatrix} 1 \\ 2 \\ 3 \\ 4 \\ 5 \\ 6 \end{bmatrix}$$

We want to construct a new data vector C where each element is to be computed by squaring the corresponding element of A and dividing the result by the corresponding element of B. One way to accomplish this is by using a subscripted formula to connect the elements. We type **n:0;5**, **C[n:A[n^2/B[n**. We display the results by typing: **C[n=**, **C=**. We should see:

$$n := 0 ..5$$

$$c_n := \frac{A_n^2}{B_n} \quad \text{(Element formula)}$$

C_n
4
8
12
16
20
24

$$C := \begin{bmatrix} 4 \\ 8 \\ 12 \\ 16 \\ 20 \\ 24 \end{bmatrix}$$

Note that each component of C is equal to the square of the corresponding component of A divided by the corresponding component of B. Also note that the subscript range must first be defined in order to use a formula involving variable subscripts.

An alternative way to achieve the same result is to *vectorize* the equation. Instead of the subscripted formula above, we use a *vectorized* equation created with the following key strokes: $\boxed{\text{C:}\{\text{<Alt>}-\}\text{(A^2/B)}}$. The following worksheet illustrates vectorization of an equation:

---

n := 0 ..5

$$C := \left[\overrightarrow{\frac{A^2}{B}} \right] \quad \text{(Vectorized equation)}$$

Cn

4
8
12
16
20
24

$$C = \begin{bmatrix} 4 \\ 8 \\ 12 \\ 16 \\ 20 \\ 24 \end{bmatrix}$$

Note that $\{\text{<Alt>}-\}$ (i.e., by holding the **<Alt>** key depressed while typing the hyphen key) initiates the vectorization process. The vectorized expression on the right-hand side must be enclosed in parentheses. The expression being vectorized is displayed with a *hooked line* above it. Also note that while the results obtained here are the same as those obtained with subscripted formulas, the vectorized method does not require an index variable unless the data is to be displayed in a table or as individually subscripted numbers. All vectors involved in a vectorized equation must have the *same* number of elements. In this example, the number was six. The elements are labeled as 0–5 with the ORIGIN set equal to zero and 1–6 with the ORIGIN set equal to one.

ANALYZING DATA AND PERFORMING LINEAR CURVE FITTING

Imagine that a corporation is studying its income for the past five years. Let a vector representing the years (labeled 1 through 5) be called X. Furthermore, let the corporation's revenues (in millions of dollars) be represented by a vector Y. We will begin our worksheet with the following assignments:

ORIGIN := 1   n := 1 ..5

$$X := \begin{bmatrix} 1 \\ 2 \\ 3 \\ 4 \\ 5 \end{bmatrix} \qquad Y := \begin{bmatrix} 1.9 \\ 4.2 \\ 5.9 \\ 8.4 \\ 9.8 \end{bmatrix}$$

To create the vector X, type $\boxed{\text{X:}\{\text{<Alt>M}\}}$ and set the array size to 5. Complete the process by filling in the placeholders and repeat for Y.

Using this data, we would like to:

a. plot revenues versus years to see the trend;

b. plot the straight line that best fits this data; and

c. project the revenues for year number six.

The straight line that best fits the data is obtained by performing a *linear regression*. The line used is one for which the sum of the squares of the vertical distances from the data points to the line is smallest. MathCAD automatically determines the slope and intercept of this line along with the *correlation* factor, which estimates how close the data points actual fit a straight line. MathCAD uses three functions to accomplish this: **slope**, **intercept**, and **corr**. We continue the previous worksheet with the following:

$$
\begin{array}{lll}
\texttt{m := slope(X,Y)} & \texttt{b := intercept(X,Y)} & \sigma \texttt{:= corr(X,Y)} \\
\texttt{m = 2} & \texttt{b = 0.04} & \sigma \texttt{= 0.997} \\
\quad\texttt{y}_n \texttt{:= m·X}_n \texttt{+ b} & &
\end{array}
$$

The first three objects calculate the slope, intercept and correlation coefficient (Pearson's r) for the line that best fits the data—the results being stored respectively in m, b, and σ. These curve-fitting functions require that their arguments be two vectors of the same size. Note that the vector containing the independent variable (in this case the year) goes first in these functions. The next three objects display the results. The closer the correlation coefficient σ is to ± 1, the closer the data points fit a straight line.

Finally, a subscripted variable is used to define points on the straight line. Note that since MathCAD is case sensitive, Y_n and y_n are treated as different variables.

Continuing the worksheet, using the @ key, we produce a plot as shown in Fig. 2.3. The graph `type` parameters are set to `1x` so that the straight line y_n is plotted using a continuous line and the data Y_n is plotted with exes.

We complete the worksheet with the following objects:

$$
\begin{array}{ll}
\texttt{Y}_6 \texttt{:= m·6 + b} & \qquad \texttt{Y}_6 \texttt{= 12.04}
\end{array}
$$

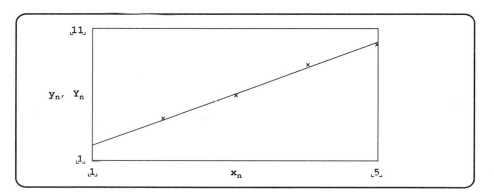

FIGURE 2.3

The linear regression line is extrapolated and evaluated at year six and displayed. The revenues for the sixth year are therefore projected to be 12.04 million dollars.

UNITS AND DIMENSIONS
Global Assignment

We now explain MathCAD's *global assignment* operation $\equiv$. This operation is generated using the tilde key (~). It is an assignment statement and acts in a manner similar to the := operation. The difference is that a global assignment may be placed *anywhere* in the worksheet—even *after* other objects that use it. It is generally used to establish a relationship that remains constant throughout the worksheet. As we shall show, it is particularly useful in defining units and dimensions.

Units

You may have noticed that when you assign a value to a variable and then display it, the worksheet shows:

```
A := 4.712389        A = 4.712 ■
```

The cursor rests on the placeholder. As soon as you leave the display object (using {**Enter**} or an arrow key), the placeholder disappears. Why is the marker displayed in the first place? The answer is that MathCAD allows you to fill the marker with information. If you fill the place holder with π and leave the object. you will see the following:

```
A := 4.712389        A = 1.5·π
```

You have requested that MathCAD display the data in units of π; the result shows that the value of A is 1.5 times π. This is a useful way of displaying a result in units or multiples of another quantity.

To illustrate the use of global assignment of units, we create a trigonometry table that gives the sine of an angle for values which range from zero to ninety degrees in increments of ten degrees. We perform the calculations using radians (MathCAD's natural unit) but express the results in degrees. Consider the worksheet in Fig. 2.4.

The first object globally defines the variable *rad* (our abbreviation for radian) as having the value of unity (i.e., MathCAD's natural unit). The second definition globally assigns $\pi/180$ to the variable *deg* (our abbreviation for degree). The third object assigns values to the range variable θ ({**<Alt>Q**}) in radian measure. The increment $\pi/18$ and range $\pi/2$ correspond to 10 degrees and 90 degrees respectively. We next assign the sine function to the variable $y(x)$.

The first object on the second row assigns $\pi/2 \cdot rad$ to A. It is created by typing **A:{<Alt>P}/2∗rad**. (The quantity rad has previously been defined as one). Next, we display A and fill the placeholder with deg. The value of A is multiplied by the

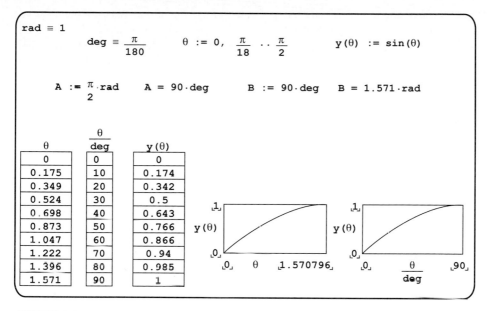

rad ≡ 1

$deg \equiv \dfrac{\pi}{180}$ $\theta := 0, \dfrac{\pi}{18} .. \dfrac{\pi}{2}$ $y(\theta) := \sin(\theta)$

$A := \dfrac{\pi}{2} \cdot rad$ $A = 90 \cdot deg$ $B := 90 \cdot deg$ $B = 1.571 \cdot rad$

θ	$\dfrac{\theta}{deg}$	$y(\theta)$
0	0	0
0.175	10	0.174
0.349	20	0.342
0.524	30	0.5
0.698	40	0.643
0.873	50	0.766
1.047	60	0.866
1.222	70	0.94
1.396	80	0.985
1.571	90	1

FIGURE 2.4

defined value of deg and displayed as A = 90·deg. The objects involving B reverse the operation and convert from degrees to radians. By defining units and filling the placeholders appropriately, it is possible to assign variables in one set of units and express them in another.

To list θ in radians, simply type θ= and {**Enter**}. To list θ in degrees, type θ/**deg**= and {**Enter**}. In the last two objects, we have plotted the function first in radians and then in degrees. (Recall that to create a graph template, type the @ key.) To plot in degrees, fill the θ-axis middle marker with θ/**deg**. Note that MathCAD will automatically adjust the θ-axis plot range to 0–90 degrees.

The global assignment has another interesting use. Often we wish to see how an object such as a plot changes when we change a set of parameters in a long worksheet. If the parameters are at the beginning of the worksheet and the plot at the end, we are constantly forced to scroll the screen back and forth to study the "what-if" situation. If we use the global assignment ≡ to assign the values of the parameters, we can place the parameters alongside the plot at the end of the worksheet. This eliminates the need to scroll.

Dimensions

In engineering and science, physical quantities are treated not just as pure numbers but as entities having *dimensions*. Suppose we wish to represent a distance of 10 miles. The quantity being described here is called a *displacement* and is said to have the dimension of *length* (abbreviated L). Similarly, the time to travel this distance (e.g., in hours) has the dimension of *time* (abbreviated T). The rate of motion or velocity is represented by the dimensions L/T (e.g., miles/hour). The other two dimensions used in MathCAD are *mass* (abbreviated M) and *charge* (abbreviated Q). [As we show in Chapter 5, you can change MathCAD's default *base* dimensions by typing: **{F10}** (menu), **C** (compute), **D** (dimension).] Length, time, mass, and charge, (L, T, M, and Q), are the standard base dimensions of physics. Other physical quantities (such as velocity = L/T) are hybrids. Each dimension can be represented in a system of units. For example, length can be represented in centimeters, meters, inches, feet, miles, kilometers, etc. Similarly time can be measured in seconds, minutes, hours, days, years, etc. Mass is typically measured in slugs, grams, or kilograms while charge is measured in coulombs or statcoulombs. MathCAD can *automatically* keep track of units and check the physical consistency of your equations.

   We use Newton's second law of mechanics to demonstrate how MathCAD handles units and dimensions. Newton's law states that the net force F on a body of mass m is directly proportional to its acceleration a. Consider the following worksheet:

$$cm \equiv 1L \qquad gm \equiv 1M \qquad sec \equiv 1T$$

$$meter \equiv 100 \cdot gm \qquad kg \equiv 1000 \cdot gm \qquad dyne \equiv gm \cdot \frac{cm}{sec^2} \qquad N \equiv kg \cdot \frac{meter}{sec^2}$$

$$m := 1 \cdot gm \qquad a := 2 \cdot \frac{cm}{sec^2} \qquad F := m \cdot a$$

The first three objects define the units for the base dimensions. We are using C.G.S. (centimeter-gram-second) units in this example. If the first object were translated into words, it would read "cm is the unit of length." Note that the definition is entered as 1L and has no multiplication symbol between the characters. The letters M, L, and T may be used anywhere in the worksheet as variable names without concern of conflict. The next three objects define derived units from the base units. Dyne is the unit of force in the C.G.S. system whereas N (Newton) is the unit in the M.K.S. (meter-kilogram-second) system. The next two objects assign both numerical values and units to the mass and acceleration. The last object applies Newton's Law by making the appropriate assignment to F.

   To display F, type **F=**. You should see:

$$F = 2 \cdot mass \cdot length \cdot time^{-2} \ \blacksquare$$

with the cursor residing on the placeholder.

   MathCAD automatically displays the numerical value of a dimensioned variable in the base units followed by its dimensions. Fill the placeholder by typing **dyne**; then leave the object by typing the **{Enter}** key. The dimensions should disappear and you should see:

$$F = 2 \cdot dyne$$

If we fill the placeholder with **N**, we obtain:

$$F = 2 \cdot 10^{-5} \cdot N$$

Note that MathCAD automatically keeps track of units and performs the necessary conversions. If we change the mass assignment from m := 1·gm to m := 1·kg, the results change to:

$$F = 2 \cdot 10^{3} \cdot dyne \qquad \text{and} \qquad F = 0.02 \cdot N$$

In the next chapter we will apply MathCAD to elementary concepts in calculus. We will study derivatives, integrals, and series and learn more about MathCAD's predefined functions.

PROBLEMS

1. Find the coordinates of the points of intersection between the curves $f(x) = e^{-x}$ and $g(x) = \cos(x)$ for positive x using the following steps:
   (a) Plot both functions from 0 to π and estimate the x-coordinate x_0 of the point of intersection.
   (b) Construct the function diff$(x) = f(x) - g(x)$. Using the estimate from part (a) as a guess, and applying the root function to diff(x), find the exact value of the x-coordinate of the point of intersection x_0. Use $TOL \equiv 0.00001$.
   (c) Evaluate the y-coordinate of the point of intersection y_0 by evaluating either $f(x)$ or $g(x)$ at x_0.
2. Repeat Problem 1 as follows:
   (a) Make the guess for the solution to be: $x = 1$, $y = 1$.
   (b) Using a Given/Find, solve the constraining equations $y \approx f(x)$ and $y \approx g(x)$ for x_0 and y_0. Use $TOL \equiv 0.00001$. Hint. Use **[◄Alt►M]** to make the assignment,

$$\begin{bmatrix} x_0 \\ y_0 \end{bmatrix} := \text{Find}(x,y)$$

3. Create a vector A with nine elements $(n = 0, \ldots 8)$ where the first element has a value of two and where each successive element is the square of the previous one. Do so using the following steps:
   (a) Keep the default value of ORIGIN=0 and define an appropriate range for the variable n.
   (b) Set $A_0 = 2$ and define the successive values of A_n using,

$$A_{n+1} = A_n^2.$$

   (c) Display the results as a table $A_n = $ and as a vector $A =$.
4. An experiment is performed to determine the acceleration of gravity near the earth's surface. An object is dropped from a height of h and the time to reach the floor t is recorded. The experiment is repeated five times for different heights. The data is as follows:

$$h(\text{ft}) = 4,\ 5,\ 6,\ 7,\ 8$$

and

$$t(\text{s}) = 0.5,\ 0.559,\ 0.612,\ 0.661,\ 0.707.$$

The acceleration of gravity is determined using the formula:

$$g = 2 \cdot h/t^2.$$

(a) Set up a range variable n= 0 ..4 and enter the above data into two data tables h and t.

(b) Using the above expression, set up a vectorized equation for the g-vector and display the vector.

(c) What do the elements of the vector g suggest about the acceleration of gravity (within experimental error)? Hint: After assigning the range by typing **n:=0;4**, create the data table by typing, for example, **h[n:4,5,6,7,8**. Do the same for the t table. Create the g-vector by typing: **g:{<Alt>-}((2∗h)/t^2)**.

5. We can also measure the acceleration of gravity g using a pendulum. The formula relating the period T of a pendulum to its length L is:

$$T = 2 \cdot \pi \cdot [L/g]^{1/2}.$$

If we set $TT = [T/(2 \cdot \pi)]^2$, we have: $L = g \cdot TT$. Thus if we measure the pendulum period for various pendulum lengths and plot the data points of L_n versus $[T_n/(2 \cdot \pi)]^2$, we should obtain a straight line whose slope is g.

Suppose we obtain the following data:

$$L_n = 2,\ 3,\ 4,\ 5,\ 6,\ 7,\ 8$$

and

$$T_n = 1.571,\ 1.923,\ 2.220,\ 2.481,\ 2.717,\ 2.898,\ 3.151$$

From this data find the acceleration of gravity using the following steps:

(a) Assign a range variable, n= 0 ..6 and create the data tables for L and T.

(b) Using vectorization, create the vector $TT = [T/(2 \cdot \pi)]^2$ and display it.
  [Use the keystrokes: **TT:{<Alt>-}((T/(2*{<Alt>P}))^2)**.]

(c) Plot L_n versus TT_n.

(d) Using MathCAD's **slope** function, determine the slope of the line which best fits the data and determine the value of g. How good is the fit? Hint: Use **g=slope(TT,L)** and σ=**corr(TT,L)**.

6. Display the sine, cosine and tangent functions as follows:

(a) Create a table for the angle θ ranging from $0°$ to $180°$ in steps of $10°$.

(b) Create the corresponding tables for the sine, cosine, and tangent. Hint: Begin by using the global assignment deg $\equiv \pi/180$. Then type, **{<Alt>Q}:0∗deg,10∗deg;180∗deg** and generate the range, $\theta := 0 \cdot \text{deg}, 10 \cdot \text{deg}\ ..180 \cdot \text{deg}$. Set the global format (type **{Esc} FORM**) to zt=10 to display all numbers smaller than 10^{10} as zero. To display the θ table in degrees, type **{<Alt>Q}/deg=**. Similarly, use sin(θ)=, cos(θ)=, and tan(θ)= to display the trigonometric functions. Since tan$(90°) = \infty$, the table should give an overflow condition. Overflow does not occur because Math-CAD approximates tan$(90°)$ as a very large but finite number.

(c) Produce a graph of the above three trigonometric functions versus θ in degrees for the range specified in part (a). Hint: Create a graph template (type **@**) and plot sin(θ), cos(θ), and tan(θ) versus θ/deg. To produce a meaningful plot, manually set the vertical scale to go from -2 to $+2$ and the horizontal scale to range from $0°$ to $180°$. Place the cursor in the graph area, type **f**, and set the graph format to `subdivs=2,2` and `size=5,30`.

7. A person is traveling at a speed of $v = 60$ mph. Given the following conversions:

$$\texttt{cm = 0.01 m,   in = 2.54 cm, km = 1000 m, ft = 12 in, mi = 5280 ft}$$

$$\texttt{min = 60 sec,   hr = 60 min,   day = 24 hr,}$$

express this speed in:

$$\texttt{km/hr, in/sec,   ft/sec,   cm/min,   km/sec,   mi/day.}$$

Use the basic dimensions $m \equiv 1L$ and $s \equiv 1T$.

BASIC
OPERATIONS II

MATHCAD'S BUILT-IN FUNCTIONS

We begin with a discussion of some of MathCAD's built-in functions.

Ordinary Functions

Trigonometric Functions	
`sin(x)`	sine
`cos(x)`	cosine
`tan(x)`	tangent
`asin(x)`	inverse sine
`acos(x)`	inverse cosine
`atan(x)`	inverse tangent
`angle(x,y)`	gives the angle in radians to the Cartesian point (x, y). Angle ranges from zero to $2 \cdot \pi$ radians.

Note: The **angle** function is a generalized *two-argument* **atan** function; its relationship to the **atan** function is demonstrated by the rule $\text{angle}(x, y) = \text{atan}(y/x)$ provided the coordinates (x, y) are in the first or fourth quadrants. All arguments in the trigonometric functions are assumed by MathCAD to be in radians. Furthermore, angles generated by the inverse trigonometric functions are in radians.

Log and Exponential Functions

`exp(x)`	exponential (e^x)
`log(x)`	common log (base 10)
`ln(x)`	natural log (base e)

Hyperbolic Functions

`sinh(x)`	hyperbolic sine
`cosh(x)`	hyperbolic cosine
`tanh(x)`	hyperbolic tangent
`asinh(x)`	inverse hyperbolic sine
`acosh(x)`	inverse hyperbolic cosine
`atanh(x)`	inverse hyperbolic tangent

Operation	Keystroke
addition	**+**
subtraction	**-**
multiplication	*****
division	**/**
exponentiation	**^**
square root	****
absolute value	**¦ (pipe key)**

We illustrate the last two operations with the following objects: **a:64**, **b:-4.32**, **c:\a**, **d:¦b**, **c=**, and **d=**. You should see:

```
a := 64    b := -4.32    c :=√a    d := |b|    c = 8    d = 4.32
```

To take the square root or the absolute value of an expression such as $x^2 + 2$, set the expression off in parentheses, that is, type **\(x^2+2)** or **¦(x^2+2)** respectively.

Special Functions

MathCAD provides the user with the following special functions: **floor**, **ceil**, **if**, **mod**, and **rnd**.

The `floor(x)` function returns the largest integer that is *smaller than* or *equal* to x. The `ceil(x)` returns the smallest integer that is *larger than* or *equal* to x. Any number x always satisfies the inequality $floor(x) \leq x \leq ceil(x)$. The functions are illustrated with the following objects:

```
a := 2.34                              b := -4.23
floor(a) = 2    ceil(a) = 3    floor(b) = -5    ceil(b) = -4
```

The **if** function has the following structure: if(cond,a,b) where cond stands for a Boolean number (a number that represents true or false). The variable names cond, a, and b have been chosen arbitrarily. If cond is one (i.e., true), then the function returns the value of a. If it is zero (false), then it returns the value of b. This is verified with the following worksheet:

```
a: = 100       b := -500
cond := 1           c := if(cond,a,b)         c = 100
cond := 0           c := if(cond,a,b)         c = -500
```

In the second row, cond is one and is therefore true; the variable c is equal to a and therefore displays as c = 100. In the third row, cond has been changed to zero and is now false; the variable c becomes equal to b and therefore displays as c = -500.

The cond in the **if** function is generally represented by one of the following *relational* conditions:

Condition	Keyboard entry	Screen display
greater than	>	>
less than	<	<
greater than or equal to	<Alt>)	≥
less than or equal to	<Alt>(	≤
not equal to	<Alt>#	≠
equal to	<Alt>=	≈

Consider the following objects:

```
Larger_of(a,b)  := if(a > b,a,b)      Smaller_of(a,b)  := if(a < b,a,b)
a: = 1    b := 2        Larger_of(a,b) = 2        Smaller_of(a,b) = 1
Status1 := a > b     Status1 = 0        Status2 := a < b     Status2 = 1
```

We define two functions Larger_of and Smaller_of using **if** functions. With Larger_of(a,b), if a > b then the function is equal to the first variable a; otherwise it is equal to the second b. A similar approach is used for Smaller_of(a,b). When they are evaluated at the assigned values of a and b, the functions return the larger (or smaller) of the two values. In the last row we illustrate the fact that it is possible to assign a relational condition to a Boolean variable. This variable can be either zero (false) or one (true).

We can use **floor, ceil**, and **if** to separate any number x into its integer and decimal parts. Consider the following worksheet:

```
a := 2.34      DecimalPart(x)  :=  |x| - floor(|x|)
               IntegerPart(x)  := if(x ≥ 0,floor(x),ceil(x))
               IntegerPart(a) = 2        DecimalPart(a) = 0.34
```

To extract the decimal part, we subtract the integer whose value is directly below the number (i.e., the **floor**) from the number itself. Absolute values are used because the decimal part is always positive. [Recall that to take the absolute value $|x|$, type |**x**.] For the integer part, we check to see whether the number is positive or negative. If the number is positive, the condition in the **if** statement is true. Consequently, the integer part is equal to the **floor** function. If, however, the number is negative, the condition is false and the function returns the negative value of $ceil(x)$. For example, if the number is equal to -2.34, the **ceil** function returns -2 since this is the integer immediately *above* -2.34.

The $mod(y,x)$ (modulus) function allows us to divide one number y by another number x and obtain the *remainder*. As examples of the **mod** function, consider the following worksheet:

```
a := 14        b := 5        c := mod(a,b)      c = 4
y(n,x) := if(mod(n,2)≈0, cos(n·x), sin(n·x))
```

The first line verifies that 14 divided by 5 is 2 with a remainder of 4. The second line shows how the **mod** function can be used to assign $\cos(n·x)$ to a function $y(n,x)$ if n is even and $\sin(n·x)$ to that function if n is odd.

The $rnd(x)$ function generates a (pseudo) random number in the range:

$$0 \le rnd(x) \le x$$

Create the following display object by typing **rnd(4)=**, leaving the cursor on the placeholder. You should see something like,

```
rnd(4) = 0.005 ■
```

With the cursor on the placeholder, type the **{F9}** (recalculate) key. Whenever the **{F9}** key is typed, the value of $rnd(4)$ changes randomly between 0 and 4. The numbers generated are not truly random but follow a preprogrammed sequence determined by a *seed* number. The default seed number is one and can be changed using the **{Esc}** **RAndom** command. The message line will allow you to set a new seed number. (You can also reset the seed number by typing: **{F10}** (menu), **C** (compute), **R** (randomize).) Every time the worksheet is reloaded, the sequence is reinitialized according to the seed number. A random set of subscripted variables can be produced as follows:

```
k := 0 ..5          Aₖ := rnd(10)
```

A_k

1.933
5.85
3.503
8.228
1.741
7.105

The assignment object is repeated six times ($k=0$ ..5), each time assigning to A_k a different random number from 0 to 10. The table is generated by typing **A[k=** .

The Φ (Heaviside) Function

The Heaviside (unit step) function is one of MathCAD's special functions and is generated with the Greek letter Φ by typing **<Alt>H**. It is defined mathematically as:

$$\Phi(x) = 0 \qquad \text{for} \qquad x < 0$$

$$\Phi(x) = 1 \qquad \text{for} \qquad x \geq 0$$

(If you wish to use Φ as the Heaviside function, make sure you do not assign the letter Φ to another function.) Figure 3.1 shows a graph of the Heaviside function. In the graph, we have overridden MathCAD's vertical axis autoscale values (-1 to 1) changing them to (-2 to 2).

The Heaviside function is an example of a *piecewise* continuous function. A nonrigorous condition for a function to be continuous on an interval is that it can be drawn without lifting the pencil from the paper. While functions such as the sine, cosine and the exponential are continuous everywhere, the Heaviside function is continuous to the right and to the left of the origin, but is discontinuous at the origin itself. In Fig. 3.1, the line connecting the portions to the left and to the right of the origin should, in theory, be vertical.

The Heaviside function in MathCAD can be used to construct other piecewise continuous functions. To do so, we assign the following function,

```
pulse(x,a,b)  := Φ (x - a)  - Φ (x - b)
```

The independent variable of the function is x; the parameters are a and b ($a < b$). Careful inspection shows that the pulse function is 1 in the interval $a \leq x \leq b$ and 0 otherwise. Using engineering terminology, we say that our user-defined pulse function turns *on* at x=a and turns *off* at x=b. A worksheet verifying this is shown in Fig. 3.2. The function shown in Fig. 3.2 has been set to turn on at x=2 and off at x=4. We have manually set the vertical scale to (-2 to 2).

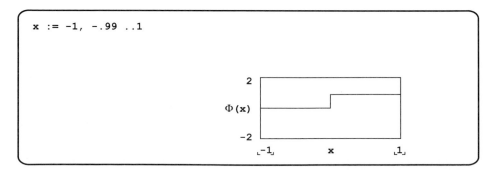

FIGURE 3.1

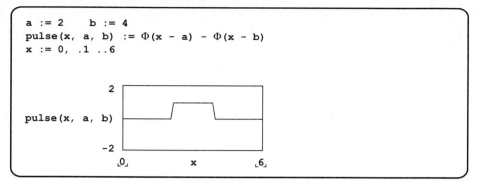

FIGURE 3.2

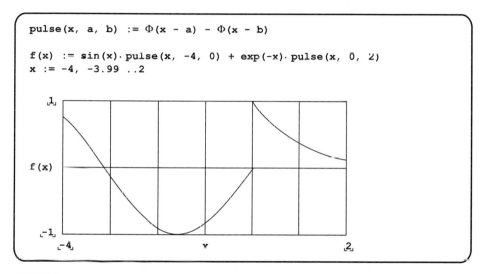

FIGURE 3.3

To generate the piecewise continuous function:

$$f(x) = \sin(x) \qquad -2 < x < 0$$
$$f(x) = e^{-x} \qquad\quad 0 < x < 2$$

we set up the worksheet shown in Fig. 3.3. The graph settings are `subdivs = 2,6` and `size = 10,30`. Note that the function is a sine to the left of the origin and an exponential to the right. Actually, the above function could have been generated more easily using MathCAD's **if** function as:

```
y(x) := if(x ≥ 0, e⁻ˣ, sin(x))
```

However, for a piecewise function that is defined differently over *more* than two intervals, the Heaviside function approach is more convenient.

Piecewise Periodic Functions

We often encounter a *periodic* function $f(x)$ which is piecewise continuous. The function is defined explicitly over a single period (or cycle) and is understood to repeat itself periodically outside that interval over the entire x-axis. For example, consider the square wave function defined as follows:

$$f(x) = +1 \qquad (0 < x \leq L/2)$$

$$f(x) = -1 \qquad (L/2 < x \leq L)$$

$$f(x + L) = f(x) \quad (-\infty < x < \infty)$$

The last relation extends the range of definition to include values of x outside the *primitive* interval $[0, L]$ and requires that the function repeat itself after a period L. Using MathCAD's **if** function, we define the function in the primitive interval as:

```
f(x)  = if(x ≤ L/2, 1, -1)
```

To extend the definition outside the primitive interval, consider the following use of the **if** function:

```
f(x)=if(x ≥ L,f(mod(x,L)),f(x))
```

and

```
f(x)=if(x ≤ 0,f(mod(x,L)+L),f(x))
```

If x is in the primitive interval, the original definition is unaffected. If x is greater than L, the function is evaluated at the point mod(x,L). Note that this brings the point x back to the corresponding position in the primitive interval. For example, if $L = 2$ and $x = 7.4$, then mod(x,L) = 1.4. The second **if** function makes corrections for values x ≤0. The effect of the two **if** functions is shown in Fig. 3.4. As can be seen from the graph, the effect is to convert the single step function to a periodic square wave.

DERIVATIVES AND INTEGRALS

Derivatives

In calculus, we define the derivative of a function $y(x)$ with respect to x as:

$$\frac{d}{dx}y(x) = \lim_{h \to 0} \frac{y(x + h) - y(x)}{h}$$

Consider a function $y(x) = \sin(x)$. We would like to find its derivative $y'(x)$. Create the following worksheet by typing: **y(x):sin(x)**, **y'(x):x?y(x)**. You should see:

```
y(x)  := sin(x)

            y'(x)  :=  d/dx y(x)
```

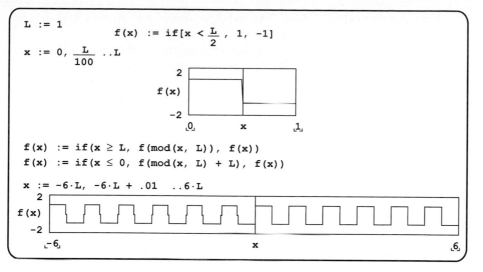

FIGURE 3.4

The prime symbol is generated by typing the single *backquote* key ('). It is used here as a literal to denote the derivative of the function. The single quote key (') produces a pair of parentheses and is *not* to be used for variable notation.

MathCAD uses the question mark (**?**) to create the derivative template. If you type **x?**, the variable x is set as the differentiation variable and you see:

$$\frac{d}{dx}\ \blacksquare$$

You need only insert the function $y(x)$ at the placeholder. If, however, you type just **?**, you see:

$$\frac{d}{d\blacksquare}\ \blacksquare$$

and you must fill in both placeholders.

In summary, to generate a derivative template we use either method (a) or (b) below:

a. Type **x?** and see

$$\frac{d}{dx}\ \blacksquare$$

We then fill the placeholder for the function.

b. Type **?** and see

$$\frac{d}{d\blacksquare}\ \blacksquare$$

We then fill *both* the placeholders.

The worksheet shown in Figs. 3.5a and 3.5b verifies that the first derivative of sin(x) is cos(x) and that the second derivative is $-$ sin(x).

The first three objects in Fig. 3.5a define the function and its derivatives. They are generated by typing: **y(x):sin(x)**, **y'(x):x?y(x)**, and **y"(x):x?y'(x)**. The double prime is generated with two backquotes. The next two lines are a clever way to generate a "what-if" template for defining a range. The left-most boundary of the range (in this case $-\pi$) is assigned to start, while the right-most boundary (in this case π) is assigned to finish. (Recall that to get π, type **{<Alt>P}**. Unless otherwise

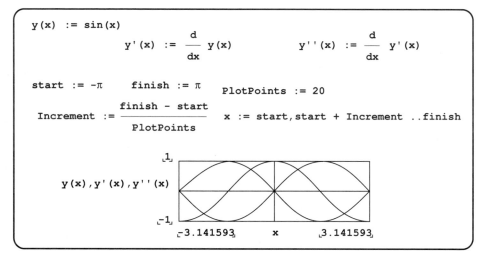

FIGURE 3.5a

x	cos(x)	y'(x)	−sin(x)	y''(x)
−3.142	−1	−1	0	0
−2.827	−0.951	−0.951	0.309	0.309
−2.513	−0.809	−0.809	0.588	0.588
−2.199	−0.588	−0.588	0.809	0.809
−1.885	−0.309	−0.309	0.951	0.951
−1.571	0	0	1	1
−1.257	0.309	0.309	0.951	0.951
−0.942	0.588	0.588	0.809	0.809
−0.628	0.809	0.809	0.588	0.588
−0.314	0.951	0.951	0.309	0.309
0	1	1	0	0
0.314	0.951	0.951	−0.309	−0.309
0.628	0.809	0.809	−0.588	−0.588
0.942	0.588	0.588	−0.809	−0.809
1.257	0.309	0.309	−0.951	−0.951
1.571	0	0	−1	−1
1.885	−0.309	−0.309	−0.951	−0.951
2.199	−0.588	−0.588	−0.809	−0.809
2.513	−0.809	−0.809	−0.588	−0.588
2.827	−0.951	−0.951	−0.309	−0.309
3.142	−1	−1	0	0

FIGURE 3.5b

assigned, MathCAD assumes π to have the value 3.14159. ...) The number of points to be plotted is assigned to `PlotPoints`. The increment is computed and assigned accordingly. Finally the range for x is assigned. The variable names `start`, `finish`, `PlotPoints`, and `Increment` are arbitrary; any valid names work. To get better resolution, we can increase `PlotPoints`; however, this increases the time it takes for MathCAD to complete the calculations.

Typing the @ key, we generate the graph template and then plot `y(x)`, `y'(x)`, and `y"(x)` using the graph setting `subdivs = 2,2`. Each graph will appear be in a different color on a color monitor. The reader should easily be able to identify the $\sin(x)$, $\cos(x)$, and $-\sin(x)$ graphs.

To get the tabular results in Fig. 3.5*b*, we type **x=**, **cos(x)=**, **y'(x)=**, **-sin(x)=**, and **y"(x)=**. The global zero tolerance was set at `zt=5` using the **{Esc} FORM** command. All numbers smaller than 10^{-5} display as zero. Note how the tables match up. We have thus demonstrated that the derivative of a sine is a cosine and that the second derivative is the negative of the sine.

NOTE ON HIGHER DERIVATIVES. In the worksheet in Fig. 3.5, we used two steps to compute a second derivative. We can also take a second derivative using a single operation. If we type **y:sin(x)**, **y"(x):⌄?x?y(x)**, we see:

$$y(x) \;:= \; \sin(x)$$
$$y''(x) \;:= \; \frac{d}{dx}\,\frac{d}{dx}\,y(x)$$

Warning: As a general rule, MathCAD tends to calculate slowly and gives progressively poorer results if the order of the derivative is too large. One should therefore use analytical expressions for derivatives where possible.

Derivatives and Tangent Lines

Consider the graph of a function $y(x)$. The derivative at some point on the curve, let us say x_0, is equal to the slope of the line tangent to the curve at that point. In Fig. 3.6 we set up a worksheet in which we graph an arbitrary function (in this case $\sin(x)$) along with the tangent line to the curve at an arbitrary point x_0 (in this case $\pi/4$).

The first three objects define the function $y(x)$, the reference point x_0, and the derivative of the function. The three objects on the second line evaluate the function at x_0 (assigned to y_0), the slope of the tangent line at x_0, and the intercept of that line.[1]

In general, a variable name used for a function (e.g., $y(x)$) cannot later be used for a subscripted variable (e.g., y_n) and vice-versa. The later definition overrides the earlier one. Note that the subscripts used here on the variables x and y are purely

---

[1]The intercept is obtained by transforming the point-slope form $(y - y_0)/(x - x_0) = m$ into the standard form $y = m \cdot x + b$.

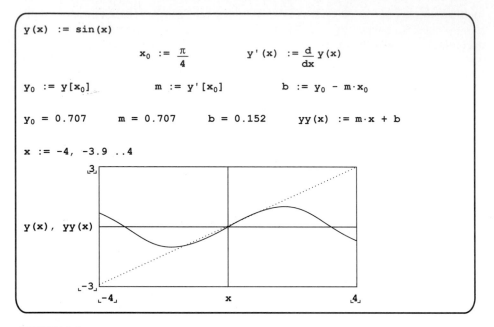

FIGURE 3.6

notational (or literal) and are *not* mathematical subscripts. We type **x.0** and **y.0** to produce these subscripts and *not* **x[0** and **y[0**.

The first three objects on the third line display the corresponding values of y_0, m, and b. The last object on that line defines the straight line equation yy (x). Finally, x is assigned a range and y (x) and yy (x) are plotted. The graph format settings are subdivs = 2,2 and type = 1d. This type setting causes the second function plotted (i.e., the straight line) to appear as a series of dots. To answer the "what-if" question, simply change the value of x_0. You should see the tangent line to the curve change accordingly.

The Maxima-Minima Problem

Consider the function $y = e^{-x} \cdot \cos(10 \cdot x)$. We wish to graph the function for positive x and find the first root, the first local (relative) minimum, and the first local (relative) maximum. Local minima and maxima are called extrema. In calculus, it is shown that the first derivative vanishes at the extrema. Furthermore, an extremum will be a local maximum if the second derivative is negative and a local minimum if it is positive. We use the worksheet shown in Fig. 3.7 to find the first few extrema and to classify them.

We have assigned the range variable x, the function y (x), and its first two derivatives. The graph of the function is displayed using subdivs = 2,10. From the graph, we see that the first root (or zero) occurs for a value of x slightly larger than 0.1. Using this value as our guess, we apply the **root** function to find the first

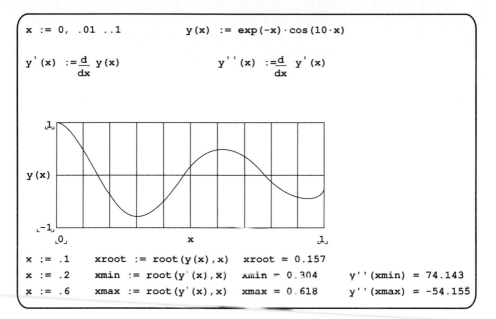

```
x := 0, .01 ..1          y(x) := exp(-x)·cos(10·x)

y'(x) :=d  y(x)                  y''(x) :=d  y'(x)
        dx                               dx
```

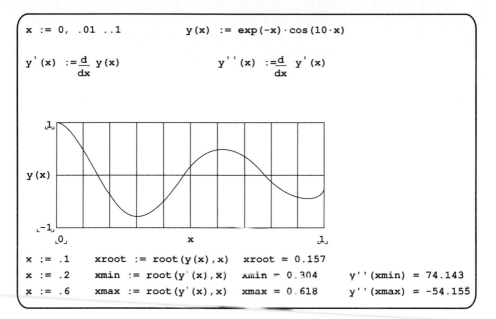

```
x := .1     xroot := root(y(x),x)   xroot = 0.157
x := .2     xmin := root(y'(x),x)   xmin = 0.304     y''(xmin) = 74.143
x := .6     xmax := root(y'(x),x)   xmax = 0.618     y''(xmax) = -54.155
```

FIGURE 3.7

root (xroot=0.157). Next, we find the first value at which the first derivative vanishes (i.e., the first minimum). This occurs to the right of x=0.2. Using this value as our guess, we apply the **root** function to the derivative function y'(x) and find xmin=0.304. We evaluate the second derivative at xmin and find that it is positive, confirming that it is indeed a minimum. The first maximum is found in a similar manner (xmax=0.618).

Definite Integrals

The area of the region bounded by the x-axis ($y = 0$), the lines $x = a$ and $x = b$, and the curve represented by the function $y(x)$ is given by the definite integral:

$$\text{Area} = \int_a^b y(x)dx = F(b) - F(a)$$

The function $F(x)$ is called the *antiderivative* of $y(x)$ because

$$y(x) = \frac{d}{dx}F(x)$$

To compute a definite integral with MathCAD, we use the *ampersand* key **&**. If we type **a:0**, **b:π**, **y(x):sin(x)**, **Area:x&** we see:

```
a := 0       b := π
y(x) := sin(x)
                 Area := ∫▪ ▪ dx
```

We fill the placeholder for the integrand with y(x). Using the arrow keys or the {Tab} key, move to the limit holders and fill the upper one with b and the lower one with a. Finally, we type **Area=** and obtain:

```
a := 0          b := π
y(x) := sin(x)
                        ⌠b
              Area :=   │   y(x) dx           Area = 2
                        ⌡a
```

Thus the area under the function $y(x) = \sin(x)$ between $x = 0$ and $x = \pi$ is 2. By changing the values of a and b or changing the function y(x), we can compute areas under different curves over different intervals.

In summary, to generate a definite integral template we use either method (a) or (b) as follows.

a. Type **x&** and see

$$\int_{\blacksquare}^{\blacksquare} \blacksquare \; dx$$

We then fill the placeholders for the integrand and for the limits.

b. Type **&** and see

$$\int_{\blacksquare}^{\blacksquare} \blacksquare \; d\blacksquare$$

We then fill *all* the placeholders.

Integrals with a Variable Upper Limit, Antiderivatives

It is possible to define a function as follows:

$$F(x) = \int_{0}^{x} f(t)dt$$

Note that a different (dummy) variable t is used in the integration process. (While this is not absolutely necessary with MathCAD, it is the accepted notation.) Because of the variable in the upper limit, the resulting integral is a function of x. As discussed previously, $F(x)$ is also called the *antiderivative* of $f(x)$ because

$$f(x) = \frac{d}{dx} F(x)$$

When an arbitrary constant is added to $F(x)$, the result is called an *indefinite* integral. Using the rule,

$$\frac{d}{dx} \sin(x) = \cos(x)$$

we may write the following integral relation:

$$F(x) = \int_0^x \cos(t)dt = \sin(t)\Big|_0^x = \sin(x) - \sin(0) = \sin(x)$$

To verify this relation with MathCAD, we develop the worksheet shown in Fig. 3.8. We assign the function $F(x)$ using an integral with a variable upper limit and plot both the function and sin(x). The graph setting is type = lo. This allows the graph points of the sine function to be displayed with rectangles. The tables are displayed by typing **x=**, **F(x)=**, and **sin(x)=** . The command **{Esc} FORM** zt=5 is invoked to display numbers smaller than 10^{-5} as zero. Since the two graphs coincide, we have verified that $F(x) = \sin(x)$.

Improper Integrals

There are two situations which make an integral *improper*:

1. the integrand becomes infinite at isolated points on the interval of integration; or
2. the upper or lower limit on the integral is infinity.

We must calculate an improper integral using a limiting process. Only if this limit exists, do we say that the integral exists. Consider the integral:

$$I = \int_1^\infty \left(\frac{1}{x^2}\right) dx$$

To evaluate this integral (if it exists), we must compute:

$$I = \lim_{x \to \infty} F(x)$$

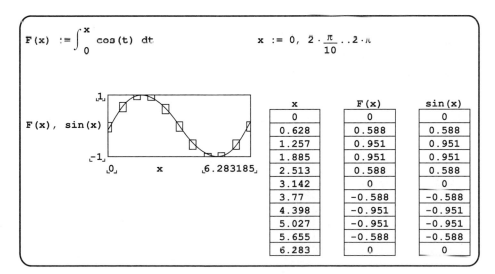

x	F(x)	sin(x)
0	0	0
0.628	0.588	0.588
1.257	0.951	0.951
1.885	0.951	0.951
2.513	0.588	0.588
3.142	0	0
3.77	-0.588	-0.588
4.398	-0.951	-0.951
5.027	-0.951	-0.951
5.655	-0.588	-0.588
6.283	0	0

FIGURE 3.8

where

$$F(x) = \int_1^x \left(\frac{1}{t^2}\right) dt$$

Using basic calculus, it can be shown that $F(x) = 1 - 1/x$. Thus in the limit $x \to \infty$, $F(x) \to 1$. Hence the integral exists and is equal to 1.

To use MathCAD to verify the result, consider the worksheet shown in Fig. 3.9. The range variable x and the integral function F (x) are assigned and listed for three values of x (by typing **x=** and **F(x)=**). Note that as x goes from 100 to 150, F (x) only changes in the third decimal place. This suggests that the limit is one. Note how slow the process is; MathCAD computes this type of integral with some difficulty. In fact if we try to display F (200), we get a not converging error. To speed convergence and obtain better results, consider the worksheet shown in Fig. 3.10,

In Fig. 3.10 we break up the original integral into two separate integrals. The first integral is over the fixed interval [1,100] and gives a constant G. The second integral is over the interval [100,x] and generates a function H (x). The function F (x) is the sum of these two integrals. In this format, MathCAD performs the integral

$$F(x) := \int_1^x \frac{1}{t^2} dt \qquad x := 100, \; 125 \; ..150$$

x	F (x)
100	0.99
125	0.992
150	0.993

FIGURE 3.9

$$G := \int_1^{100} \frac{1}{t^2} dt \qquad H(x) := \int_{100}^x \frac{1}{t^2} dt \qquad F(x) := G + H(x)$$

$$x := 100, \; 500 \; ..4900$$

x	F (x)
100	0.99
500	0.998
900	0.999
1300	0.999
1700	0.999
2100	1
2500	1
2900	1
3300	1
3700	1
4100	1
4500	1
4900	1

FIGURE 3.10

more rapidly and the results clearly show that the limit of $F(x)$ (as x approaches infinity) is one. To avoid overflow to exponential format in the x list, increase the global exponential tolerance by typing **{Esc} FORM** and setting et=6.

MathCAD can also perform multiple (iterated) integrals. If we type **I:&&**, we see:

$$I \; := \; \int_{\blacksquare}^{\blacksquare} \; \int_{\blacksquare}^{\blacksquare} \; \blacksquare \; \mathrm{d}\blacksquare \; \mathrm{d}\blacksquare$$

Typing **&** twice generates a double integral. We need only fill in the placeholders. Using **&** n times leads to an n-fold integral. We shall discuss multiple integrals in Chapter 4.

SEQUENCES, SERIES SUMS, SERIES PRODUCTS, AND FACTORIALS

Sequences

A *sequence* is a pattern of numbers defined by some rule. The rule can be established by requiring that the numbers of the sequence be subscripted and that their values be related to their subscripts. The subscripts n are assumed to be integers ranging from zero to infinity. For example, we might have a sequence defined by the symbol $\{n\}$ which means that every number in the sequence is equal to its own subscript, that is, $a_n = n$. If we start with the subscript 0, then we have $\{n\} = 0, 1, 2, 3, 4, 5, \ldots$. Similarly we could have:

$$\{n^2 + 1\} = 1, 2, 5, 10, 17, \ldots$$

or

$$\{2^n\} = 0, 1, 2, 4, 8, 16 \ldots$$

To generate sequences with MathCAD, we define an integer range variable for use as a subscript. We next construct a variable using this subscript and assign values to it with a given formula. The subscripted variable can be displayed in tabular form. Using the following objects: **n:0;10**, **a[n:n**, **b[n:n^2+1**, **c[n:2^n**, **d[n:.5^n**, **n=**, **a[n=**, **b[n=**, **c[n=**, **d[n=**, the worksheet appears as shown in Fig. 3.11. The (integer) subscript is n and ranges from 0 to 10. Four subscripted variables, a_n, b_n, c_n, and d_n, are assigned using different formulas. The values of each are displayed in tabular form.

Series Sums

A finite series is defined as the sum of a finite number of terms in a sequence. Suppose we have the sequence $\{n\}$ and wish to sum all the numbers of the sequence starting

$n := 0 \ ..10$

$a_n := n$ $\qquad$ $b_n := n^2 + 1$ $\qquad$ $c_n := 2^n$ $\qquad$ $d_n := .5^n$

n	a_n	b_n	c_n	d_n
0	0	1	1	1
1	1	2	2	0.5
2	2	5	4	0.25
3	3	10	8	0.125
4	4	17	16	0.063
5	5	26	32	0.031
6	6	37	64	0.016
7	7	50	128	0.008
8	8	65	256	0.004
9	9	82	512	0.002
10	10	101	1024	0.001

FIGURE 3.11

at zero and ending at some number, let us say, N. We write this series sum as:

$$\sum_{n=0}^{N} n = 0 + 1 + 2 + 3 + \cdots + N$$

The summation symbol $\sum$ (sigma) is used to designate a series sum. Other examples are:

$$\sum_{n=0}^{N} (n^2 + 1) = 1 + 2 + 5 + 10 + 17 + \cdots + (N^2 + 1)$$

$$\sum_{n=0}^{N} (2^n) = 1 + 2 + 4 + 8 + 16 + \cdots + 2^N$$

MathCAD can evaluate a finite series of a sequence of subscripted variables. We must first assign an integer range variable to represent the index or subscript in our summation. To perform the summation with MathCAD, enter the objects: **n:0;5**, **A:$**. The screen should appear as shown in Fig. 3.12*a*. The summation template is created using the **$** key. Fill the placeholder after the summation symbol with the appropriate subscripted variable (or function of n) to be summed. Using the arrow keys or the **{Tab}** key, move to the placeholder below the summation sign and enter the subscript or index variable. This tells MathCAD to sum over the preassigned range.

In summary, to generate a summation template we use either method (a) or (b) listed here.

a. Type **n$** and the screen should appear as shown in Fig. 3.12*b*. Then fill the placeholder with the subscripted quantity to be summed.

b. Type **$** and the screen should appear as shown in Fig. 3.12*c*. Then fill *both* the placeholders.

n := 0 ..5

$$A := \sum_{\blacksquare} \blacksquare$$

FIGURE 3.12*a*

$$\sum_{n} \blacksquare$$

FIGURE 3.12*b*

$$\sum_{\blacksquare} \blacksquare$$

FIGURE 3.12*c*

Note that the index for a summation is an integer range variable and must be defined *before* the summation is performed.

Create a worksheet by typing the following: **N:6**, **n:0;N**, **a[n:n**, **b[n:n^2+1**, **c[n:2^n**, **SumA:$a[n{Tab}n**, **SumB:$b[n{Tab}n**, **SumC:$c[n{Tab}n**, **SumA=**, **SumB=**, **SumC=**. The screen should appear as in Fig. 3.13. In the worksheet, we assign an upper limit $(N=6)$ for our summation index (i.e., the range variable, n). Next, we make the range assignment for the index variable as well as assignments for three different subscripted variables. The next row of objects performs summations for a_n, b_n, c_n and assigns them to the variables SumA, SumB, SumC. The results are displayed in the last row of objects.

N := 6   n := 0 ..N

$a_n := n$ $b_n := n^2 + 1$ $c_n := 2^n$

$$SumA := \sum_{n} a_n \qquad SumB := \sum_{n} b_n \qquad SumC := \sum_{n} c_n$$

SumA = 21   SumB = 98   SumC = 127

FIGURE 3.13

The worksheet in Fig. 3.13 demonstrates the following:

$$\sum_{n=0}^{6} n = 0 + 1 + 2 + 3 + 4 + 5 + 6 = 21$$

$$\sum_{n=0}^{6} (n^2 + 1) = 1 + 2 + 5 + 10 + 17 + 26 + 37 = 98$$

$$\sum_{n=0}^{6} (2^n) = 1 + 2 + 4 + 8 + 16 + 32 + 64 = 127$$

We can evaluate each of the above series for any number of terms by changing the assigned value of N.

Series Products

We next consider the *product* of a group of elements of a sequence $\{n\}$ which we write as,

$$\prod_{n=1}^{N} n = 1 \cdot 2 \cdot 3 \cdot 4 \cdot \ \cdots \ \cdot N$$

The symbol π (pi) is used to denote a product. To generate a product template with MathCAD, we use the **#** key. Create a worksheet by typing the following: **n:1;5**, **c[n:n**, **Prod:#c[n{Tab}n**, **Prod=**. The screen should appear as in Fig. 3.14.

The series product follows a format similar to that of the series sum. The worksheet in Fig. 3.15 gives more examples of series products. The worksheet shown in Fig. 3.15 verifies that:

$$1 \cdot 2 \cdot 3 = 6$$

$$2 \cdot 5 \cdot 10 = 100$$

$$2 \cdot 4 \cdot 8 = 64$$

By changing the value of N, we change the number of terms in the product.

Factorial

A simple type of product is the *factorial* of a nonnegative integer written as $n!$. By definition, we have:

$$n! = 1 \cdot 2 \cdot 3 \cdot \ \cdots \ \cdot n$$

```
n := 1 ..5      c_n := n
                          Prod := ∏ c_n       Prod = 120
                                   n
```

FIGURE 3.14

$$N := 3 \qquad n := 1 \, .. N \qquad a_n := n$$

$$b_n := n^2 + 1 \qquad c_n := 2^n$$

$$ProdA := \prod_n a_n \qquad ProdB := \prod_n b_n \qquad ProdC := \prod_n c_n$$

$$ProdA = 6 \qquad\qquad ProdB = 100 \qquad\qquad ProdC = 64$$

FIGURE 3.15

Thus $3! = 6$, $4! = 24$, $5! = 120$, etc. ($0!$ is *defined* to be 1.) To represent a factorial in MathCAD, simply follow the number or the variable name with an exclamation mark !. The worksheet shown in Fig. 3.16 summarizes the factorial, series sum, and series products.

VECTORS

Elements of Vector Algebra

To complete this chapter, we consider how MathCAD handles vector algebra. A vector is a quantity that has both magnitude and direction. A scalar has just magnitude. We consider a vector in a three dimensional space. Such a vector can be represented by specifying the components along the x, y, and z axes of a Cartesian reference frame. A vector $\mathbf{A}$ can be resolved into its components A_x, A_y, and A_z and displayed as a column array:

$$A = \begin{bmatrix} A_x \\ A_y \\ A_z \end{bmatrix}$$

If two vectors are equal, their corresponding components are equal.

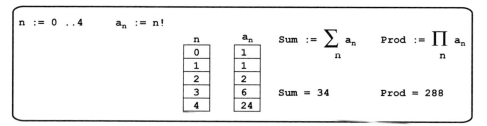

$$n := 0 \, .. 4 \qquad a_n := n!$$

n	a_n
0	1
1	1
2	2
3	6
4	24

$$Sum := \sum_n a_n \qquad Prod := \prod_n a_n$$

$$Sum = 34 \qquad Prod = 288$$

FIGURE 3.16

The following rules apply to vectors:

a. Magnitude of a vector:

$$A = |\mathbf{A}| = [A_x^2 + A_y^2 + A_z^2]^{1/2}$$

b. Addition (or subtraction) of vectors:

$$\mathbf{C} = \mathbf{A} \pm \mathbf{B} \qquad C_x = A_x \pm B_x \qquad C_y = A_y \pm B_y \qquad C_z = A_z \pm B_z$$

$$\begin{bmatrix} C_x \\ C_y \\ C_z \end{bmatrix} = \begin{bmatrix} A_x \\ A_y \\ A_z \end{bmatrix} \pm \begin{bmatrix} B_x \\ B_y \\ B_z \end{bmatrix} = \begin{bmatrix} A_x \pm B_x \\ A_y \pm B_y \\ A_z \pm B_z \end{bmatrix}$$

c. Multiplication of a vector by a scalar:

$$\mathbf{D} = a \cdot \mathbf{A} \qquad D_x = a \cdot A_x \qquad D_y = a \cdot A_y \qquad D_z = a \cdot A_z$$

$$\begin{bmatrix} D_x \\ D_y \\ D_z \end{bmatrix} = a \cdot \begin{bmatrix} A_x \\ A_y \\ A_z \end{bmatrix} = \begin{bmatrix} a \cdot A_x \\ a \cdot A_y \\ a \cdot A_z \end{bmatrix}$$

d. Scalar (dot) product of two vectors:

$$c = \mathbf{A} \cdot \mathbf{B} \qquad c = A_x \cdot B_x + A_y \cdot B_y + A_z \cdot B_z$$

e. Vector (cross) product of two vectors:

$$\mathbf{C} = \mathbf{A} \times \mathbf{B} \qquad \begin{aligned} C_x &= (A_y \cdot B_z - A_z \cdot B_y) \\ C_y &= (A_z \cdot B_x - A_x \cdot B_z) \\ C_z &= (A_x \cdot B_y - A_y \cdot B_x) \end{aligned}$$

Note that (b), (c), and (e) lead to vectors whereas (a) and (d) lead to scalars. The following is also true:

f.

$$c = \mathbf{A} \cdot \mathbf{B} = |\mathbf{A}| \cdot |\mathbf{B}| \cdot \cos(\theta)$$

where θ is the angle between **A** and **B**.

g.

$$|\mathbf{C}| = |\mathbf{A} \times \mathbf{B}| = |\mathbf{A}| \cdot |\mathbf{B}| \cdot \sin(\theta)$$

where θ is the angle between **A** and **B**.

Applying MathCAD to Vector Algebra

MathCAD handles vector algebra in a straightforward manner. To assign a vector A, we use the method of matrices introduced in the previous chapter. We type: **A:{<Alt>M}**. The message line appears as follows:

no file	Array size (rows columns):	9	10	auto

in version 2.0; and

Array size (rows columns):	9	10	auto

in version 2.5.

To produce a column vector template, enter **n 1** after the colon where n represents the number of elements in the vector. Use a space to separate the n from the 1. (You may also omit the 1 and just type **n**.) For example, if we enter **3 1**, the following template appears:

$$A := \begin{bmatrix} \blacksquare \\ \blacksquare \\ \blacksquare \end{bmatrix}$$

Simply fill the placeholders with the appropriate values and the vector will be assigned. To evaluate the magnitude of a vector, use the absolute value symbol | | (type the ¦ key). To add or subtract vectors, use the ordinary plus **+** and minus **-** keys. To take the scalar product of two vectors use the asterisk **∗**. Finally, to take the cross product, type **{<Alt>∗}** (and see the ✕ symbol appear). The worksheet in Fig. 3.17 illustrates these operations.

The deg unit is first globally defined using the ~ (tilde) key. A scalar and two vectors are assigned. The following operations are also assigned: multiplication of a vector by a scalar, addition of two vectors, the scalar product, and the vector product. (Use **∗** for the dot product and **{<Alt>∗}** for the cross product.) The quantities are displayed on the next line. The magnitudes of the vectors are displayed next. On the last row we have displayed a *mixed product*, that is, one involving both the dot and cross products. Finally, we compute the angle between the vectors **A** and **B** using Rule (**f**) above. The key strokes for this assignment are as follows:

$$\text{deg} \equiv \frac{\pi}{180} \qquad a := 2 \qquad A := \begin{bmatrix} 2 \\ 1 \\ 3 \end{bmatrix} \qquad B := \begin{bmatrix} 1 \\ -2 \\ 4 \end{bmatrix}$$

$$C := a \cdot A \qquad D := A + B \qquad c := A \cdot B \qquad E := A \times B$$

$$C := \begin{bmatrix} 4 \\ 2 \\ 6 \end{bmatrix} \qquad D := \begin{bmatrix} 3 \\ -1 \\ 7 \end{bmatrix} \qquad c := 12 \qquad E := \begin{bmatrix} 10 \\ -5 \\ -5 \end{bmatrix}$$

$$|A| = 3.742 \qquad |B| = 4.583 \qquad |C| = 7.483 \qquad |D| = 7.681 \qquad |E| \ 12.247$$

$$(A \times B) \cdot E = 150 \qquad \theta := \text{acos}\left[\frac{A \cdot B}{|A| \cdot |B|} \right] \qquad \theta = 45.585 \cdot \text{deg}$$

FIGURE 3.17

$$a := \begin{bmatrix} 2 \\ 1 \\ 4 \end{bmatrix} \qquad b := \begin{bmatrix} 1 \\ 5 \\ 2 \end{bmatrix} \qquad \begin{array}{l} c := a \cdot b \\ c = 15 \end{array} \qquad \begin{array}{l} d := \overrightarrow{(a \cdot b)} \\ \\ d := \begin{bmatrix} 2 \\ 5 \\ 8 \end{bmatrix} \end{array}$$

FIGURE 3.18

{<Alt>Q}:acos((A∗B)/(|A∗|B)). To display the angle θ in degrees, type **{<Alt>Q}=** and fill the placeholder with the user-defined unit, deg.

Warning: Do not confuse a vector operation with a vectorized operation! As an example of the difference between the two, consider the worksheet shown in Fig. 3.18. The scalar (dot) product of the two vectors gives a scalar value of c=15. The vectorized product d generates a vector array in which each element is the product of the corresponding elements of a and b. The vector **d** has *no* special significance in vector algebra. (Recall from Chapter 2, that the vectorized object is generated using: **d:{<Alt>-}(a∗b){Enter}.**)

In the next chapter, we use the tools presented here to develop applications to general calculus. We will study derivatives and integrals and their applications. Worksheets involving polar coordinates, parametric equations, and multivariable calculus will also be presented.

PROBLEMS

1. Using calculus, it can be shown that,

$$\frac{d[\sin^{-1}(x)]}{dx} = \frac{1}{[1 - x^2]^{1/2}}$$

Verify this result as follows:
   (a) Assign the function $f(x) = \text{asin}(x)$ and its derivative $f'(x) = df(x)/dx$
   (b) Assign the function $h(x) = 1/[1 - x^2]^{1/2}$
   (c) Plot both $f'(x)$ and $h(x)$ versus x. Use the plot range $x = 0, 0.05 \,..0.95$ and the plot format type=lo.

2. Let a pure harmonic waveform be represented by $y(t) = A \cdot \sin(t)$ where A is the amplitude of the signal. Noise on the signal can be simulated with a random number generator. Assume that random noise whose amplitude is B is added to the signal. Simulate and plot the signal over one cycle as follows:
   (a) Assign t values as follows:

$$N = 100, \qquad n = 0 \,..N \qquad \text{and} \qquad t_n = 2 \cdot \pi \cdot n/N$$

   (b) Assign the harmonic wave as:

$$A = 10 \qquad \text{and} \qquad \text{Signal}_n = A \cdot \sin(t_n)$$

   (c) Assign the noise function using:

$$B = 1 \qquad \text{and} \qquad \text{Noise}_n = 2 \cdot B \cdot (\text{rnd}(1) - 0.5)$$

Note that since rnd(1) produces random numbers ranging from zero to one, the Noise values fall randomly between $-B$ and $+B$.

(d) Construct the composite signal as:

$$\text{Composite}_n = \text{Signal}_n + \text{Noise}_n$$

(e) Plot Composite_n versus t_n.

3. Consider the following piecewise continuous function:

$$y(x) = -\sin(x) \qquad\qquad\qquad (-2 \cdot \pi \le x < -\pi)$$

$$= \cos\left(\frac{x}{2}\right) \cdot \exp[-0.1 \cdot x^2] \quad (-\pi \le x \le \pi)$$

$$= \sin(x) \qquad\qquad\qquad (\pi < x \le 2 \cdot \pi)$$

Plot the function and its derivative on the interval $[-2 \cdot \pi, \ 2 \cdot \pi]$ using the Heaviside function. Hint: As shown in the text, construct the composite function $y(x)$ using:

$$y(x) = -\sin(x) \cdot \text{pulse}(x, -2 \cdot \pi, -\pi) + \cdots$$

$$+ \cos\left(\frac{x}{2}\right) \cdot \exp(-0.1 \cdot x^2) \cdot \text{pulse}(x, \ \pi, \pi) + \cdots$$

$$+ \sin(x) \cdot \text{pulse}(x, \pi, 2 \cdot \pi)$$

where,

$$\text{pulse}(x, a, b) = \Phi(x - a) - \Phi(x - b)$$

4. Find the roots of the cubic polynomial,

$$y(x) = 2 \cdot x^3 + x^2 - 4 \cdot x - 2$$

Use the following steps:
(a) Plot the function on the interval $[-2, \ 2]$.
(b) Make guesses of $x_1 = -2$, $x_2 = 0$ and $x_3 = +2$ for the roots. Then use MathCAD's **root** function to precisely determine the three roots.
(c) By filling the placeholders appropriately, show that two of the roots are $\pm\sqrt{2}$.

5. We can *define* the natural log of x as follows:

$$\ln(x) \equiv \int_1^x \frac{1}{t} dt$$

(a) Verify this definition by assigning the functions,

$$f(x) = \int_1^x \frac{1}{t} dt \qquad \text{and} \qquad g(x) = \ln(x)$$

(b) Plot $f(x)$ and $g(x)$ versus x using a plot range of $x = 1, 1.5 \ .. 5$ and a plot **type** =lo.

6. (a) The logarithm of x to any base b can be computed from the natural logarithm using,

$$\log_b(x) = \frac{\ln(x)}{\ln(b)}$$

Verify that the formula is valid for the common log (i.e., base = 10). Hint: Define a function $\text{Log}(x, b) = \ln(x)/\ln(b)$. Then plot $\text{Log}(x, 10)$ and $\log(x)$ versus x using the plot parameters of Problem 5.

(b) The derivative of a general logarithm is given by,

$$d\frac{[\log_b(x)]}{dx} = \left[\frac{1}{\ln(b)}\right] \cdot \left[\frac{1}{x}\right]$$

Verify the above formula for the common logarithm. Hint: Continuing from part (a), assign the functions,

$$y'(x,b) = \frac{d}{dx}\text{Log}(x,b) \quad \text{and} \quad Y'(x,b) = \left[\frac{1}{\ln(b)}\right] \cdot \left[\frac{1}{x}\right]$$

Set $b = 10$ and plot both $y'(x,b)$ and $Y'(x,b)$ versus x as in part (a).

7. Consider the infinite series,

$$1 - \frac{1}{3} + \frac{1}{5} - \frac{1}{7} + \frac{1}{9} -, \cdots \infty$$

Show that this series converges (adds up) to $\pi/4$. Hint: Using $N = 1000$ and a subscript range of $n = 1 ..N$, set up the sum,

$$\text{Sum} = \sum_n \frac{(-1)^{(n-1)}}{(2 \cdot n - 1)}$$

Display the result, filling the placeholder with $\pi/4$.

8. Any three, nonparallel vectors **a**, **b**, and **c** span a parallelepiped whose volume is given by,

$$V = \mathbf{a} \cdot (\mathbf{b} \times \mathbf{c})$$

(a) Using this formula, compute the volume of the parallelpiped spanned by the vectors,

$$a = \begin{bmatrix} 1 \\ 3 \\ -2 \end{bmatrix} \qquad b = \begin{bmatrix} 1 \\ 2 \\ 3 \end{bmatrix} \qquad c = \begin{bmatrix} 3 \\ 2 \\ -1 \end{bmatrix}$$

(b) Show that the result is the same if we use,

$$V = \mathbf{c} \cdot (\mathbf{a} \times \mathbf{b})$$

APPLICATIONS TO GENERAL CALCULUS

INTRODUCTION

In the next two chapters we present applications of MathCAD to topics in general calculus and physics. For each topic we offer some background material, followed by a sample worksheet. Text is added to the worksheet to clarify the material. In most cases, text is underlined to distinguish it from computational work. Keystrokes for creating MathCAD objects in the worksheets are explained where necessary. For the basic keystrokes, however, it is assumed that the student is familiar with the material covered in the first three chapters. A summary of MathCAD's keystrokes is presented in Appendix A for the student's convenience.

SKETCHING A POLYNOMIAL

As our first application of MathCAD to calculus, we study the properties of the following fourth-degree polynomial,

$$y(x) = x^4 - 5 \cdot x^2 + 4$$

To begin the analysis, we find the roots of the function corresponding to the crossing points on the x-axis. As the function goes through these points, it changes sign, going from positive to negative or negative to positive.

Next, we find the points at which the first derivative vanishes. The slope of the tangent line to the curve becomes zero (horizontal) at these *stationary* points. At such a point, the curve has a relative extremum (i.e., a maximum or a minimum) provided the second derivative does not also vanish at the point. The extremum is a maximum if the second derivative is negative and a minimum if the second derivative is positive. Since the slope of the curve changes sign at the relative extrema, the curve goes from increasing to decreasing or from decreasing to increasing as the function passes through these points.

Finally, we find the points where the *second* derivative passes through zero and changes sign. At these *inflection* points, the curve changes concavity, going from concave up to concave down or vice versa. Once all these points are found, it is a

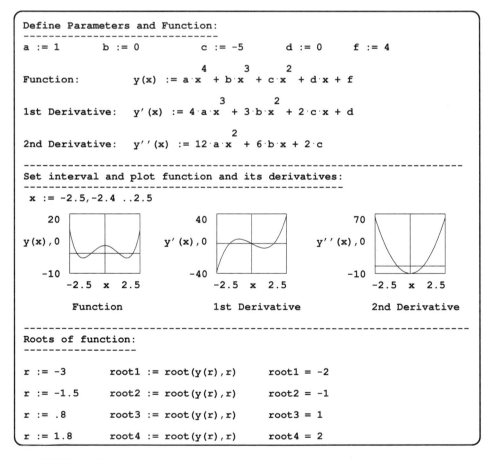

WORKSHEET 4.1
Sketching a polynomial (*cont. below*).

straightforward matter to sketch the function. An analysis of a polynomial is presented in Worksheet 4.1.

> **MathCAD solution: Worksheet 4.1.** We set the `zt` (global zero tolerance) parameter to `zt=3`. We then define a fourth-degree polynomial using the coefficients of the terms as parameters. To speed up computations, we assign the derivatives using analytical expressions rather than apply MathCAD's derivative operation. Recall that the prime symbol in `y'` is generated using the backquote key. We graph the function and its derivatives on the interval $[-2.5, 2.5]$ using `subdivs = 1,2`. This interval contains all the critical points of the polynomial. On each plot we also graph the constant `y= 0` to generate the x-axis.
>
> We next compute the roots (zeros) of the function. The graph of the function suggests that there are zero-crossing points in the vicinity of -3, -1.5, 1.5, and 3. Using these values as guesses, we apply MathCAD's **root** function to find the actual roots. The results for the four roots are: -2, -1, 1, and 2.
>
> The graph of the function shows that the polynomial has three relative extrema. This is confirmed by the fact that the first derivative has three zero-crossing points given by the roots of `y'(x)=0`. These roots are situated in the vicinity of -2, 0, and 2. Using the **root** function, their values are found to be -1.581, 0, and $+1.581$. An extremum point will be a relative minimum if the second derivative at that point is

```
Roots of 1st Derivative:
------------------------

r := -5      root1' := root(y'(r),r)     root1' = -1.581     First extremum

r := .1      root2' := root(y'(r),r)     root2' = 0          Second extremum

r := 3       root3' := root(y'(r),r)     root3' = 1.581      Third extremum



------         ------------------------------------------------------------
                     Classifying Extrema
                     -------------------
Stationary points:    root1' = -1.581     root2' = 0        root3' = 1.581

Second derivatives:
                   y''(root1') = 20
                              y''(root2') = -10
                                        y''(root3') = 20

 Classification:          (Minimum)         (Maximum)          (Minimum)

 ------------------------------------------------------------------------
Roots of 2nd Derivative:
------------------------

 r := -1     root1'' := root(y''(r),r)    root1'' = -0.913    Inflection Pt.

 r := 1      root2'' := root(y''(r),r)    root2'' = 0.913     Inflection Pt.
```

WORKSHEET 4.1
(*cont.*)

positive; it will be a relative maximum if the second derivative is negative. We see from the graph of the polynomial that `root1'` (x= -1.581) and `root3'` (x= 1.581) are minima while `root2'` (x= 0) is a maximum.

The function is *increasing* where the first derivative is positive and *decreasing* where the first derivative is negative. The function is therefore increasing on the intervals [-1.581, 0] and [+1.581, +∞] and decreasing on the intervals [-∞, -1.581] and [0, +1.581]. The second derivative has two roots. These roots, which mark the points of inflection, are found to be `root1"=-0.913` and `root2"=+0.913`. The function is concave *up* where the second derivative is positive and concave *down* where the second derivative is negative. Within the interval [-0.913, +0.913], the function is concave down; elsewhere it is concave up. The concavity changes at the inflection points. This is again confirmed by the graphs.

RELATED RATES

Consider the following problem. A lighthouse beacon located two miles off a straight shore line is rotating at a constant rate $d\theta/dt = \omega = \pi$ rad/s (0.5 revs/s). The beacon projects a moving spot of light onto a very long wall on the shoreline. A point P is situated on the wall directly opposite the lighthouse. Consider a point on the wall a distance x from the point P (see Fig. 4.1). We will see in Worksheet 4.2 that although the beacon rotates at a constant rate, the spot velocity along the wall is nonuniform. We wish to determine how fast the spot is moving along the wall when $x = 1$ mi.

This related rate problem is solved analytically using the following steps:

a. Establish the relationship between the variables x and θ. From Fig. 4.1, the desired relation is,

$$x(\theta) = 2 \cdot \tan(\theta)$$

or

$$\theta(x) = \arctan\left(\frac{x}{2}\right)$$

b. Using the chain rule, differentiate both sides of the equation in (a) *with respect to time*.

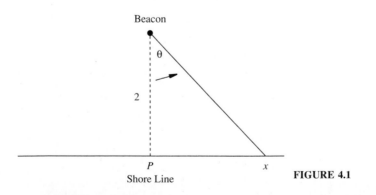

FIGURE 4.1

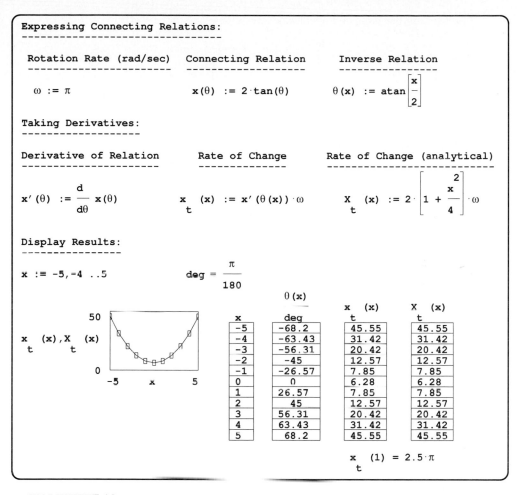

WORKSHEET 4.2
Related rates.

Differentiation gives,

$$\frac{dx}{dt} = [x'(\theta)] \cdot \left[\frac{d\theta}{dt}\right] \qquad \text{where} \qquad x'(\theta) = \frac{dx}{d\theta}$$

$$\frac{dx}{dt} = 2 \cdot [\sec^2(\theta)] \cdot \left[\frac{d\theta}{dt}\right]$$

c. Express the right-hand side of (b) in terms of x and evaluate it at the point in question.

Performing the indicated operations, we find

$$\frac{dx}{dt} = 2 \cdot [\sec^2(\theta)] \cdot [\pi]$$

$$= 2 \cdot [1 + \tan^2(\theta)] \cdot \pi$$

$$= 2 \cdot \left[1 + \frac{x^2}{4}\right] \cdot \pi$$

Evaluating the last expression at $x = 1$, we obtain $dx/dt = 2.5 \cdot \pi$ mi/s.

MathCAD solution: Worksheet 4.2. We assign the beacon rotation rate to the parameter ω and define both the direct and inverse connecting relations between x and θ, as required by (a). In the second row, we assign the derivative of x (with respect to θ) to the function x' (θ). The rate of change of x with respect to t is then computed using the chain rule and assigned to x_t (x). The last object on the row assigns the analytical result to X_t (x) and is presented here only to verify that our results are correct. Note that MathCAD treats x and X as different variables. Finally, the results are displayed in graphical and tabular form on the interval $[-5, \ 5]$.

We note that the beam spot moves the slowest (6.28 mi/s) when the beam is perpendicular to the shore line ($\theta = 0°$). As it moves away from this position on either side, the spot velocity increases rapidly. In particular, when $x = 1$ mi ($\theta = 26.57°$), the velocity of the spot is 7.85 mi/s or $2.5 \cdot \pi$ mi/s as the last object shows. MathCAD's direct calculations agree with the analytical results (plotted on the graph using rectangles). The last result is established by typing **X.t(1)=** and filling the placeholder with π (**{<Alt>P}**).

MAXIMA-MINIMA PROBLEMS

Consider the following problem. A person has the option to purchase a rectangular piece of property which he wants to enclose (Fig. 4.2). The price of decorative fencing for the front is $2.00/ft. whereas the price of plain fencing for the sides and rear is $1.00/ft. Assuming that the property must be a rectangular shape of area $= 1000$ ft^2, what should the dimensions be in order to minimize the fencing cost? What will that minimum cost be? The analytical solution to the problem involves the following steps:

a. Express the quantity to be minimized (the cost) in terms of the relevant variables (the dimensions x and y). The desired relation is,

$$\text{Cost}(x, y) = \text{Price}_{\text{Front}} \cdot x + \text{Price}_{\text{Rest}} \cdot (2 \cdot y + x)$$

b. Reduce the above expression to one involving only a single variable, for example, x. Since Area $= x \cdot y$, we have $y(x) = \text{Area}/x$. We therefore write,

$$\text{Cost}(x) = \text{Price}_{\text{Front}} \cdot x + \text{Price}_{\text{Rest}} \cdot \left(2 \cdot \frac{\text{Area}}{x} + x\right)$$

or

$$\text{Cost}(x) = 2 \cdot x + 1 \cdot \left(2 \cdot \frac{1000}{x} + x\right)$$

where we have substituted values for the area and the price of the fencing.

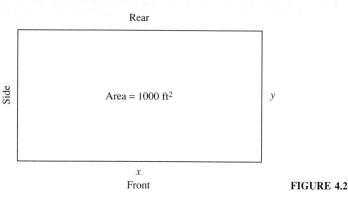

FIGURE 4.2

c. Take the derivative of the cost function derived in (b) and find the root x_{opt} (the optimum frontage) consistent with the constraints of the problem. In this case there is only one solution. Verify that the result is indeed a minimum either by checking the second derivative or by examining the graph of the cost function. Substitute x_{opt} into $y(x)$ and $Cost(x)$ to find y_{opt} (the optimum depth) and $Cost_{min}(x)$ (the minimum cost) of the fencing.

MathCAD solution: Worksheet 4.3. We fix the constants of the problem, namely the total area and the price of the fencing. Next, we express the side dimension y and the total cost Cost in terms of the front dimension x. The cost function Cost (x) is plotted versus x on the interval [10, 50] in steps of 0.5. The graph shows that the cost function has a minimum in the vicinity of x= 25.

To precisely fix the x value for the minimum, we differentiate the cost function and then use MathCAD's **root** function to find the root of the derivative x_{opt}. To increase the accuracy of the root search, we add **TOL ≡ .0001** to the worksheet. The results for x_{opt}, y_{opt}, and Cost are displayed in the last line. The answer to our problem is therefore,

$$x_{opt} = 25.82 \text{ ft} \qquad y_{opt} = 38.73 \text{ ft} \qquad Cost_{Min} = \$154.92$$

It is interesting to note that if we change the worksheet by making the price of the front fencing the same as that of the sides and rear, MathCAD gives the result,

$$x_{opt} = 31.623 \text{ ft} \qquad y_{opt} = 31.623 \text{ ft} \qquad Cost_{Min} = \$126.49$$

This demonstrates that given a set of rectangles of the same area, the square has the smallest perimeter.

INTEGRALS AND AREAS

The area of a region enclosed by a set of curves will be computed using the integral calculus. The computation is done by either adding infinitesimally thin *vertical* strips (integration with respect to x) or by adding infinitesimally thin *horizontal* strips (integration with respect to y). The two methods give the same result. However,

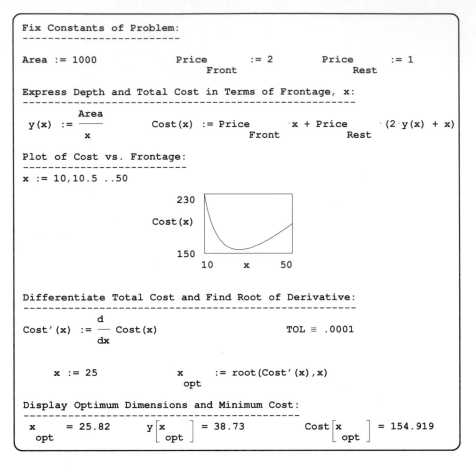

WORKSHEET 4.3

Maximum-minimum problem.

depending on the particular problem, one method may be simpler to use than the other.

As an example, we consider the area bounded by the parabola $f(x) = (1 - x^2)$, the straight line $g(x) = m \cdot x$, and the y-axis (Fig. 4.3). This problem is easier to solve using vertical strips. Each strip has a width of dx and a height equal to the difference between the upper function and the lower one. The differential area of any strip is therefore,

$$dA = [f(x) - g(x)] \cdot dx$$

The lower limit of integration for x is the y-axis ($x = 0$). The upper limit is determined by the x coordinate of the intersection point of the two curves, which we call x_2. The total area is therefore computed using,

$$A = \int_0^{x_2} [f(x) - g(x)] \cdot dx$$

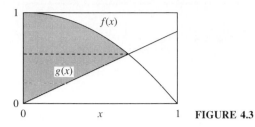

FIGURE 4.3

To solve the problem using horizontal strips, we divide the total area into two areas separated by a horizontal line passing through the intersection point of the curves (x_2, y_2) as shown in Fig. 4.3. The lower region has strips which are bounded on the left by the y-axis ($x = 0$) and on the right by the straight line $G(y)$. The upper region has strips which are bounded on the left by the y-axis ($x = 0$) and on the right by the parabola $F(y)$. The functions $G(y)$ and $F(y)$ are obtained by inverting the expressions $y = g(x)$ and $y = f(x)$ (i.e., solving for x in terms of y). The inversions give,

$$F(y) = \sqrt{(1 - y)} \qquad G(y) = \frac{y}{m}$$

In the lower region, horizontal strips ranging from $y = 0$ to $y = y_2$ are added. In the upper region, we add the strips ranging from $y = y_2$ to $y = 1$ (the y-intercept of the parabola). This fixes the limits of integration. The total area is the sum of the areas of the regions,

$$A = \int_0^{y_2} F(y) \cdot dy + \int_{y_2}^1 G(y) \cdot dy$$

Note that before either method can be applied, the coordinates of the point (x_2, y_2) must be computed. This problem is solved in Worksheet 4.4.

MathCAD solution: Worksheet 4.4. We assign the equations of the parabola and the straight line. The slope of the line is assigned as a parameter m (m=0.8). The two curves are plotted from zero to one using increments of one-tenth. MathCAD's **root** function is used to find the point of intersection of the curves (x₂=0.677, y₂=0.542). The area is then computed by integration with vertical strips; the area is found to be A= 0.39. Recall that the template for an integral is generated by typing **&**.

For comparison, the area is recomputed using horizontal strips. The total area integral, which is the sum of two separate integrals, is calculated by typing **Area:y&**. The following template will appear,

$$\text{Area} := \int_{\blacksquare}^{\blacksquare} \blacksquare \; dy$$

We place the cursor on the **y** and type **+y&** and observe,

We then move the cursor within the object and fill the placeholders accordingly.

Note that two methods give the same result. If we change the value of m, the computed area changes. However the result is still the same whether horizontal strips or vertical strips are used for the computation.

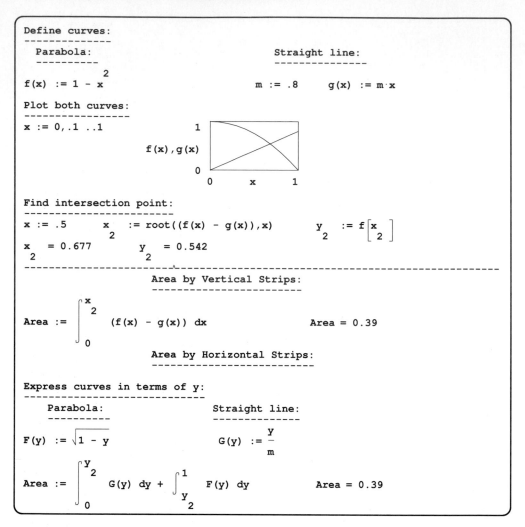

WORKSHEET 4.4
Integrals and areas.

SEQUENCES, SERIES, RECURSION

As discussed in Chapter 3, a sequence is a set of subscripted numbers whose values are related to their subscripts. Examples are,

$$\{n^2 + 1\}_0 = 1, 2, 5, 10, 17, \ldots,$$

or

$$\{2^n\}_0 = 1, 2, 4, 8, 16, \ldots,$$

The symbol $\{\ \}_0$ indicates that the subscripts begin with zero. A sequence may also start with a value other than zero.

Suppose we wish to compute the sum of the terms of an infinite sequence. A sum computed by starting with the first term and ending with the Nth term ($n = N$) is called an *N*th *partial sum*. For the two sequences above, the Nth partial sums are,

$$\text{Sum}_N = \sum_{n=0}^{N}(n^2 + 1) = 1 + 2 + 5 + 10 + 17 + \cdots + (N^2 + 1)$$

$$\text{Sum}_N = \sum_{n=0}^{N}(2^n) = 1 + 2 + 4 + 8 + 16 + \cdots + 2^N$$

The sum of an *infinite* series is defined as the limit of the Nth partial sum as N goes to infinity or

$$\text{Sum} = \sum_{n=0}^{\infty} a_n = \lim_{N \to \infty} \text{Sum}_N = \lim_{N \to \infty} \sum_{n=0}^{N} a_n$$

If this limit exists, the series is said to *converge*; if not, the series is said to *diverge*.

We consider the properties of a (finite) *geometric* series defined as,

$$\text{Sum}_N = \sum_{n=0}^{N} r^n = 1 + r + r^2 + r^3 + \cdots + r^N$$

The parameter r represents the *ratio* of the series. It is shown in calculus texts that for the geometric series the partial sum is evaluated by the analytical formula,

$$\text{Sum}_N = \left[\frac{1 - r^{(N+1)}}{1 - r} \right]$$

Using this expression, we determine that if $r < 1$, the infinite geometric series (taken as $N \to \infty$) converges to,

$$\text{Sum} = \frac{1}{1 - r}$$

If $r \geq 1$, the series diverges. Thus the geometric series,

$$1 + .5 + .5^2 + .5^3 + \cdots = \frac{1}{1 - .5} = 2$$

converges, whereas the geometric series,

$$1 + 1.5 + 1.5^2 + 1.5^3 + \cdots$$

diverges. The properties of the geometric series are examined in Worksheet 4.5.

A DIGRESSION ON RECURSION. Consider the following four objects:

Ratio: r := .5

Range: k := 0 ..10

Seeding: $\text{Sum}_0 := 1$

Recursion: $\text{Sum}_{(k+1)} := \text{Sum}_k + r^{k+1}$

The first object above assigns the value of the ratio. The second object defines the range for the index of recursion. The third object assigns a value to the first partial sum Sum_0. This last assignment is called *seeding* or *initialization*. The final object performs the required recursion and computes the succeeding partial sums. Each partial sum is evaluated by adding the current term of the series to the previous sum. There is a total of eleven (10+1) partial sums. The first few partial sums are computed as follows:

$k=0$ $\text{Sum}_1 = \text{Sum}_0 + r^1 = 1 + .5^1 = 1.5$

$k=1$ $\text{Sum}_2 = \text{Sum}_1 + r^2 = 1.5 + .5^2 = 1.75$

$k=2$ $\text{Sum}_3 = \text{Sum}_2 + r^3 = 1.75 + .5^3 = 1.875$

Note: To assign a subscripted variable of the form $\text{Sum}_{(k+1)}$:=, type **Sum[(k+1):**. If you omit the parentheses, the +1 term will be added to the subscripted variable rather than to the subscript. A similar rule holds for an expression in an exponent or superscript.

MathCAD solution: Worksheet 4.5. We define the ratio $(r=0.5)$, the number of terms to be summed $(N=6)$, and the range for the summation index n. We compute the sum of the five terms first by using MathCAD's summation operation and then by using the analytical formula given above. (Recall to generate the summation template, type **{<Alt>$}**.) If we change the value of N, the results change but both methods give the same value.

We would like to study the convergence of the geometric series by examining its behavior as N increases. The problem with using MathCAD's summation operation is that it only computes the results for one value of N at a time. We can study convergence more effectively using *recursion*.

Using the recursive steps described above, we evaluate the partial sums using a range k= 0 ..10. The results are plotted and tabulated. It can be seen that $\text{Sum}_6 = 1.984$. This result agrees with the earlier one using MathCAD's summation template. From both the graph and the table, we observe that as k gets larger, the partial sums tend to a value of two. Thus the geometric series for r= 0.5 appears to converge to two. When we change the ratio to r= 1.5, we find that the partial sums appear to increase without limit, suggesting divergence. These conclusions are consistent with the theory presented above. It must be stressed that MathCAD's analysis does not rigorously prove convergence or divergence, but only suggests it.

HALTING RECURSION WITH THE until FUNCTION

Let us return to the geometric series presented above and consider the following question. With a ratio $r = 0.5$, how many terms are required to just exceed some value, let us say, $M = 1.9$? To find the answer, we could simply examine the results of the previous worksheet. From the table in Worksheet 4.5, we note that the partial

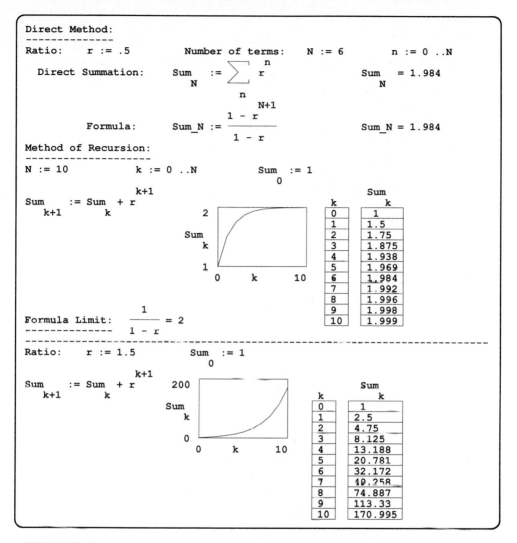

```
Direct Method:
--------------
Ratio:     r := .5        Number of terms:    N := 6          n := 0 ..N
                                         n
   Direct Summation:     Sum   :=   ∑   r                  Sum   = 1.984
                           N                                  N
                              n
                                  N+1
                          1 - r
        Formula:     Sum_N :=  ─────────               Sum_N = 1.984
                          1 - r
Method of Recursion:
--------------------
N := 10            k := 0 ..N          Sum   := 1
                                          0
                    k+1                                    Sum
Sum      := Sum   + r                          k           k
   k+1        k                                0           1
                                               1           1.5
                          Sum                  2           1.75
                            k                  3           1.875
                                               4           1.938
                                               5           1.969
                       0    k    10            6           1.984
                                               7           1.992
                                               8           1.996
                    1                          9           1.998
Formula Limit:    ───────  = 2                10           1.999
---------------   1 - r
---------------------------------------------------------------------
Ratio:    r := 1.5         Sum   := 1
                             0
                    k+1                                    Sum
Sum      := Sum   + r     200                   k           k
   k+1        k                                 0           1
                          Sum                   1           2.5
                            k                   2           4.75
                            0                   3           8.125
                                                4           13.188
                       0    k    10             5           20.781
                                                6           32.172
                                                7           49.258
                                                8           74.887
                                                9           113.33
                                               10           170.995
```

WORKSHEET 4.5
Geometric series.

sum first exceeds 1.9 after *five* terms (i.e., n= 0 .. 4) when it acquires a value of
$Sum_4 = 1.938$.

    We can also answer the above question using MathCAD's **until** function
which allows us to perform a series of recursive operations until a certain condition
is met. The recursion is then halted. The syntax of the **until** function is as follows,

       until(TestExpr,RecursExpr)

We use the arbitrary names RecursExpr to represent a recursive operation and
TestExpr to represent the condition for termination. Recursion continues only while

```
The Geometric Series:
---------------------

Ratio        Allow for 100 Terms      Set Range for Recursion      Sum Maximum
-----        -------------------      -----------------------      -----------
r := .5         N := 100                    k := 0 ..N              MaxSum := 1.9


  Seed the Sum            Compute Partial Sums Recursively Using 'Halting'
  -----------            ------------------------------------------------
    Sum  := 1                                                          k+1
       0                    Sum    := until  ⎡⎡MaxSum - Sum ⎤, Sum + r   ⎤
                               k+1           ⎣⎣            k⎦    k       ⎦


      Highest Non-Zero Element                     Partial Sum for this Element
      ------------------------                     ----------------------------
Max_k := last(Sum) - 1        Max_k = 4                 Sum      = 1.938
                                                           Max_k

Display computed elements:
--------------------------
k := 0 ..last(Sum)


Element            Tabular Results                   Vector Form
-------            ---------------                   -----------
                        Sum
                          k
  k           ┌─────────────┐                            ┌     ┐
  0           │     1       │                            │    1│
  1           │    1.5      │                            │  1.5│
  2           │    1.75     │                            │ 1.75│
  3           │    1.875    │                 Sum =      │1.875│
  4           │    1.938    │                            │1.938│
  5           │     0       │                            │    0│
              └─────────────┘                            └     ┘
```

WORKSHEET 4.6
Using the until function to terminate recursion.

TestExpr is positive or zero and terminates when TestExpr becomes negative. In Worksheet 4.6, we illustrate how the **until** function works.

> **MathCAD solution: Worksheet 4.6.** We assign the ratio term (r= 0.5) for the geometric series and an arbitrary upper limit (N= 100) for the recursive index. Using N, we define a range for the index k (k= 0.. N). We set the value sum for which the geometric series is to just exceed MaxSum (MaxSum= 1.9). The recursive process is seeded with Sum_0= 1. Next we apply the **until** function. Note that RecursExpr= Sum_k+ r^{k+1} is the same recursive form used in Worksheet 4.5. The halting expression is set to TestExpr= (MaxSum − Sum_k). Because of the **until** function, the recursion continues only until (MaxSum − Sum_k) < 0. When this occurs, the function produces a value of zero and the recursion terminates.
>
> The results of the recursive calculations are stored in the vector Sum. The last element of the vector contains the value zero, while the next to last element contains the results of the last recursive calculation. The subscript or index for the last element is obtained by applying MathCAD's **last** function to the vector Sum as last(Sum). Note that our answer is given by the function Max_k= last(Sum) − 1. The next to last element (Max_k= 4) has a value of Sum_{Max_k}= 1.938. This verifies that with the terms zero through four, the sum of our geometric series will just exceed the preset

value of MaxSum= 1.9. The computed partial sums are displayed in both tabular and vector forms.

CONIC SECTIONS AND PARAMETRIC EQUATIONS

The subject of analytic geometry deals with functions that represent curves in general and *conic sections* in particular. A conic section is a curve generated by the intersection of a right circular cone and a plane. Such a curve is classified as either an ellipse, a parabola, or a hyperbola. We consider the case of an ellipse.

The equation of an ellipse in standard form is,

$$\frac{(x - x_0)^2}{a^2} + \frac{(y - y_0)^2}{b^2} = 1$$

where a and b represent the lengths of the symmetry axes of the ellipse. (For $a > b$, a is called the *semi-major axis* and b the *semi-minor axis*. For $a < b$, the reverse is true.) The coordinates x_0 and y_0 locate the center of the ellipse.

MathCAD does not plot equations; it plots functions. A function $y(x)$ gives a single value of y for every value of x. If we solve the equation given above for y as a function of x, we actually get *two* different functions namely,

$$y(x) = \pm b \cdot \left[1 - \frac{(x - x_0)^2}{a^2} \right] + y_0$$

The positive root generates the upper branch of the ellipse and the negative root the lower branch.

It is often easier to plot a curve by representing its equation in *parametric* form. This is accomplished by writing the original equation $f(x, y) = 0$ as two functions,

$$x = x(t) \qquad \text{and} \qquad y = y(t)$$

The variable t is called the *parameter* of the equation. It is not necessary that t have any special significance, although it often does. When t is eliminated from the two (parametric) equations $x(t)$ and $y(t)$, the resulting equation is equivalent to the original equation $f(x, y) = 0$. For example, by eliminating the variable t from the parametric equations,

$$x(t) = a \cdot \cos(t) + x_0$$

and

$$y(t) = b \cdot \sin(t) + y_0$$

we obtain the equation for the ellipse given above. To trace the complete ellipse, the parameter t must range from zero to $2 \cdot \pi$. The properties of an ellipse are analyzed in Worksheet 4.7.

MathCAD solution: Worksheet 4.7. The first part of the worksheet shows how to plot an ellipse directly. The geometric parameters (a, b, x_0, y_0) are assigned and the upper and lower branch functions $(y_u(x), y_l(x))$ are defined. A plot range is chosen for the variable x. This range is expressed in terms of the semi-major axis to guarantee that the plot will cover the domain of definition of the ellipse. Finally both branches are

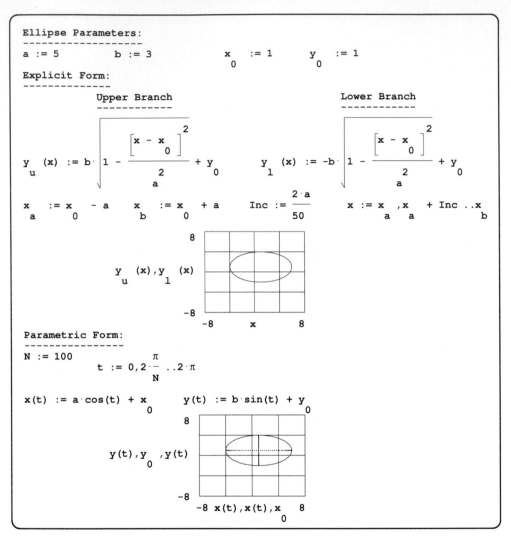

WORKSHEET 4.7
Plotting an ellipse.

plotted. The scales have been manually set to [-8, 8] on both axes and the graph parameters are set to subdivs= 4,4 and size= 8,17. We have tried to adjust the graph size dimensions so that the actual distances along the two axes appear equal. With this choice, the boxes generated by the subdivisions appear as squares. This assures that when the ellipse parameters a and b are equal, the curve which becomes a circle will actually look like a circle.

We continue the worksheet using the parametric form to represent the ellipse. The graph is generated by plotting the function x(t) on the horizontal axis and y(t) on the vertical. The plot format is the same as that used for the graph above. Note that we have plotted more than one function on each axis. MathCAD pairs these functions for plotting. Thus we have three plots—`y(t)` vs. `x(t)`, followed by `y₀` vs. `x(t)`, followed by `y(t)` vs. `x₀`. The last two pairs generate the major and minor axes of the ellipse. The horizontal symmetry axis is generated by plotting the horizontal line `y=y₀` versus the variable `x(t)`. Plotting `y(t)` versus the vertical line `x=x₀` produces the vertical symmetry axis. We are using the graph format `type = 1dd`.

POLAR COORDINATES

Until now we have considered applications in Cartesian coordinates. In many situations, it is more convenient to study equations in polar coordinates defined by the transformation,

$$x = r \cdot \cos(\theta) \qquad y = r \cdot \sin(\theta) \qquad \text{(polar to Cartesian)}$$

$$r = [x^2 + y^2]^{1/2} \qquad \theta = \tan^{-1}\left(\frac{y}{x}\right) \qquad \text{(Cartesian to polar)}$$

The variable r represents the distance from the origin to the coordinate point (x, y). The variable θ is the angle from the positive x-axis to the line defined by r.

A function in polar coordinates is written $r = r(\theta)$. Consider, for example, the function $r = 5 \cdot \sin(\theta) \cdot \cos(\theta)$. The graph of this function is a four-leaf clover. The graph of the function $r = 1$ is a circle of radius one about the origin. These functions are plotted in the first quadrant in Fig. 4.4.

Consider the following area problem. Find the area in the first quadrant between the curves $r_1(\theta)$ and $r_2(\theta)$ where $r_2(\theta) = 5 \cdot \sin(\theta) \cdot \cos(\theta)$ is a cloverleaf and $r_1(\theta) = 1$ is a circle (see Fig. 4.4). Note that the curves intersect at the angles θ_1 and θ_2. According to the rules of calculus, the area between the outer curve (the cloverleaf) and the inner curve (the circle) is given by,

$$\text{Area} = \frac{1}{2} \cdot \int_{\theta_1}^{\theta_2} [r_2^2(\theta) - r_1^2(\theta)]d\theta$$

This problem is solved in Worksheet 4.8.

> **MathCAD solution: Worksheet 4.8.** After defining the degree unit, we assign the functions for the transformation from polar to Cartesian coordinates. We use the method of *global assignment* ($\equiv$) by typing ~ (tilde). We could have also used the ordinary

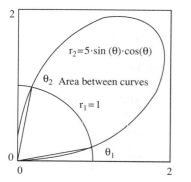

$r_2 = 5 \cdot \sin(\theta) \cdot \cos(\theta)$

θ_2 Area between curves

$r_1 = 1$

θ_1

FIGURE 4.4

$$deg \equiv \frac{\pi}{180}$$

Define the transformation:

$$x(r,\theta) \equiv r \cdot \cos(\theta)$$

$$y(r,\theta) \equiv r \cdot \sin(\theta)$$

Define the two curves:

Clover leaf: $r_2(\theta) := 5 \cdot \sin(\theta) \cdot \cos(\theta)$

Unit circle: $r_1(\theta) := 1$

Plot the curves in first quadrant:

$$\theta := 0, \frac{\pi}{80} \ .. \ \frac{\pi}{2}$$

$$y\left[r_2(\theta), \theta\right], y\left[r_1(\theta), \theta\right]$$ (vertical axis, 0 to 2)

$$0 \quad x\left[r_2(\theta), \theta\right], x\left[r_1(\theta), \theta\right] \quad 2$$

Find intersections of curves:

$\theta := .5$ Given $r_1(\theta) \approx r_2(\theta)$ $\theta1 := \text{Find}(\theta)$ $\theta1 = 11.789 \cdot deg$

$\theta := 1$ Given $r_1(\theta) \approx r_2(\theta)$ $\theta2 := \text{Find}(\theta)$ $\theta2 = 78.211 \cdot deg$

Compute area between curves:

$$\text{Area} := .5 \cdot \int_{\theta1}^{\theta2} \left[r_2(\theta)^2 - r_1(\theta)^2 \right] d\theta \qquad \text{Area} = 1.805$$

WORKSHEET 4.8

Area between two curves in polar coordinates.

method of assignment $(:=)$ by typing :. In the second row, we assign the polar functions representing the two curves. Next we plot the functions in the first quadrant by limiting the plot range variable θ to the first quadrant $(0 \leq \theta \leq \pi/2)$. To produce plots of the cloverleaf and the circle on a single graph, we plot $x[r_2(\theta), \theta]$ and $x[r_1(\theta), \theta]$ on the horizontal axis and $y[r_2(\theta), \theta]$ and $y[r_1(\theta), \theta]$ on the vertical axis. For example, place the cursor on the middle placeholder on the horizontal axis and type: x(r.2({<Alt>Q}),{<Alt>Q}),x(r.1({<Alt>Q}),{<Alt>Q}).

Using MathCAD's **Find** function, we compute the angular intersections of the two curves. The two angles are displayed in degrees by filling the placeholders with deg. Note that these angles are complementary, as might be expected from the symmetry of the problem. Finally, the integration formula above is applied to compute the area. The last object displays the result as Area= 1.805.

The radius r_1 (θ) of the circle can be varied. If it is set equal to zero, the area computed represents that of the entire cloverleaf (in the first quadrant). As the radius increases to $r_1 = 2.5$ (i.e., to the tip of the cloverleaf), the area approaches zero.

ARC LENGTH

The arc length along a curve represented by a function $y(x)$ between two points x_1 and x_2 is given by the formula,

$$L = \int_{x_1}^{x_2} \left[1 + \left(\frac{dy}{dx} \right)^2 \right]^{1/2} dx$$

provided that the tangent line to the curve is never vertical on the interval; otherwise, dy/dx is undefined.

It is often easier to compute the arc length if the curve is represented in parametric form as $x = x(t)$ and $y = y(t)$. The arc length can be expressed as,

$$L = \int_{t_1}^{t_2} \left[\left(\frac{dx}{dt} \right)^2 + \left(\frac{dy}{dt} \right)^2 \right]^{1/2} dt$$

where t_1 and t_2 are the parameter values corresponding to the end points of the arc (x_1, y_1) and (x_2, y_2). As in the first integral above, the derivatives must be defined everywhere on the interval of integration. We demonstrate the computation of arc lengths for a cycloid and for an ellipse in Worksheet 4.9.

MathCAD solution: Worksheet 4.9. We first calculate the distance along an arch of a cycloid. We define the equation of the cycloid in parametric form as,

$$x(t) = a \cdot (t - \sin(t))$$

and

$$y(t) = a \cdot (1 - \cos(t))$$

where we have arbitrarily set **a**= 2.

We next assign the appropriate derivatives. It can be seen that y(t) vanishes when t= 0, $2 \cdot \pi$, $4 \cdot \pi$, etc. It follows that one arch of the cycloid is traced out as t goes from zero to $2 \cdot \pi$. The arc length is computed and the result displayed first as L= 16 and then, by filling the placeholder with a, as L= $8 \cdot a$. Finally, the cycloid is plotted over two arches (0 to $4 \cdot \pi$). The placeholders for the upper limits of the graph scale have been manually set to x= $4 \cdot \pi \cdot a$ and y= $2 \cdot a$. By changing the value of a, you can compute the arc lengths for different cycloids. However you will note that the result remains L= $8 \cdot a$. This suggests that the expression is an analytical one and is valid for all cycloids of this type.

Continuing, we use the arc length formulas to compute the circumference of an ellipse whose semi-major and semi-minor axes are a and b respectively. We express the equation of the ellipse in parametric form. Note that to trace the complete ellipse, the parameter t must range from 0 to $2 \cdot \pi$. The arc length integral is computed and the circumference displayed as L= 9.688. The ellipse is plotted. It turns out that the integral for the circumference of an ellipse, unlike the one above for the cycloid, cannot be evaluated analytically in terms of elementary functions. It belongs to a family

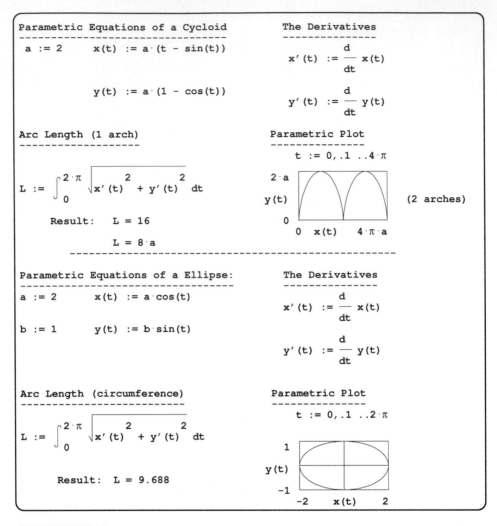

Parametric Equations of a Cycloid
----

a := 2   x(t) := a·(t - sin(t))

y(t) := a·(1 - cos(t))

The Derivatives

$$x'(t) := \frac{d}{dt} x(t)$$

$$y'(t) := \frac{d}{dt} y(t)$$

Arc Length (1 arch)

$$L := \int_0^{2\cdot\pi} \sqrt{x'(t)^2 + y'(t)^2}\, dt$$

Result: L = 16

L = 8·a

Parametric Plot
----

t := 0, .1 ..4·π

2·a

y(t)   (2 arches)

0

0   x(t)   4·π·a

Parametric Equations of a Ellipse:
----

a := 2   x(t) := a·cos(t)

b := 1   y(t) := b·sin(t)

The Derivatives

$$x'(t) := \frac{d}{dt} x(t)$$

$$y'(t) := \frac{d}{dt} y(t)$$

Arc Length (circumference)

$$L := \int_0^{2\cdot\pi} \sqrt{x'(t)^2 + y'(t)^2}\, dt$$

Result: L = 9.688

Parametric Plot
----

t := 0, .1 ..2·π

1

y(t)

-1

-2   x(t)   2

WORKSHEET 4.9
Arc length along a curve.

of integrals aptly termed *elliptic*. These integrals are computed numerically and are available in reference tables. If we set $a = b = 1$, the ellipse becomes a circle of radius one. The circumference becomes L= 6.283 or L= 2·π which is consistent with the formula for the circle C= 2·π·R.

USING SOLVE BLOCKS TO COMPUTE INVERSE FUNCTIONS

Suppose we have an equation of the form $F(x, y) = 0$ defined on some domain $a \leq x \leq b$. If the curve passes the *vertical-line* test on the interval, we can regard y as a function of x and solve the equation as $y = f(x)$. The vertical-line test requires that no vertical line exists (on the interval $[a, b]$) which intersects the curve $F(x, y) = 0$ at more than one point. For example, the equation of a circle of unit radius centered at the origin, $x^2 + y^2 = 1$, does not represent a function $y(x)$ because at least one vertical line exists which intersects the circle at two points.

The *inverse* of a function $y(x)$, which we call $y_{inv}(x)$, exists on the interval $[a, b]$ if the function passes the *horizontal-line* test. This test requires that no horizontal line exists (on the interval $[a, b]$) which intersects the curve $y = y(x)$ at more than one point. For example, the function $y = x^3$ has an inverse on the interval $[-\infty, \infty]$ whereas the function $y = x^2$ does not.

To compute the inverse of a function $y(x)$ analytically (if it exists), we perform the following operations:

a. Interchange x and y in the equation.

b. Label y as y_{inv} and solve for y_{inv} in terms of x.

For example, the inverse function of $y = 2 \cdot x + 3$ is found to be $y_{inv} = (x - 3)/2$. The inverse of $y = x^3$ is $y_{inv} = x^{(1/3)}$. The following rule holds for any function and its inverse:

$$y[y_{inv}(x)] = x$$

Furthermore, the plots of $y(x)$ and $y_{inv}(x)$ are symmetric about the $45°$ line, $y = x$. The *domain* (the x-range of definition) of the inverse function becomes the *range* (the y-range of definition) of the original function and vice versa.

Some inverse functions cannot be expressed analytically in terms of familiar functions. Consider, for example, the function:

$$y(x) = x \cdot \sin(x) \qquad \text{on the interval} \qquad 0 \le x \le \left(\frac{\pi}{2}\right)$$

A plot of this function shows that it passes the horizontal-line test and thus has an inverse in the specified interval. The inverse function can be written:

$$y_{inv}(x), \qquad \text{on the interval} \qquad 0 \le x \le \left(\frac{\pi}{2}\right)$$

The fact that the domain (x-range) of the function and that of its inverse are the same is a coincidence.

Unfortunately, it is not possible to solve analytically for x in terms of y. However MathCAD can provide us with a numerical solution using the **Given/Find** solve block. Suppose that we wish to find the value of x when $y = 1$. Consider the following objects:

```
f(x) := x·sin(x)     y := 1
x := .5    Given   y ≈ f(x)     x := Find(x)     x = 1.114
```

The function $f(x) = x \cdot \sin(x)$ is defined and a value of $y = 1$ assigned. A guess is made for x and a solve block used to find the value of x. We have thus "inverted" the function for a *single* point, determining that $f_{inv}(1) = 1.114$.

If we remove the assignment object for y, we see the following:

```
f(x)  := x·sin(x)
x := .5     Given     y ≈  f(x)      x := Find(x)      x = 0.5
             |                                 |
        undefined            error in solve block
```

This is expected since the solve block does not have the value of y for which the solution x is being sought.

Consider next the following set of objects:

```
f(x)  := x·sin(x)
x := .5         Given       y ≈  f(x)          g(y) := Find(x)
x := 1                    g(x)  = 1.114
```

Note that we have replaced the left-hand side of the **Find** object with a *function g(y)*. Since a function does not actually perform a computation until its argument is given, no error occurs in the solve block. When a value of y is specified in the function $g(y)$, the solve block *subroutine* is processed and the value of g is returned. Hence the solve block actually gives a function $g(x)$ which is the inverse of the function $f(x)$.

We examine the inverse function of $f(x) = x \cdot \sin(x)$ in Worksheet 4.10.

MathCAD solution: Worksheet 4.10. In this worksheet we label the function f(x) and its inverse g(x). We define the function f(x) = x·sin(x) and assign its domain [a,b] where a=0 and b=π/2. [MathCAD's version 2.0 **Given/Find** algorithm has some difficulty computing the inverse of this function at the origin and so we use a=0.001. With version 2.5, setting a=0 presents no problem.]

A guess for x is made using a point at the middle of the interval. The solve block is used to generate the function x(y). This inverse function is reassigned to the variable g. The functions f(x) and g(x) and the line y= x are plotted. Note that f(x) and g(x) are symmetric with respect to the 45° line, y= x.

Finally, the function f(g(x)) is plotted versus x. Since f(g(x))=x, the plot represents a 45° line through the origin, confirming that g(x) is the inverse function of f(x).

MULTIPLE INTEGRALS

Multiple or iterated integrals are used for computing areas and volumes. While Math-CAD performs multiple integrals, computing anything beyond a triple integral is impractical. Fortunately, in many cases it is possible to simplify a computation by reducing the level of iteration of an integral.

We compute the volume of an ellipsoid whose equation in Cartesian coordinates is,

$$\left(\frac{x}{a}\right)^2 + \left(\frac{y}{b}\right)^2 + \left(\frac{z}{c}\right)^2 = 1$$

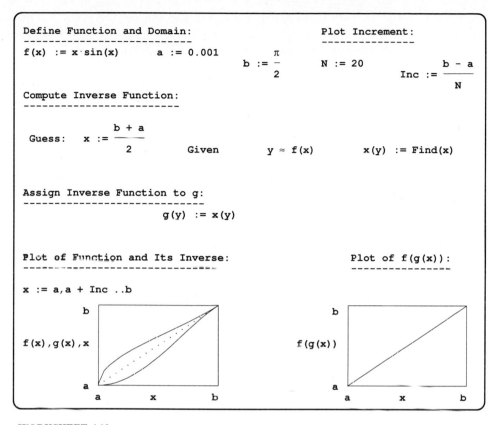

Define Function and Domain:
----

f(x) := x·sin(x)   a := 0.001

Plot Increment:
----

b := $\dfrac{\pi}{2}$ N := 20   Inc := $\dfrac{b - a}{N}$

Compute Inverse Function:

Guess: x := $\dfrac{b + a}{2}$ Given   y ≈ f(x)   x(y) := Find(x)

Assign Inverse Function to g:
----

g(y) := x(y)

Plot of Function and Its Inverse:

Plot of f(g(x)):
----

x := a,a + Inc ..b

WORKSHEET 4.10
Inverse of a function.

The ellipsoid has semi-axes a, b, c and is centered at the origin. Solving for z, we obtain,

$$z = \pm g(x, y) = \pm c \cdot \left[1 - \left(\frac{x}{a}\right)^2 - \left(\frac{y}{b}\right)^2\right]^{1/2}$$

where the $\pm$ signs represent the surfaces above and below the plane $z = 0$ (i.e., the xy-plane). The general form of the volume integral for the ellipsoid is,

$$V = 8 \cdot \int_0^a \int_0^{f(x)} \int_0^{g(x,y)} 1 \, dz \, dy \, dx$$

where

$$f(x) = b \cdot \left[1 - \left(\frac{x}{a}\right)^2\right]^{1/2}$$

The function $\pm f(x)$ represents the upper (or lower) branches of an ellipse generated by the intersection of the ellipsoid and the xy-plane. This ellipse has semi-axes a and *b.* The integral covers the volume only in the first octant; symmetry suggests that the entire volume is obtained by multiplying the integral by eight.

The innermost integration (with respect to z) expands a differential cube $dx\ dy\ dz$ into a thin vertical *column* of height $g(x)$ and a cross section $dy\ dx$. The second innermost integral (with respect to y) expands the column into a thin sheet of thickness dx. The last integration (with respect to x) adds these sheets to form the volume.

The triple integral can be reduced to a double integral by performing the z-integration analytically. The volume of the ellipsoid can now be written as the double integral,

$$V = 8 \cdot \int_0^a \int_0^{f(x)} g(x,y)\ dy\ dx$$

where

$$g(x,y) = c \cdot \left[1 - \left(\frac{x}{a}\right)^2 - \left(\frac{y}{b}\right)^2\right]^{1/2}$$

It is interesting to note that when we replace the integrand with one, the integral represents twice the area of an ellipse of dimensions a and b. Thus for the area of the ellipse, we have,

$$A = 4 \cdot \int_0^a \int_0^{f(x)} dy\ dx$$

where

$$f(x) = b \cdot \left[1 - \left(\frac{x}{a}\right)^2\right]^{1/2}$$

This double integral can be reduced to a single integral by performing the y integration analytically. The area of the ellipse is then given by the integral,

$$A = 4 \cdot \int_0^a f(x)\ dx$$

The calculations described above are performed in Worksheet 4.11.

MathCAD solution: Worksheet 4.11. We define the semi-axes of the ellipsoid as a=3, b=2, and c=1 and assign the functions g(x,y) and f(x). The volume integral is computed and displayed. The double integral is generated by entering **V:8∗&&**. The placeholders in the integral are filled appropriately. The volume of the ellipsoid is displayed as V= 25.125. When the placeholder is filled with the constant expression 4·π·(a·b·c)/3, the displayed numerical value of V changes to one. When we vary the values of a, b, and c, the volume expression displayed remains constant. This suggests that the general formula for the volume of an ellipsoid is V= 4·π·(a·b·c)/3.

Continuing with the worksheet, we compute the area of an ellipse using both the double and single integral methods. Note that both methods give the same result, A= 18.844. By filling the placeholders with π·a·b, we obtain the result V=1·π·a·b which is the general formula for the area of an ellipse.

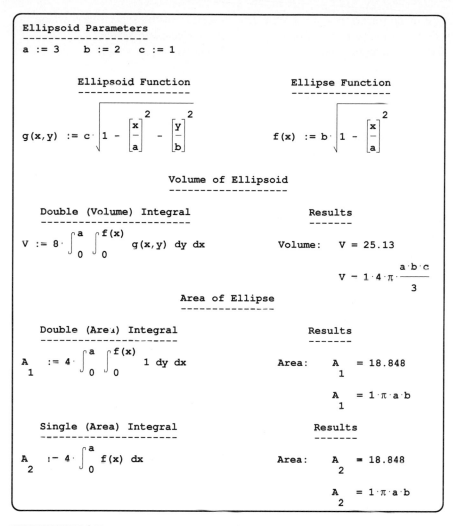

WORKSHEET 4.11
Multiple integrals.

TAYLOR AND MACLAURIN SERIES

It is often possible to represent a function $f(x)$ as a power series of the form,

$$f(x) = \sum_{n=0}^{\infty} a_n \cdot (x - x_0)^n$$

If the series converges to the function, the coefficients are found using Taylor's formula,

$$a_n = \frac{1}{n!} \left. \frac{d^n f(x)}{dx^n} \right|_{x=x_0}$$

This type of power series is a called a *Taylor Series*. In the special case where the center of expansion is $x_0 = 0$, the series is called a *Maclaurin Series*.

Let us assume that the Taylor series converges on an interval about x_0 defined by,

$$(x_0 - R) < x < (x_0 + R)$$

The largest value of R for which the series converges is called the *radius of convergence* of the series and the corresponding interval the *interval of convergence*. For example, the Taylor series for $\sin(x)$ about $x_0 = 0$ has a radius of convergence of $R = \infty$, that is, it converges for all x. The Taylor series for the function $1/(1 - x)$ about $x_0 = 0$ has a radius of convergence of $R = 1$. It converges on the interval $(-1, 1)$.

In Worksheet 4.12, we consider the Maclaurin expansion of the sine function. The nth derivative of the $y = \sin(x)$ evaluated at zero is,

$$\left. \frac{d^n \sin(x)}{dx^n} \right|_{x=0} \begin{array}{ll} = 1 & n = 1, 5, 9, \; .. \\[6pt] = -1 & n = 3, 7, 11, \; .. \\[6pt] = 0 & \text{otherwise} \end{array}$$

The Maclaurin coefficients can therefore be expressed as,

$$a_n = \frac{[-1]^{(n-1)/2}}{n!} \qquad (n = \text{ odd})$$

$$a_n = 0 \qquad (n = \text{ even})$$

We apply this formula in Worksheet 4.12.

MathCAD solution: Worksheet 4.12. We compute the coefficients for the first ten (nonzero) terms of the series. We then assign the range for the summation index as `n=1,3 ..2·N-1` so that it includes only odd integers up to and including the value `2·N-1` (in our case `N=10` so that $n_{max} = 19$). The odd coefficients are assigned using analytical expressions. Using its derivative operation, MathCAD can directly compute these coefficients from Taylor's formula. However, using an analytical form leads to more accurate results and faster computation.

Next, a finite series (a Maclaurin polynomial) `zα (x)` is constructed by summing the first *six* nonzero terms. A similar construction is performed for `zβ (x)` by summing the first *eight* nonzero terms. Finally, the results are compared to the sine function using a plot over the range `[0,2·π]` in steps of `π/6`. To subdivide the axes, we use a graph format `subdivs 2,1`. The graph format `type 10x` generates a line graph for the sine, rectangles for `zα (x)`, and exes for `zβ (x)`. By filling the plot scale placeholders, we manually set the scale to `[0,2·π]` for x and `[-2,2]` for y. Note that both Maclaurin series represent good approximations near the expansion point. The series with `N=6` terms deviates markedly from the sine function as we approach `2·π`. As more terms are included `(N=8)`, the series better approximates the sine function over the entire plot interval. The eight coefficients are tabulated for reference.

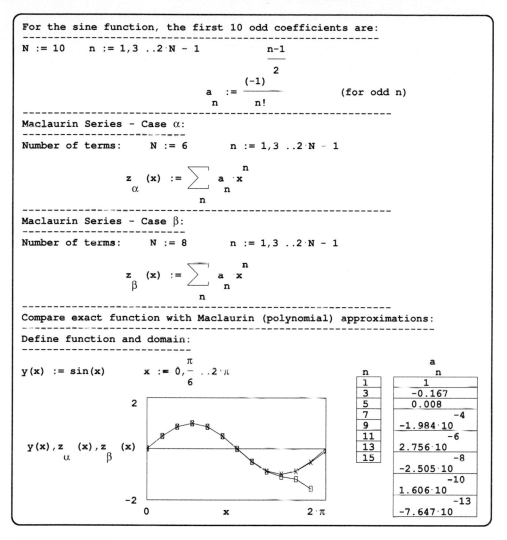

For the sine function, the first 10 odd coefficients are:

N := 10   n := 1,3 ..2·N - 1

$$a_n := \frac{(-1)^{\frac{n-1}{2}}}{n!} \qquad \text{(for odd n)}$$

Maclaurin Series - Case α:

Number of terms: N := 6   n := 1,3 ..2·N - 1

$$z_\alpha(x) := \sum_n a_n \cdot x^n$$

Maclaurin Series - Case β:

Number of terms: N := 8   n := 1,3 ..2·N - 1

$$z_\beta(x) := \sum_n a_n \cdot x^n$$

Compare exact function with Maclaurin (polynomial) approximations:

Define function and domain:

----

y(x) := sin(x) $x := 0, \frac{\pi}{6} ..2 \cdot \pi$

$y(x), z_\alpha(x), z_\beta(x)$

n	a_n
1	1
3	-0.167
5	0.008
7	-4
9	$-1.984 \cdot 10^{-4}$
11	-6
13	$2.756 \cdot 10^{-6}$
15	-8
	$-2.505 \cdot 10^{-8}$
	-10
	$1.606 \cdot 10^{-10}$
	-13
	$-7.647 \cdot 10^{-13}$

WORKSHEET 4.12
Using a Maclaurin series to approximate a sine function.

MULTIVARIABLE CALCULUS, THE GRADIENT

We conclude this chapter with applications of calculus to functions of more than one independent variable. A function of three variables may be written $f(x, y, z)$. For every point in space, the function has a defined value. For example, $f(x, y, z)$ might represent the temperature at various points in a three dimensional solid. The derivative of this function is represented by three separate derivatives known as *partial* derivatives. They are written,

$$f_x = \frac{\partial f}{\partial x} \qquad f_y = \frac{\partial f}{\partial y} \qquad f_z = \frac{\partial f}{\partial z}$$

With f_x, for example, we differentiate with respect to x holding y and z constant. The operation f_x is called the *partial derivative with respect to x*. (The subscript x on the function is the conventional notation for the partial derivative with respect to x.) Similar rules apply to f_y and f_z. The Cartesian vector function, which has the separate functions f_x, f_y, and f_z as its components, is written *grad f* (or ∇f) and is called the *gradient* of f. By definition, the gradient vector points along the direction of maximum increase of the function, $f(x, y, z)$; its magnitude represents the rate of change of the function with respect to distance along that direction. MathCAD uses the ordinary derivative symbol $df(x, y, z)/dx$ to compute partial derivatives. Thus the operation,

$$\text{f}_\text{x}(\text{x},\text{y},\text{z}) \; := \; \tfrac{\text{d}}{\text{dx}} \; \text{f}(\text{x},\text{y},\text{z})$$

generates the partial derivative with respect to x and treats the other variables as constants for the purpose of differentiation.

A (differential) displacement is represented by a vector $\boldsymbol{\delta}\mathbf{s}$ whose components δx, δy, and δz represent the displacements along the three axes. The approximate change in a function for a differential displacement can be computed using differentials as,

$$\delta f = f(x + \delta x, y + \delta y, z + \delta z) - f(x, y)$$
$$\approx f_x \cdot \delta x + f_y \cdot \delta y + f_z \cdot \delta z = \; \text{grad } f \cdot \boldsymbol{\delta}\mathbf{s}$$

The last term on the right is the scalar product of the two vectors. The smaller the magnitude of $\boldsymbol{\delta}\mathbf{s}$, the better the approximation.

In Worksheet 4.13, we apply the concepts of partial derivatives to the function $f(x, y, z) = x^2 \cdot \sin(y) \cdot \cos(z)$. In particular, we will compute the approximate change in this function when we change the coordinates from (1, 2, 3) to (1.01, 2.02, 3.03).

MathCAD solution: Worksheet 4.13. We assign the function and its three partial derivatives. The first partial derivative (with respect to **x**) is generated with the keystrokes,

f.x(x,y,z):x?f(x,y,z)

This is repeated for the other two partial derivatives. The coordinates of the point are chosen and the differential displacements assigned.

A vector function with the name arbitrarily chosen as Grad_f(x,y,z) is assigned. The matrix template is created by typing: **Grad_f(x,y,z):{<Alt>M}**. We respond to the prompt for the matrix dimensions on the message line with the numbers **3 1** and then type {**Enter**}. We next fill the element placeholders with the functions f_x(x,y,z), f_y(x,y,z), and f_z(x,y,z) as required. The vector Grad_f is obtained by evaluating Grad_f(x,y,z) at the point (1,2,3).

The differential displacements are assigned. (The Greek symbol δ is generated using {**<Alt>D**}.) Next the gradient vector and its magnitude are displayed. (As mentioned, the vector Grad_f, points in the direction in which the function increases most rapidly; the magnitude of the vector gives the rate of change with distance along that direction.) The displacement vector is assigned and displayed. The change in the function is computed using differentials (δf=-0.014) and computed using an exact calculation (δf=-0.013).

```
Define the Function:
--------------------
                 2
    f(x,y,z) := x ·sin(y)·cos(z)

Compute the Gradient Function:
------------------------------
            d
  f  (x,y,z) := —— f(x,y,z)
   x           dx

                     d
          f  (x,y,z) := —— f(x,y,z)
           y            dy

                             d
                f  (x,y,z) := —— f(x,y,z)
                 z            dz

Evaluate at Some Point in Space:
--------------------------------
      Initial Point                  Differential Displacement
      -------------                  -------------------------
   x := 1   y := 2   z := 3      δx := .01   δy := .02   δz := .03

        Gradient Vector                   Displacement Vector
        ---------------                   -------------------
                    ┌            ┐                    ┌  ┐        ┌    ┐
                    │ f  (x,y,z) │                    │δx│        │0.01│
                    │  x         │              δs := │δy│   δs = │0.02│
                    │ f  (x,y,z) │                    │δz│        │0.03│
   Grad_f(x,y,z) := │  y         │                    └  ┘        └    ┘
                    │ f  (x,y,z) │
                    │  z         │
                    └            ┘

   Grad_f := Grad_f(x,y,z)            ┌       ┐
                                      │  1.8  │
                        Grad_f =      │ 0.412 │    |Grad_f| = 1.851
                                      │-0.128 │
                                      └       ┘

   Approximate Change in Function (using differentials):
   -----------------------------------------------------
      δf := Grad_f·δs                        δf = -0.014

   Exact Change in Function:
   -------------------------
      δf := f(x + δx,y + δy,z + δz) - f(x,y,z)    δf = -0.013
```

WORKSHEET 4.13
Gradient of a function.

LINE INTEGRALS AND GREEN'S THEOREM

Consider two arbitrary functions $f(x, y)$ and $g(x, y)$. Assume that both functions are continuous and that they have continuous first partial derivatives in some region of the xy-plane. Consider some curve (or contour) situated in that region represented by $y = y(x)$ and extending from one point a to another point b. We define the *line integral* of the functions along this curve as,

$$I = \int_{a \atop C}^{b} f(x, y) \cdot dx + g(x, y) \cdot dy$$

where C represents the contour. To compute the integral explicitly, we express all quantities in the integrand in terms of one variable, let us say x. We then have,

$$I = \int_{x_a}^{x_b} \left\{ f[x, y(x)] + g[x, y(x)] \cdot \frac{dy}{dx} \right\} \cdot dx$$

If the contour is a closed loop, the integral above is written,

$$I = \oint_C f(x, y) \cdot dx + g(x, y) \cdot dy$$

where the circle on the integral designates a closed contour (taken counterclockwise). In general, a closed contour integral is not zero.

It is often easier to evaluate a line integral whether open or closed if the contour is represented in parametric form. If the contour is represented by $x = x(t)$ and $y = y(t)$, then the line integral can be expressed as,

$$I = \int_{t_a}^{t_b} \left\{ f[x(t), y(t)] \cdot \frac{dx}{dt} + g[x(t), y(t)] \cdot \frac{dy}{dt} \right\} \cdot dt$$

where t_a and t_b are the parameters which define the limits of the contour.

An important theorem pertaining to closed contour integrals is Green's Theorem. The theorem states that the line integral over a closed contour can also be computed using an area-type integral over the region enclosed by the contour. Specifically, Green's Theorem is,

$$\oint_C f(x, y) \cdot dx + g(x, y) \cdot dy = \int_A \int [g_x(x, y) - f_y(x, y)] \cdot dx \, dy$$

where A is the area enclosed by the contour, and

$$g_x = \frac{\partial g}{\partial x}$$

and

$$f_y = \frac{\partial f}{\partial y}$$

In Worksheet 4.14, we demonstrate Green's Theorem.

MathCAD solution: Worksheet 4.14. We choose a pair of arbitrary functions,

$$f(x, y) = x \cdot y \qquad \text{and} \qquad g(x, y) = x \cdot y^2$$

As our closed contour, we take a unit circle about the origin,

$$x^2 + y^2 = 1$$

which in parametric form is represented by,

$$x(t) = \cos(t) \qquad \text{and} \qquad y(t) = \sin(t) \qquad \text{for} \qquad 0 \le t < 2 \cdot \pi$$

The contour is plotted parametrically by plotting x(t) and y(t) on the horizontal and vertical axes respectively. The plot range for the parameter is t=0 to t=2·π. The functions f[x(t),y(t)] and g[x(t),y(t)] are expressed in terms of t as F(t)

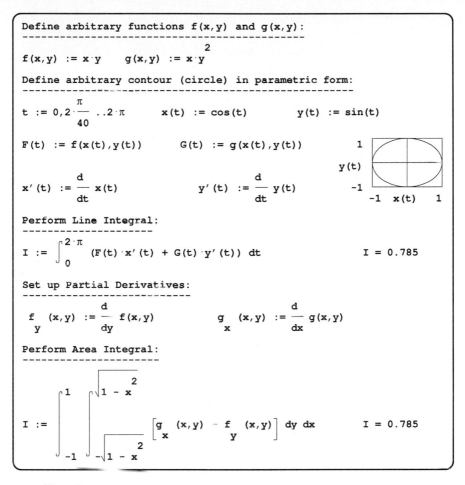

```
Define arbitrary functions f(x,y) and g(x,y):
-----------------------------------------------
                                  2
f(x,y) := x·y      g(x,y) := x·y

Define arbitrary contour (circle) in parametric form:
-----------------------------------------------------
          π
t := 0,2·—— ..2·π      x(t) := cos(t)        y(t) := sin(t)
         40

F(t) := f(x(t),y(t))      G(t) := g(x(t),y(t))           1

                                                        y(t)
         d                              d
x'(t) := —— x(t)            y'(t) := —— y(t)            -1
         dt                             dt
                                                          -1   x(t)   1

Perform Line Integral:
----------------------
       ⌠2·π
I :=   ⌡    (F(t)·x'(t) + G(t)·y'(t)) dt                I = 0.785
        0

Set up Partial Derivatives:
---------------------------
        d                            d
 f (x,y) := —— f(x,y)        g (x,y) := —— g(x,y)
  y         dy                x        dx

Perform Area Integral:
----------------------
             _____
            √      2
       ⌠1   ⌠ 1 - x
       ⌡    ⌡        ⎡g (x,y) - f (x,y)⎤ dy dx          I = 0.785
I :=        |        ⎣ x         y     ⎦
            |_____
            √      2
      -1  -√ 1 - x
```

WORKSHEET 4.14
Green's Theorem.

and $G(t)$. The appropriate derivatives are taken, the line integral evaluated, and the result displayed ($I = 0.785$).

To verify Green's Theorem, we evaluate the area integral by first taking the appropriate partial derivatives. The area integral over the interior of the unit circle is computed and the result is shown to agree with that of the line integral method above.

The worksheet computes relatively slowly because we are dealing with an iterated integral whose integrand contains derivatives which are computed by MathCAD. The computations proceed more quickly if we assign all the derivatives analytically rather than have MathCAD compute them. To do this for the functions and contour of our problem, we would make the replacements,

```
    x'(t) := -sin(t),   y'(t) := cos(t)
    fy := x      gx := y²
```

In the next chapter, we apply the tools of MathCAD to topics in general physics. We will study problems in mechanics, heat transfer, calorimetry, and sound. Topics involving electrostatics, circuit analysis, optics, and nuclear physics will also be presented.

PROBLEMS

1. Consider the function $y(x) = \cos(x) \cdot \exp(-x/2)$ on the interval $[0, 2 \cdot \pi]$.
   (a) Find the coordinates of the two relative extrema and classify them. Indicate the regions where the function is increasing and where it is decreasing.
   (b) Find the two points of inflection and indicate the regions where the function is concave up and where it is concave down. Hint: Assign the function $y(x)$ and its first two derivatives $y'(x)$ and $y''(x)$. Plot all three on the interval. Use the **root** function to find the extrema and inflection points.

2. A video camera is situated 2000 ft from the launch pad of a rocket. The rocket is launched vertically and is rising at a rate of $v_0 = 600$ ft/s. The angle of elevation of the camera lens θ increases with time in such a way that the lens remains oriented toward the rocket.
   (a) Plot the angle of elevation and its rate of change versus time.
   (b) Determine the rate of increase of the angle (in rad/s and in deg/s) and the rate at which the rocket is moving away from the camera at $t = 5$ seconds after launch. The following steps are suggested:
      (i) Use the global assignments $\mathtt{rad} \equiv 1$, $\mathtt{sec} \equiv 1$ and $\mathtt{deg} \equiv \pi/180$.
      (ii) Assign the function for the height of the rocket $y(t)$.
      (iii) Use the Pythagorean formula to relate the camera-rocket distance $s(t)$ to $y(t)$. Compute its derivative $s'(t)$.
      (iv) Use the appropriate inverse trigonometric relation to express the elevation angle $\theta(t)$ in terms of $y(t)$.
      (v) Use MathCAD to define the derivative $\theta'(t)$ and then plot $\theta(t)$ and $\theta'(t)$ versus t.
      (vi) Display the value of $\theta'(5)$ twice. In the first case, fill the placeholder with $\mathtt{rad/sec}$; in the second, fill it with $\mathtt{deg/sec}$.
      (vii) Evaluate the expression, $s'(5)$.

3. An offshore oil well is located 3 mi from the closest shorepoint A. A holding tank is situated 6 mi from point A along the straight shoreline at a second shorepoint B. A pipe line is to be constructed from the oil well to the holding tank in two straight sections. The first section will extend underwater from the well to some point P on the shore located x mi from point A. The second will run above ground parallel to the shore from point P to point B. The underwater section will cost \$150,000 per mi while the above ground section will cost \$100,000 per mi. Find the value of x and the length of each section to minimize the cost of the project. Find the minimum cost using the following steps:
   (a) Construct the functions for the underwater and the above ground pipe section lengths $l_1(x)$ and $l_2(x)$.
   (b) Define the total cost function $\mathrm{Cost}(x)$ and compute the derivative function $\mathrm{Cost}'(x)$.
   (c) Plot $\mathrm{Cost}(x)$ versus x on the interval $[0, 6]$ and estimate the value of x for which $\mathrm{Cost}(x)$ is a minimum.
   (d) Using the value obtained in part (c) as a guess, apply the **root** function to the derivative function $\mathrm{Cost}'(x)$ to determine the precise position of the optimum x_o.
   (e) Display x_o, $l_1(x_o)$, $l_2(x_o)$, and $\mathrm{Cost}(x_o)$.

4. Find the area of the region bounded from above by the curve $f(x) = 5 \cdot \sin(x)$ and from below by the straight line $g(x) = x + 1$ for positive x. Use the following steps:

(a) Plot both functions on the interval $[0, \pi]$ and estimate the points of intersection.

(b) Construct the function $\text{diff}(x) = f(x) - g(x)$ and use the **root** function to find the (two) roots in the interval.

(c) Find the area by integrating $\text{diff}(x)$. Use the roots found in part (b) as limits.

5. A p-series is defined as,

$$1 + \frac{1}{2^p} + \frac{1}{3^p} + \frac{1}{4^p} + \cdots = \sum_{k=1}^{\infty} \frac{1}{k^p}$$

It can be shown that the series converges if $p > 1$ and diverges if $p \leq 1$.

(a) Examine the behavior of the p-series for $p = 1$ and for $p = 2$ taking the first 20 terms in the series and using the following steps.

  (i) Set up an expression for the partial sums using,

$$p = 2, \qquad N = 20, \qquad k = 1 .. N$$

and

$$\text{Sum}_1 = 1, \qquad \text{Sum}_{(k+1)} = \text{Sum}_k + \frac{1}{(k+1)^p}$$

  (ii) Make a plot of the kth partial sum, Sum_k, versus k.

  (iii) List the results as tables using $k =$ and $\text{Sum}_k =$.

(b) Examine the behavior of the integral function,

$$I(x) = \int_1^x \frac{1}{t^p} dt, \qquad \text{as} \qquad x \to \infty$$

If this function approaches a limit, the corresponding p-series converges; otherwise it diverges.

  Compare the cases $p = 1$ and $p = 2$ for all parts above.

6. The equation $y(x) = (x - x_0)^2/(4 \cdot p) + y_0$ represents a parabola whose symmetry axis is parallel to the y-axis (Fig. 4.5). The *vertex* coordinates are (x_0, y_0). The *focus* is situated on the symmetry axis inside the parabola a distance p from the vertex. The line perpendicular to the axis situated a distance p from the vertex outside the parabola is called the *directrix*.

(a) Plot the parabola described above using different values of x_0, y_0, and p. Show how the graph changes as these parameters vary.

(b) Show that the distance from any point on the parabola to the focus is the same as the perpendicular distance from that point to the directrix. Hint: The equation of the

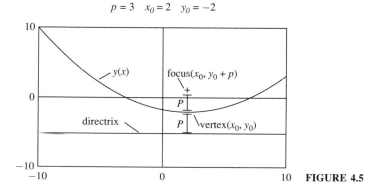

$p = 3 \quad x_0 = 2 \quad y_0 = -2$

FIGURE 4.5

directrix is $y = d = y_0 - p$. The distance from a point on the curve (x, y) to the directrix is,

$$s_1(x) = y(x) - d$$

The coordinates of the focus are $(x_0, y_0 + p)$. The distance from the point (x, y) to the focus is,

$$s_2(x) = [\{x - x_0\}^2 + \{y(x) - (y_0 + p)\}^2]^{1/2}$$

Using a plot, show that $s_1(x)$ and $s_2(x)$ are equal.

7. A cardioid can be represented in polar form as,

$$r(\theta) = 1 - \cos(\theta)$$

(a) Plot this function and compute the area in the first quadrant.

(b) Show that the analytical solution is $3 \cdot \pi/8 - 1$. Hint: Display the computed result from item (a) and fill the placeholder with the above expression. The numeric factor should be one.

8. A curve can be represented parametrically by,

$$x(t) = \ln(\cos(2 \cdot t)) \quad \text{and} \quad y(t) = 2 \cdot t \quad \text{for} \quad 0 \le t \le \left(\frac{\pi}{6}\right)$$

(a) Plot the curve in parametric form.

(b) Find the arc length for the curve. By filling the placeholder appropriately, show that the analytic solution for the arc length is $\ln(2 + \sqrt{3})$.

9. The volume enclosed by the paraboloid $z = 4 - x^2 - y^2$ and the xy-plane $z = 0$ is computed as,

$$\text{Volume} = 4 \cdot \int_0^2 \int_0^{[4-x^2]^{1/2}} [4 - x^2 - y^2] dy \, dx$$

(a) Compute the double integral with MathCAD. Recall that a double integral template is generated by typing **&&**.

(b) Reduce the double integral to a single integral by analytically performing the integration over y. Compute this integral with MathCAD.

(c) By filling the placeholder in the result with π, show that the integrations in parts (a) and (b) give Volume $= 8 \cdot \pi$.

10. Given the coefficient $a_n = [-1]^n/n!$, examine the behavior of a Maclaurin series of the function $y(x) = e^{-x}$. Use the following steps:

(a) Assign the function $f(x) = \exp(-x)$.

(b) Construct the function,

$$g(x) = \sum_{n=0}^{8} a_n \cdot x^n$$

(c) Construct the function,

$$h(x) = \sum_{n=0}^{12} a_n \cdot x^n$$

(d) Plot the three functions $f(x)$, $g(x)$, and $h(x)$ on a graph using a plot range of $x = 0, 0.5 \ ..4$. Use a graph format type of 10X.

11. A force field has components $F_x(x, y) = x^2 + y^2$ and $F_y(x, y) = x \cdot y$. An object subjected to this force moves along the parabola $y = x^2$ from the origin $a = (0, 0)$ to the point $b = (1, 1)$. Find the work done on the object using the formula,

$$\text{Work} = \int_a^b F_x(x, y) \ dx + F_y(x, y) \ dy$$

Hint: The parabolic segment can be represented in parametric form by $x(t) = t$, $y(t) = t^2$ for $0 \leq t \leq 1$. The work integral can be written in terms of t as,

$$\text{Work} = \int_0^1 \left[F_x\{x(t), y(t)\} \cdot \frac{dx(t)}{dt} + F_y\{x(t), y(t)\} \cdot \frac{dy(t)}{dt} \right] \cdot dt$$

12. According to the *trapezoidal* rule, the area under the curve represented by the function $y(x)$ on the interval $[a, b]$ is given by:

$$\text{Area} = \sum_{j=1}^{N} \frac{[y(x_j) + y(x_{j-1})]}{2} \cdot \Delta x$$

where $\Delta x = [b - a]/N$ and $x_j = a + j \cdot \Delta x$ and N is the number of subintervals.

Applying the above rule, find the area under the curve $y(x) = \sin(x)$ on the interval $[0, \pi]$ using $N = 100$. Compare this with the exact result, namely Area = 2. What happens to the error if the number of subintervals is reduced to $N = 50$?

REFERENCES

Anton, H.: *Calculus*, Wiley, New York, 1988.

Fraleigh, J. B.: *Calculus with Analytic Geometry*, Addison-Wesley, Reading, Mass., 1990.

Larson, R. E., R. P. Hostetler, and B. H. Edwards, *Calculus*, Heath, Lexington, Mass., 1990.

Mizrahi, A., and M. Sullivan: *Calculus & Analytic Geometry*, Wadsworth, Belmont, Calif., 1990.

Stewart, J.: *Calculus*, Brooks/Cole, Pacific Grove, Calif., 1991.

Thomas, G.B., and R. L. Finney: *Calculus*, Addison-Wesley, Reading, Mass., 1979.

CHAPTER
5

APPLICATIONS TO GENERAL PHYSICS

DIMENSIONS AND UNITS

A physical quantity is defined not only by its numerical value but also by the *dimensions* of which it is composed. There are seven basic dimensions of physics.* As was shown in Chapter 2, MathCAD supports the following four: *length*, *mass*, *time*, and *electric charge* and designates them by L, M, T, and Q respectively. You can redefine any of these four. Physical quantities are composed of products and/or quotients of the basic dimensions. For example, velocity has dimensions of length·time^{-1} whereas energy is composed of mass·length^2·time^{-2}.

Three systems of units are usually used to express these dimensions. They are the *C.G.S*, *M.K.S.*, and *British* systems. The units of length, mass, and time in these systems are:

Dimension	C.G.S.	M.K.S.	British
length	centimeters	meters	feet
mass	grams	kilograms	slugs
time	seconds	seconds	seconds

---

*The basic seven dimensions are: length, mass, time, charge, temperature, mole number, and luminous intensity.

A quantity such as velocity is expressed in units of cm·s^{-1}, m·s^{-1}, and ft·s^{-1} in the C.G.S., M.K.S., and British system respectively.

In an equation with physical quantities, not only must the numerical value of both sides be the same, but the dimensions must also match. Often errors can be detected by examining the dimensions of each side of an equation. MathCAD allows you to attach dimensions to physical quantities. It then proceeds to check your equations for dimensional consistency. It also allows you to define unit conversions so that physical quantities can be computed and displayed in more than one system.

We illustrate dimensional analysis with the *ideal gas law*,

$$P \cdot V = n \cdot R \cdot T$$

where P is the pressure, V the volume, T the absolute (or Kelvin) temperature, and n the number of moles in the gas. The quantity R is a universal constant known as the *ideal gas constant*. While the dimensions of R are fixed, the numerical value depends on the choice of units. Physicists, chemists, and engineers each prefer their own system of units. For example, physicists often express R in joules · kg_mole$^{-1} \cdot K^{-1}$ or cal·g_mole$^{-1} \cdot K^{-1}$ while chemists prefer R in liter·atmospheres· g_mole$^{-1} \cdot K^{-1}$. Chemical engineers commonly express R in BTU · lb_mole^{-1} · Rankine^{-1}. In Worksheet 5.1, we show how MathCAD handles the dimensions and units of the ideal gas constant. We also show how the dimension of charge is replaced by the dimension of temperature with MathCAD.

> **MathCAD solution: Worksheet 5.1.** Before we begin the worksheet, we reset the basic dimensions by making the fourth dimension absolute temperature instead of charge. We make the change using the following key sequence: **{F10}** (menu), **C** (compute), **D** (dimension). The pull-down menu (or message line in ver. 2.0) will show MathCAD's default dimensions. Replace the word charge appearing after the Q with the word temp and press **{Enter}**. The dimension Q will now be used for temperature. [The dimension letters M, L, T, Q cannot be changed.] We use the M.K.S. system units to express our primary dimensions. For example, to globally assign the dimension longth to the unit m (meter), type **m~1L**. The other dimensions are assigned by typing **kg~1M**, **s~1T**, and **K~1Q**. We are taking the unit of absolute temperature to be the *Kelvin* (K).
>
> We proceed to use global definitions to define secondary units, first for the different type of moles and then for force, length, volume, energy, and pressure. For example, to define the Newton (MKS force), we make the global assignment by typing **N~kg*m/s^2**. We define an alternative unit for absolute temperature called the *Rankine*. [The Rankine, lb-mole (molecular amount) and BTU (British thermal unit of energy) are common to the British system and are used extensively by engineers.] Once the conversion factors have been defined, we assign the accepted value of R in C.G.S. units [cal · g_mole$^{-1} \cdot K^{-1}$] by typing: **R:1.987*cal/(gm_mole*K)**.
>
> We are now ready to display the values of R in other units. When we type **R=**, we see,

```
R = 8.314·mass·length²·time⁻²·temp⁻¹
```

> This is MathCAD's way of reminding us that R has dimensions. The numerical value of R is given for the chosen units of our basic dimensions (in our case, meters, kilograms,

Meter/Length	Kilogram/Mass	Second/Time	Kelvin/Temperature
-----------	-------------	----------	------------------
$m \equiv 1L$	$kg \equiv 1M$	$s \equiv 1T$	$K \equiv 1Q$

Mole $gm\_mole \equiv 1$ $kg\_mole \equiv 1000 \cdot gm\_mole$ $lb\_mole \equiv .454 \cdot kg\_mole$

Force: $N \equiv kg \cdot \dfrac{m}{s^2}$ $d \equiv 10^6 \cdot N$ $lb \equiv \dfrac{N}{.225}$

Length: $cm \equiv .01 \cdot m$ $in \equiv 1 \cdot \dfrac{m}{39.37}$ $ft \equiv 12 \cdot in$

Volume: $cc \equiv 1 \cdot cm^3$ $l \equiv 1000 \cdot cc$ Rankine Temp.: $Rank \equiv \left[\dfrac{5}{9}\right] \cdot K$
-------   ---------------

Energy: $J \equiv 1 \cdot N \cdot m$ $erg \equiv 1 \cdot d \cdot cm$ $cal \equiv 4.184 \cdot J$ $ft\_lb \equiv ft \cdot lb$
------ $BTU \equiv 1.055 \cdot 10^3 \cdot J$

Pressure: $Pa \equiv 1 \cdot \dfrac{N}{m^2}$ $atm \equiv 1.013 \cdot 10^5 \cdot Pa$ $bar \equiv 10^5 \cdot Pa$ $psia \equiv \dfrac{bar}{14.5}$

Assigned Value of R: $R := 1.987 \cdot \dfrac{cal}{gm\_mole \cdot K}$

Displayed Values of R:

$R = 0.082 \cdot \dfrac{l \cdot atm}{gm\_mole \cdot K}$ $R = 8.314 \cdot 10^3 \cdot \dfrac{J}{kg\_mole \cdot K}$ $R = 83.136 \cdot cm^3 \cdot \dfrac{bar}{gm\_mole \cdot K}$

$R = 8.314 \cdot 10^{-4} \cdot \dfrac{erg}{gm\_mole \cdot K}$ $R = 1.988 \cdot \dfrac{BTU}{lb\_mole \cdot Rank}$

$R = 10.737 \cdot psia \cdot \dfrac{ft^3}{lb\_mole \cdot Rank}$ $R = 1.548 \cdot 10^3 \cdot \dfrac{ft\_lb}{lb\_mole \cdot Rank}$

WORKSHEET 5.1
Dimensions and units of the ideal gas constant.

seconds, and Kelvins). If we fill the placeholder with **l*atm/(gm_mole*K)**, the result is redisplayed as,

$$R = 0.082 \cdot \dfrac{l \cdot atm}{gm\_mole \cdot K}$$

If you have correctly chosen a set of units for R, then all four of the dimension names should disappear in the displayed result.
    We continue the worksheet by displaying R in different units. (Note: If you are using the student edition of MathCAD, enter all the display objects for R downward rather than across the page to avoid exceeding the 80 character limit.) As can be seen from the worksheet, MathCAD not only keeps track of dimensions but also expresses quantities in any set of dimensionally consistent units.

ADDITION OF VECTORS

A physical quantity can be classified as either a *scalar* or a *vector*.[1] Scalars have only a magnitude while vectors have both a magnitude and a direction. For example, mass is a scalar quantity and needs only a magnitude to quantify it. Velocity, on the other hand, is a vector and requires specifications involving both magnitude and direction. The algebra of vectors is different from that of scalars. While scalars follow the algebra of ordinary numbers, vectors require a more extensive treatment. Below, we consider the addition of vectors.

A vector in two dimensions can be represented in *polar form* using a magnitude and an angle (measured from the positive x-axis). For example, the vector $\mathbf{V} = (4, 45°)$ is a vector of length 4 and direction 45° above the positive x-axis. Consider the following four vectors to be added: $\mathbf{V}_1 = (4, 30°)$, $\mathbf{V}_2 = (2, 45°)$, $\mathbf{V}_3 = (3, -120°)$, and $\mathbf{V}_4 = (4, 230°)$. The sum or resultant is also a vector and is written as $\mathbf{R} = \mathbf{V}_1 + \mathbf{V}_2 + \mathbf{V}_3 + \mathbf{V}_4$. Vectors may be added graphically or analytically.

The graphical or polygon method (see Fig. 5.1) begins by placing the first vector with its tail at the origin and orienting it according to its direction. The tail of the second vector is then placed at the head of the first and oriented according to its direction. The chain is continued with the remaining vectors. Finally a vector is drawn from the origin (tail of first vector) to the head of the last vector to form a polygon. This last vector is the sum or *resultant*, $\mathbf{R}$.

An analytical method to compute the resultant is *rectangular resolution*. Each vector is *resolved* into both an x and a y component and the corresponding components added, as in the following table:

x-components	y-components
$\mathbf{V}_{1x} = \mathbf{V}_1 \cdot \cos(\theta_1)$	$\mathbf{V}_{1y} = \mathbf{V}_1 \cdot \sin(\theta_1)$
$\mathbf{V}_{2x} = \mathbf{V}_2 \cdot \cos(\theta_2)$	$\mathbf{V}_{2y} = \mathbf{V}_2 \cdot \sin(\theta_2)$
$\mathbf{V}_{3x} = \mathbf{V}_3 \cdot \cos(\theta_3)$	$\mathbf{V}_{3y} = \mathbf{V}_3 \cdot \sin(\theta_3)$
$\mathbf{V}_{4x} = \mathbf{V}_4 \cdot \cos(\theta_4)$	$\mathbf{V}_{4y} = \mathbf{V}_4 \cdot \sin(\theta_4)$
etc.	etc.
$\mathbf{R}_x = \displaystyle\sum_x V_{nx}$	$\mathbf{R}_y = \displaystyle\sum_n V_{ny}$

The magnitude and direction of the resultant is computed using,

$$\mathbf{R} = [\mathbf{R}_x^2 + \mathbf{R}_y^2]^{1/2} \qquad \theta = \tan^{-1}\left(\frac{\mathbf{R}_y}{\mathbf{R}_x}\right)$$

---

[1]Certain physical quantities have too complex a structure to be classified in this way. More generally, a quantity is classified as a *tensor*. The higher the *rank* of the tensor, the more complex the quantity. Scalars and vectors are tensors of rank zero and one respectively.

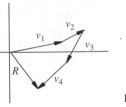

FIGURE 5.1

where the angle is adjusted for the correct quadrant. Worksheet 5.2 shows how to add vectors using rectangular resolution.

MathCAD solution: Worksheet 5.2. Since we plan to enter angles in degrees rather than in radians, we begin by defining the degree unit. We also assign the number of vectors to be added (N=8). The first two objects in the second row assign and then display the range for an integer variable n. The display is accomplished by typing **n=**. The next two objects are *tabular assignments* for the magnitude and direction of the eight vectors. The data is entered using the keystrokes, **v[n:4,2,3,4,** etc. followed by **{Enter}** and **{<Alt>Q}[n:30*deg,45*deg,-120*deg,230*deg,** etc. followed by **{Enter}**. For example, the first vector has been assigned a magnitude of 4 units and a direction of 30 degrees above the positive x-axis.

Using *vectorization*, we create a pair of tables (or MathCAD vectors). These two vectors are not to be confused with the eight physical vectors given. The keystrokes to create them are **Vx:{<Alt>-}(v*cos({<Alt>Q}))** and **Vy:{<Alt>-}(v*sin({<Alt>Q}))**. The elements of these two MathCAD vectors contain the x and y components of the eight given vectors. For example, the first elements of **Vx** and **Vy** correspond to the components of the first physical vector, i.e., $4 \cdot \cos(30°) = 3.464$ and $4 \cdot \sin(30°) = 2$. We next add the components separately to obtain the components of the resultant $\mathbf{R_x}$ and $\mathbf{R_y}$. To compute these components, type **R.x:n$Vx[n** and **R.y:n$Vy[n**.

Finally, we compute the magnitude R and the direction angle θ of the resultant. The angle is obtained from MathCAD's **angle** function. By filling the placeholder with the conversion factor **deg**, defined at the top of the worksheet, we see the angle displayed in degrees.

You can use Worksheet 5.2 to add any eight vectors by changing the values of the magnitude and direction in the assigning tables for v_n and θ_n. You can add any number of vectors by extending the tables.

PROJECTILE MOTION

When the only force acting on an object is the gravitational pull of the earth, the object, which is said to be in "free fall," will accelerate toward the center of the earth. If the object is near the surface of the earth, the acceleration will be uniform. Its horizontal and vertical coordinates x and y will vary with time t according to the parametric equations,

Horizontal motion ($a_x = 0$)	Vertical motion ($a_y = g$)
$x = v_{x_0} \cdot t + x_0$	$y = \dfrac{1}{2} \cdot g \cdot t^2 + v_{y_0} \cdot t + y_0$

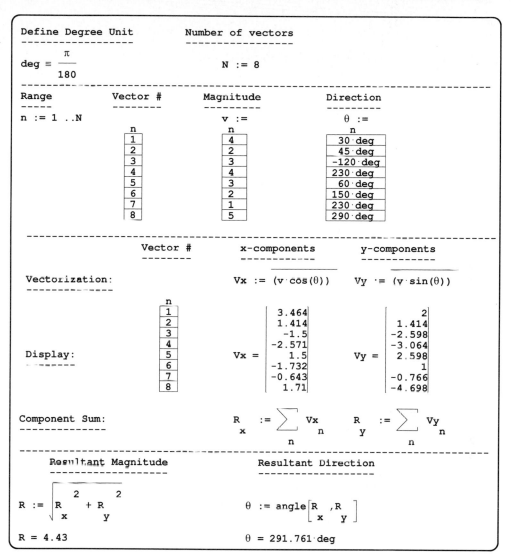

WORKSHEET 5.2
Addition of vectors.

where g is the (constant) acceleration of gravity. The value of g is -32 ft $\cdot$ s^{-2}, -980 cm $\cdot$ s^{-2}, or -9.8 m $\cdot$ s^{-2} according to the system of units being used. The initial value constants are,

$$v_{x_0} = \text{Initial } x\text{-velocity} \qquad v_{y_0} = \text{Initial } y\text{-velocity}$$

$$x_0 = \text{Initial } x\text{-coordinate} \qquad y_0 = \text{Initial } y\text{-coordinate}$$

If the object is started from the coordinate origin ($x_0 = 0$, $y_0 = 0$) and launched with a speed v_0 at an angle θ_0 above the horizontal, the above equations take the form,

$$x = [v_0 \cdot \cos(\theta_0)] \cdot t \qquad \text{and} \qquad y = \frac{1}{2} \cdot g \cdot t^2 + [v_0 \cdot \sin(\theta_0)] \cdot t$$

The object moves in a parabolic trajectory as shown in Fig. 5.2.

The object reaches a maximum height h and has a horizontal range R. Using some algebra, it can be shown that,

$$h = \frac{-v_0^2 \cdot \sin^2(\theta_0)}{(2 \cdot g)}$$

and

$$R = \frac{-v_0^2 \cdot \sin(2 \cdot \theta_0)}{g}$$

The flight time T is given by,

$$T = \frac{-2 \cdot v_0 \cdot \sin(\theta_o)}{g}$$

The maximum height and flight time of the trajectory increase with the launch angle θ_0. The range, however, increases with θ_0 until it reaches a maximum for $\theta_0 = 45°$ and then begins to decrease. We analyze projectile motion in Worksheet 5.3.

MathCAD solution: Worksheet 5.3. The degree unit and the acceleration of gravity are defined. The initial launch speed is fixed ($v_0 = 100$) but the launch angle is allowed to be a variable parameter θ. (In the worksheet, we drop the subscript zero on the launch angle.) The equations of motion for position and velocity are assigned as are the formulas for range and height. Four arbitrary launch angles (in degrees) are assigned as subscripted variables. (Note that the four angles constitute a MathCAD vector $\boldsymbol{\theta}$.) The assignment for θ_1, for example, is made using the following keystrokes,

θ[1:75∗deg

The angle α is assigned to be the maximum of the four angles above (in our case $\alpha = 75°$). This is accomplished using MathCAD's **max** function as follows,

α:max(θ)

MathCAD's **max** function retrieves the largest element of a vector. The maximum range is computed by evaluating the range formula at $45°$. The maximum time of flight and

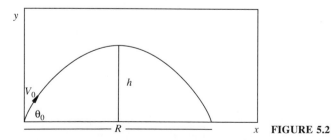

FIGURE 5.2

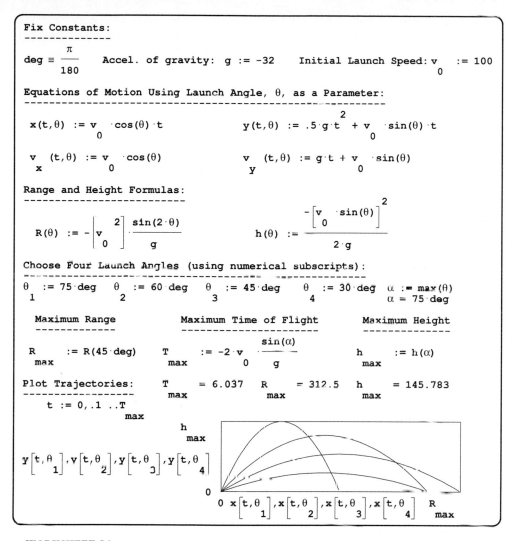

Fix Constants:

$deg \equiv \dfrac{\pi}{180}$ Accel. of gravity: $g := -32$ Initial Launch Speed: $v_0 := 100$

Equations of Motion Using Launch Angle, θ, as a Parameter:

$x(t,\theta) := v_0 \cdot \cos(\theta) \cdot t$ $y(t,\theta) := .5 \cdot g \cdot t^2 + v_0 \cdot \sin(\theta) \cdot t$

$v_x(t,\theta) := v_0 \cdot \cos(\theta)$ $v_y(t,\theta) := g \cdot t + v_0 \cdot \sin(\theta)$

Range and Height Formulas:

$R(\theta) := -\left| v_0 \right|^2 \cdot \dfrac{\sin(2 \cdot \theta)}{g}$ $h(\theta) := \dfrac{-\left[v_0 \cdot \sin(\theta) \right]^2}{2 \cdot g}$

Choose Four Launch Angles (using numerical subscripts):

$\theta_1 := 75 \cdot deg$ $\theta_2 := 60 \cdot deg$ $\theta_3 := 45 \cdot deg$ $\theta_4 := 30 \cdot deg$ $\alpha := max(\theta)$
$\alpha = 75 \cdot deg$

Maximum Range   Maximum Time of Flight   Maximum Height
-------------   ----------------------   --------------

$R_{max} := R(45 \cdot deg)$ $T_{max} := -2 \cdot v_0 \cdot \dfrac{\sin(\alpha)}{g}$ $h_{max} := h(\alpha)$

Plot Trajectories: $T_{max} = 6.037$ $R_{max} = 312.5$ $h_{max} = 145.783$

$t := 0, .1 \ .. T_{max}$

$$y\left[t, \theta_1\right], y\left[t, \theta_2\right], y\left[t, \theta_3\right], y\left[t, \theta_4\right]$$

$$0 \quad x\left[t, \theta_1\right], x\left[t, \theta_2\right], x\left[t, \theta_3\right], x\left[t, \theta_4\right] \quad R_{max}$$

WORKSHEET 5.3
Motion of a projectile.

maximum height occur for the largest launch angle (in this case α). We used α to evaluate T_{max} and h_{max}.

Finally the trajectories are plotted. Each is generated by plotting its equations of motion $x(t)$ and $y(t)$ on the horizontal and vertical axis respectively. The central placeholder on the horizontal axis is filled with,

x(t,{<Alt>Q}[1),x(t,{<Alt>Q}[2),x(t,{<Alt>Q}[3),x(t,{<Alt>Q}[4)

A similar entry, using **y**, is made for the placeholder on the vertical axis. MathCAD pairs the variables x and y and produces four plots.

The plot variable t (time) is assigned to range from zero to T_{max} to insure that all orbit points are included. By filling the scale placeholders appropriately, the x and y scales are manually set to $[0, R_{max}]$ and $[0, h_{max}]$.

Note that as θ decreases from its initial value of $75°$, the range increases until it reaches a maximum at an angle of $45°$. Thereafter it decreases. Note also that $60°$ and $30°$ launch angles have the *same* range although the larger angle reaches a greater height and has a longer flight time. (This rule holds for all pairs of complementary angles.) To observe the trajectories for different launch angles, change the assigned values of θ_n in the worksheet.

NEWTON'S SECOND LAW, MOTION OF COUPLED BODIES

Consider two masses M and m arranged as in Fig. 5.3. The angle of the incline is θ. If the system is unbalanced, the masses will accelerate. We take the positive direction of motion to be up the plane for M and vertically down for m.

The coefficient of kinetic friction between the plane and M is μ_k. By drawing free-body diagrams on each mass and applying Newton's second law, $F = m \cdot a$, we obtain the following simultaneous equations for the two unknowns a (acceleration) and T (string tension),

$$T - M \cdot g \cdot \sin(\theta) \pm \mu_k \cdot M \cdot g \cdot \cos(\theta) = M \cdot a$$

$$m \cdot g - T = m \cdot a$$

The third term in the first equation represents the force of friction. The plus sign applies if the mass M is moving *down* (i.e., negative velocity) the plane; otherwise the minus sign is used. This is because *kinetic friction always points opposite to the direction of motion.* The two equations can be solved analytically for the acceleration and the tension. The results are as follows,

$$a = \frac{g \cdot [m - M \cdot \sin(\theta) \pm \mu_k \cdot M \cdot \cos(\theta)]}{[M + m]}$$

$$T = m \cdot (g - a)$$

The numerical result for the acceleration obtained in the first equation is used in the second to compute the tension. The acceleration and tension depend on the values of the masses, the incline angle, and the coefficient of friction. The upper sign in the

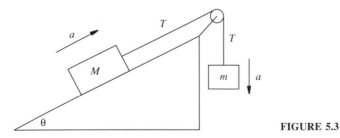

FIGURE 5.3

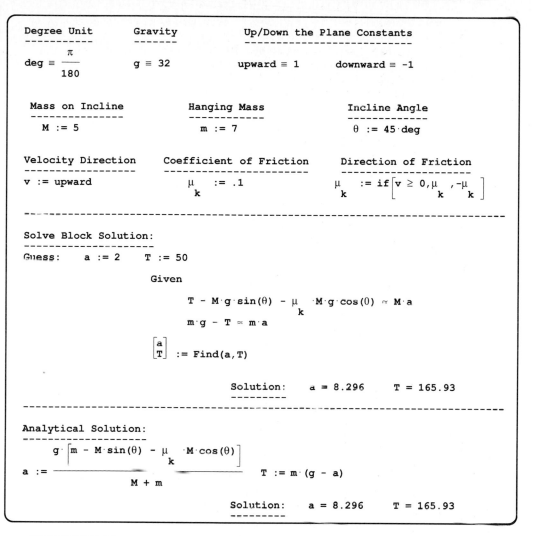

WORKSHEET 5.4
Newton's second law—motion of coupled bodies.

expression is used for motion *down* the plane. The analysis of the motion is presented in Worksheet 5.4.

MathCAD solution: Worksheet 5.4. We begin by globally assigning values to the degree unit, to the acceleration of gravity, and to a pair of constants labeled upward=1 and downward=-1. These constants assign the direction of the velocity of the mass on the incline. Setting the velocity equal to upward (i.e., to +1) indicates that the mass is moving up the plane. Setting it equal to downward (i.e., to -1) indicates that the mass is moving down the plane. Next, the values of the masses M and m and the incline angle θ are assigned. We set v=upward and assign the value of the coefficient of kinetic friction μ_k. Note that an **if** object is being used to account for the $\pm$ sign in the equations of motion. (Type **{<Alt>)}** to generate $\geq$.)

A solve block is used to numerically solve for the acceleration and tension. (The relational equals, $\approx$, is produced by typing **{<Alt>=}**.) Note that the results of the **Find** are directly assigned to a two-dimensional MathCAD vector whose elements are a and T. The assignment is made by typing **{<Alt>M}2 0{Enter}:Find(a,T)** and filling the placeholders with **a** and **T**. The results for a and T are displayed.

We also solve the problem using the analytical expression derived above and verify that the results agree with the solve block approach. By changing the values of the masses, the incline angle, the velocity direction, or the coefficient of kinetic friction, we can see how the acceleration and the tension depend on these quantities.

COLLISIONS

When two bodies move toward each other along some line, collide, and then move apart along the same line, we have a *one-dimensional* collision. We take the line of the collision to be the x-axis. The first object has a mass of m_1 while the second is α times as large, that is, $m_2 = \alpha \cdot m_1$. The masses have initial velocities v_1 and v_2. After the collision, the final velocities are v_1' and v_2'. The law of *Conservation of Linear Momentum* is valid for all such collisions and requires,

Momentum before collision = Momentum after collision

$$m_1 \cdot v_1 + m_2 \cdot v_2 = m_1 \cdot v_1' + m_2 \cdot v_2'$$

In order to solve for the two final velocities, we need a second equation. We use Newton's empirical rule for relative velocities,

[Rel. velocity after collision] = $-\epsilon \cdot$ [Rel. velocity before collision]

$$[v_2' - v_1'] = -\epsilon \cdot [v_2 - v_1]$$

The collision parameter ϵ is called the *coefficient of restitution* and is restricted to the range $0 \leq \epsilon \leq 1$. When $\epsilon = 0$, the collision is called *perfectly inelastic* (the masses stick together and heat is generated); when $\epsilon = 1$, the collision is *perfectly elastic* (kinetic energy is conserved and no heat is generated).

The two equations above can be solved for v_1' and v_2' as,

$$v_1' = \frac{[(1 - \epsilon \cdot \alpha) \cdot v_1 + \alpha \cdot (1 + \epsilon) \cdot v_2]}{[1 + \alpha]}$$

$$v_2' = \frac{[(\alpha - \epsilon) \cdot v_2 + (1 + \epsilon) \cdot v_1]}{[1 + \alpha]}$$

where $\alpha = m_2/m_1$ is the mass ratio. The heat generated as a result of the collision is computed by subtracting the final kinetic energy from the initial kinetic energy, or

$$\text{Heat generated } = \left[\frac{1}{2} \cdot m_1 \cdot v_1^2 + \frac{1}{2} \cdot m_2 \cdot v_2^2\right] - \left[\frac{1}{2} \cdot m_1 \cdot v_1'^2 + \frac{1}{2} \cdot m_2 \cdot v_2'^2\right]$$

A typical one-dimensional collision is analyzed in Worksheet 5.5.

MathCAD solution: Worksheet 5.5. The first row assigns the first mass ($m_1 = 1$) and the initial velocities ($v_1 = 10$, $v_2 = 0$). The final velocities are expressed as

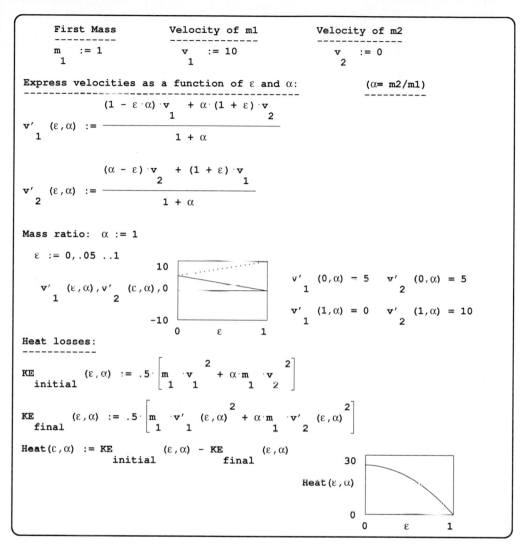

WORKSHEET 5.5
Collision of two point masses.

functions of ϵ and α. With the masses equal (α=1), the final velocities are plotted as functions of ϵ (using a solid line for v'_1 and dots for v'_2). Note that when the collision becomes perfectly inelastic (ϵ=0), the two masses stick together and move with the same velocity. When the collision becomes perfectly elastic (ϵ=1), the first mass comes to rest; the second mass acquires the initial velocity of the first. This *velocity transfer* is characteristic of billiard balls. Finally, the heat function is computed and plotted versus ϵ for α=1 (equal masses). Note that as ϵ tends to one, the heat generated approaches zero.

By changing the value of α, we can observe the results for different mass ratios. An interesting case is that of a ball striking the earth, where the mass ratio α is very large.

If the collision is perfectly inelastic $(\epsilon=0)$, the ball ends up at rest stuck to the earth, whereas if the collision is perfectly elastic $(\epsilon=1)$, the ball simply reverses its velocity. Verify this result by setting $\alpha=10000$ and considering the two cases $\epsilon=0$ and $\epsilon=1$.

SIMPLE HARMONIC MOTION IN TWO DIMENSIONS

When an object of mass M is attached to a spring with an elastic constant k_x and set into motion along the x-axis, the equations of motion can be written as,

$$x(t) = A_x \cdot \cos(\omega_x \cdot t + \phi_x)$$

$$v_x(t) = -\omega_x \cdot A_x \cdot \sin(\omega_x \cdot t + \phi_x)$$

where ω_x is the (angular) *frequency*, A_x is the *amplitude* and ϕ_x is the *phase* of the motion. These constants are determined from the equations,

$$\omega_x = \left[\frac{k_x}{M}\right]^{1/2} \qquad A_x = \left[x_0^2 + \frac{v_{x0}^2}{\omega_x^2}\right]^{1/2} \qquad \phi_x = \tan^{-1}\left[\frac{-v_{x0}}{(\omega_x \cdot x_0)}\right]$$

where x_0 and v_{x0} are the initial position and velocity respectively. The constant ω_x is called a *physical* constant because it is determined by physical conditions (the size of the mass and the stiffness of the spring) whereas the constants x_0 and v_{x0} are called *initial value* constants because they are determined from the way the object is started. The resulting motion of the mass is called *simple harmonic*; the mass oscillates back and forth indefinitely along the x-axis.

If the object moves in the xy-plane and is subjected to elastic restoring forces k_x and k_y along the x-axis and y-axis respectively, the resulting motion is a superposition of two simple harmonic motions $x(t)$ and $y(t)$. These are given by,

$$x(t) = A_x \cdot \cos(\omega_x \cdot t + \phi_x)$$

$$y(t) = A_y \cdot \cos(\omega_y \cdot t + \phi_y)$$

where $\omega_x = [k_x/M]^{1/2}$ and $\omega_y = [k_y/M]^{1/2}$. The resulting motion of the mass is determined by the two frequencies ω_x and ω_y and by the amplitudes and phases A_x, A_y, ϕ_x, and ϕ_y.

If the two frequencies are not equal, but can be written,

$$\omega_x = n \cdot \omega \qquad \text{and} \qquad \omega_y = m \cdot \omega$$

where ω is some base frequency and n and m are positive integers, then the orbit is a *Lissajous* figure. The orbit is closed which means that the mass periodically retraces its path. If $n = 1$ and m is an irrational number (e.g., $m = \sqrt{3}$), then the orbit is not closed and the mass never retraces it path.

If the two frequencies are equal, $\omega_x = \omega_y = \omega$, the orbit is an ellipse. The shape and orientation of the ellipse are determined by the amplitudes and phases of the two vibrations. The tilt angle of the ellipse ϕ is determined from the formula,

$$\tan(2 \cdot \phi) = \frac{2 \cdot A_x \cdot A_y \cdot \cos(\phi_y - \phi_x)}{[A_x^2 - A_y^2]}$$

If $\phi_y - \phi_x = \pi/2$, then the tilt angle of the ellipse is zero and its width and height are $2 \cdot A_x$ and $2 \cdot A_y$ respectively . If $\phi_y - \phi_x = 0$ or $\phi_y - \phi_x = 180°$, then the ellipse degenerates into a straight line of slope A_y/A_x or $-A_y/A_x$ respectively.

We examine simple harmonic motion in two dimensions in Worksheet 5.6.

MathCAD solution: Worksheet 5.6. We begin by assigning the base frequency $(\omega=1)$, the multipliers (n=1, m=3) and the amplitudes and phases (A$_x$=1, A$_y$=1, ϕ_x=0· deg, ϕ_y=90· deg). The equations $x(t)$ and $y(t)$ are plotted over three base periods, where the base period is T=2·π/ω.

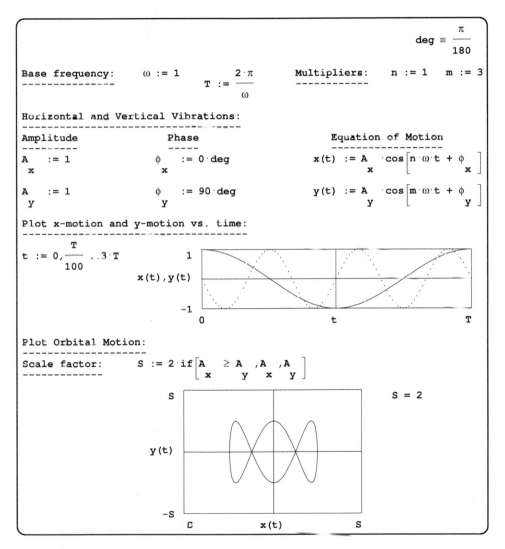

WORKSHEET 5.6
Simple harmonic motion in two dimensions.

The orbit is obtained by plotting $x(t)$ on the horizontal axis and $y(t)$ on the vertical axis. The plot format is set to `size=12,30` in order to produce an approximately square template. The scale is manually set to $-S$ to $+S$ for both axes, where S is twice the larger of the two amplitudes of motion.

For the assigned parameters, the form of the orbit is a Lissajous pattern. The orbit actually retraces after one base period. Increasing the plot range beyond this period does not produce any new orbital points.

Make the assignment `n=1` and `m=`$\sqrt{3}$ and verify that, in this case, the orbit is not closed. Increasing the plot range beyond the base period `T` extends the orbit to new points in space.

With `n=1` and `m=1`, vary the amplitudes and phases and observe the different ellipses. Note that to produce a circle, the amplitudes must be equal and the phase difference must be $90°$. Verify that for phase differences of $0°$ or $180°$, the orbit is a straight line of slope $\pm A_y/A_x$.

STATIONARY VIBRATIONS OF A STRING

If a taut string of length L is fixed at both ends, it vibrates when plucked. A set of natural modes of vibration (or harmonics) exists for the string. Each mode is characterized by an integer n. In any one mode, the string vibrates with a natural or characteristic frequency ω_n. The pattern of the string in a mode is represented by a *stationary* (or *standing*) wave. The equation of a stationary wave is,

$$y_n(x, t) = \cos(\omega_n \cdot t) \cdot \sin(k_n \cdot x) \qquad (n = 1, 2, 3 ..)$$

where y is the displacement, t is the time, and x is a point on the string. The wavenumber is $k_n = n \cdot \pi/L$ and the frequency is $\omega_n = v \cdot k_n$. The parameter v represents the velocity of transverse waves on the string and is given by

$$v = \left(\frac{\text{Tension}}{\text{Linear mass density}} \right)^{1/2}$$

The first harmonic has $n = 1$, the second $n = 2$, etc.

By plotting y versus x at different times, we see how the string changes shape. In Worksheet 5.7, we analyze the motion of a vibrating string in its various modes.

MathCAD solution: Worksheet 5.7. We assign the wave parameters and the equation of motion. Note that MathCAD does *not* support subscripted functions; therefore n is treated as variable in the wave function. The first plot is for the first harmonic (n=1) and shows the string shape at four different times. The frequency is displayed by typing **{<Alt>W}[n=** and then filling the placeholder with π (**{<Alt>P}**). The plots are repeated for the next two harmonics. Note that for n=2 and n=3 there are certain internal points that do not vibrate. These points are called *nodes* and are characteristic of the natural modes of vibration.

By changing the velocity, you can simulate the effect of a change in either the tension or density of the string.

BEATS

Consider two sources emitting harmonic sounds. The two sounds have the same amplitudes $A_1 = A_2 = A$ but slightly different frequencies ω_1 and $\omega_2 = \omega_1 + \delta\omega$.

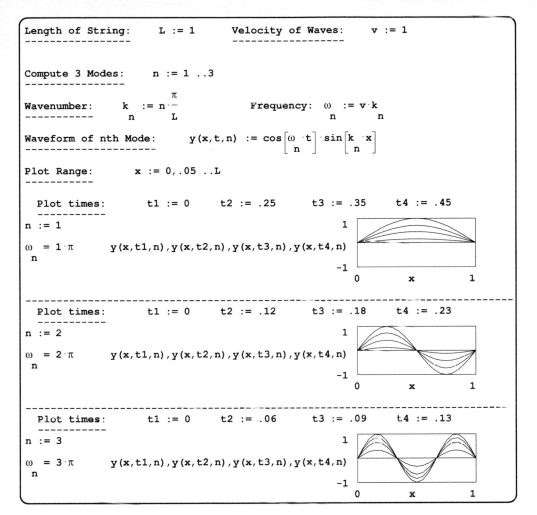

WORKSHEET 5.7
Standing waves.

It can be shown that the composite sound is nearly harmonic and has a frequency approximately equal to ω_1. The amplitude, however, is not constant but oscillates with a frequency of δw. Hence the loudness of the sound pulsates at a rate equal to the difference of the component frequencies ω_1 and ω_2. This is the phenomenon of *beats*.

To see this, let the two vibrational motions be written as,

$$y_1 = \cos[\omega \cdot t], \qquad \text{and} \qquad y_2 = \cos[(\omega + \delta w) \cdot t]$$

where the small frequency difference is δw; the amplitudes are each equal to one. The composite vibration $y = y_1 + y_2$ can be expressed as,

$$y = \cos[\omega \cdot t] + \cos[(\omega + \delta\omega) \cdot t]$$

$$= 2 \cdot \cos\left[\left(\frac{\delta\omega}{2}\right) \cdot t\right] \cdot \cos\left[\left(\frac{\omega + \delta\omega}{2}\right) \cdot t\right]$$

$$\approx 2 \cdot \cos\left[\left(\frac{\delta\omega}{2}\right) \cdot t\right] \cdot \cos[\omega \cdot t] \qquad (\text{if } \delta\omega << \omega)$$

$$\approx A(t) \cdot \cos(\omega \cdot t) \qquad \text{where } A(t) = 2 \cdot \cos\left[\left(\frac{\delta\omega}{2}\right) \cdot t\right]$$

The second equation is obtained using the identity,

$$\cos(a) + \cos(b) = 2 \cdot \cos\left[\frac{(a - b)}{2}\right] \cdot \cos\left[\frac{(a + b)}{2}\right]$$

The beat frequency of the composite wave is,

$$\omega_{\text{beat}} = 2\left[\frac{\delta\omega}{2}\right] = \delta\omega = \omega_2 - \omega_1$$

The beat pulses are $T_{\text{beat}} = 2 \cdot \pi/\delta\omega$ seconds apart. In Worksheet 5.8 below, we illustrate the phenomenon of beats.

> **MathCAD solution: Worksheet 5.8.** We choose the frequency of the first component y_1 to be $\omega_1 = 2 \cdot \pi$ rad/s corresponding to a period of T= 1s. We set the frequency difference equal to $\delta\omega = 0.1 \cdot \omega_1$ (i.e., a 10% difference). Thus the second component y_2 has a frequency $\omega_2 = \omega_1 + \delta\omega$. The two component functions are assigned and plotted over five cycles. One is displayed using solid lines and the other dots. The frequency difference of the waves is evident from the graph.
>
> Next, the composite vibration is plotted on an interval of 30 cycles. Note that there are three beat pulses in the interval. The beat period is therefore 10 s corresponding to a beat frequency which is one tenth of ω_1. We have thus demonstrated the validity of the equation above. If the frequency difference is changed to $\delta\omega = 0.2 \cdot \omega$, you will see six beat pulses on the interval.

INTERFERENCE FROM TWO SOURCES

Let waves be emitted from a pair of identical vibrating sources separated by a distance d (see Fig. 5.4). Assume that the waves are of wavelength λ and amplitude A and that they are emitted in a direction θ with the horizontal. As they approach a distant screen, the lower wave travels an extra distance $\delta = d \cdot \sin(\theta)$ relative to the upper wave. When the waves merge (at the screen) they arrive with a phase difference of,

$$\phi = 2 \cdot \pi \cdot \frac{\delta}{\lambda} = \frac{2 \cdot \pi \cdot d \cdot \sin(\theta)}{\lambda}$$

To find the resultant wave vibration, we add the two component waves y_1 and y_2 using ϕ as the phase difference between the vibrations. The resultant vibration is computed by representing each of the component vibrations by a vector-like quantity called a *phasor* and then adding the phasors (see Fig. 5.5).

Applying trigonometry to the triangle in Fig. 5.5, it can be shown that the amplitude of the resultant phasor can be written as

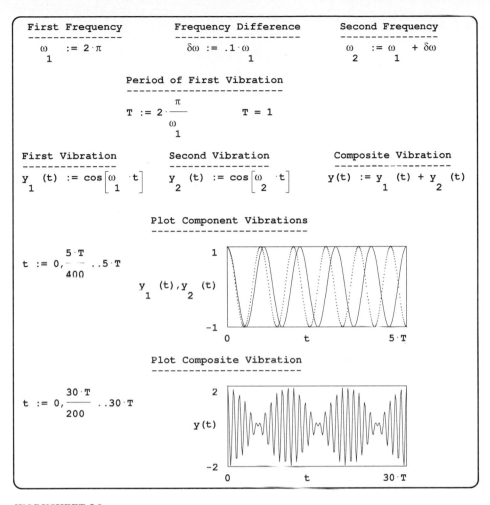

WORKSHEET 5.8
Beats.

$$A_{Res} = 2 \cdot A \cdot \cos\left(\frac{\phi}{2}\right)$$

The resultant *intensity* of the composite wave is proportional to the square of the amplitude and can be expressed as,

$$I_{Res} = 4 \cdot I_1 \cdot \cos^2\left(\frac{\phi}{2}\right)$$

where $I_1 = A^2$ is the intensity produced by a single source.

If the waves represent light coming from two slits, then the intensity represents the resultant brightness of the waves when they converge on a distant screen. As shown above, the phase angle ϕ is a function of the direction angle θ. Consequently, the

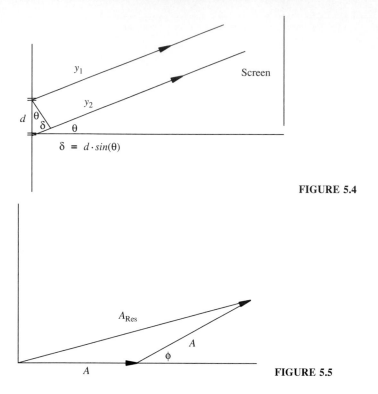

FIGURE 5.4

FIGURE 5.5

intensity varies along the screen. At certain values of θ, the intensity is a maximum; at other values it is zero. The intensity pattern of two slits is called a *Young's* interference pattern and has maxima at angles θ_n which satisfy Young's formula,

$$d \cdot \sin(\theta_n) = n \cdot \lambda \qquad \text{where} \qquad n = 0, \pm 1, \pm 2, \ldots$$

For these angles, the phase difference between the vibrations ϕ is a multiple of $2 \cdot \pi$; the waves arrive in phase and *constructively* interfere. We examine the two-slit pattern and confirm Young's formula in Worksheet 5.9, below.

> **MathCAD solution: Worksheet 5.9.** The amplitude (A=1), wavelength (λ = 0.25), and slit separation (d= 1) are assigned and the phase difference ϕ is computed. The amplitude is expressed as a function of θ, $A_{Res}(\theta)$. By squaring the amplitude, we obtain the intensity function $I_{Res}(\theta)$. The intensity is plotted as a function of θ (in degrees). (Recall that to plot θ in degrees, fill the central placeholder on the horizontal axis with θ/**deg**.) From the interference pattern, we see that the intensity has a maximum of 1 at θ=0 (central maximum). Maxima also occur symmetrically on both sides of the central maximum.
>
> We set a range for the integer n. Note that since we will be using negative subscripts as low as −4, we have used the assignment ORIGIN ≡ −4. We solve for θ_n in Young's formula. We compute the intensity for these values of n and display the results in tabular form. To list θ_n in degrees, type θ**[n/deg=**. Note that the value of the intensity at the angles θ_n is $I_{Res}(\theta_n) = 4 \cdot A^2 = 4$ (i.e., the maximum value) and occurs when n= 0, ±1, ±2,..., thus confirming Young's formula.

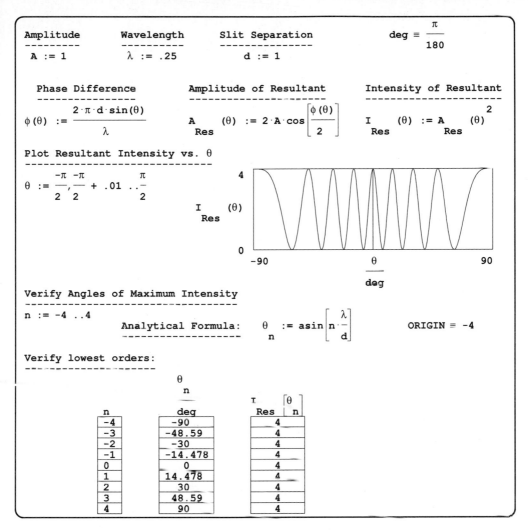

WORKSHEET 5.9
Two-slit interference.

CALORIMETRY

When two objects at different temperatures are brought into contact, heat flows from the hotter one to the colder one until the two objects reach the same temperature. If no heat is transferred to the surroundings, the heat gained by one must equal the heat lost by the other.

When a body gains or loses heat it may do so with or without changing phase (e.g., going from solid to liquid or liquid to vapor). *During a phase change, the temperature remains constant.* The rules for heat transfer are as follows:

1. No phase change.

$$\text{Heat} = m \cdot c \cdot [T_f - T_i]$$

where
$$m = \text{mass}$$

$$c = \text{specific heat}$$

$$[T_f - T_i] = \text{change in temperature}$$

2. Phase change.

$$\text{Heat} = m \cdot L$$

where
$$m = \text{mass}$$

$$L = \text{latent heat of phase change}$$

Consider the following problem. Ice of mass $m_i = 20$ g at a temperature $T_i = -30°C$ is mixed with water of mass $m_w = 200$ g at a temperature $T_w = 20°C$. The mixing process takes place in an insulating container (e.g., a vacuum bottle) which does nothing more than insure that heat is neither gained from nor lost to the surroundings. What is the final state of the system? The answer, as we shall see, depends on the masses and initial temperatures of the ice and water being mixed.

Case I. If very little water is mixed in, all the water will likely freeze and the final temperature will be below zero (but above $-30°C$). The unknown quantity is the final temperature of the system T_1.

Case II. If a larger amount of water is mixed in, it may be partially frozen by the ice so that the final state will be a mixture of ice and water at zero degrees. The unknown quantity is the amount of water that froze x_w.

Case III. If a still larger amount of water is mixed in, the ice may be partially melted by the water so that the final state is still a mixture of ice and water at zero degrees. The unknown quantity is the amount of ice that melted x_i.

Case IV. If a sufficiently large amount of water is mixed in, the ice will completely melt and the system will be composed of all water at a temperature above zero (but below $20°C$). The unknown quantity is the final temperature of the system T_2.

For Case I, we have the following equation:

$$\text{Heat Gained} = \text{Heat Lost}$$

$$m_i \cdot c_i \cdot [T_1 - T_i] = m_w \cdot c_w \cdot [T_w - 0] + m_w \cdot L + m_w \cdot c_i \cdot [0 - T_1]$$

or

$$T_1 = \frac{m_w \cdot c_w \cdot T_w + m_i \cdot c_i \cdot T_i + m_w \cdot L}{c_i \cdot (m_i + m_w)}$$

[Assumption: All ice at a temperature T_1, $T_i \le T_1 \le 0$]

For Case II, we have the following equation:

$$\text{Heat Gained} = \text{Heat Lost}$$

$$m_i \cdot c_i \cdot [0 - T_i] = m_w \cdot c_w \cdot [T_w - 0] + x_w \cdot L$$

or

$$x_w = -\frac{m_w \cdot c_w \cdot T_w + m_i \cdot c_i \cdot T_i}{L} \qquad \text{(amount of water that freezes)}$$

[Assumption: x_w is the amount of water that freezes, $x_w \leq m_w$]

For Case III, we have the following equation:

$$\text{Heat Gained} = \text{Heat Lost}$$

$$m_i \cdot c_i \cdot [0 - T_i] + x_i \cdot L = m_w \cdot c_w \cdot [T_w - 0]$$

or

$$x_i = \frac{m_w \cdot c_w \cdot T_w + m_i \cdot c_i \cdot T_i}{L}$$

[Assumption: x_i is the amount of ice that melts, $x_i \leq m_i$]

For Case IV, we have the following equation:

$$\text{Heat Gained} = \text{Heat Lost}$$

$$m_i \cdot c_i \cdot [0 - T_i] + m_i \cdot L + m_i \cdot c_w \cdot [T_2 - 0] = m_w \cdot c_w \cdot [T_w - T_2]$$

or

$$T_2 = \frac{m_w \cdot c_w \cdot T_w + m_i \cdot c_i \cdot T_i - m_i \cdot L}{c_i \cdot (m_i + m_w)}$$

[Assumption: All water at a temperature T_2, $0 \leq T_2 \leq T_w$]

To determine which case is correct, we examine the results more carefully. For example, for Case I to be correct, the final temperature must be above $-30°$ and below (or equal to) $0°$ because ice cannot be above zero degrees. For Case II to be correct, the amount of water that freezes x_w must be in the range $0 \leq x_w \leq m_w$, since only the amount of water available can be frozen. Worksheet 5.10 illustrates the solution to this problem.

MathCAD solution: Worksheet 5.10. The following data for water and ice is required for the worksheet:

Specific heats.

$$c_{\text{ice}} = 0.5 \text{ cal} \cdot \text{g}^{-1} \cdot (\text{C}°)^{-1}$$

$$c_{\text{water}} = 1 \text{ cal} \cdot \text{g}^{-1} \cdot (\text{C}°)^{-1}$$

Latent heat.

$$L_{\text{fusion}} = 80 \text{ cal} \cdot \text{g}^{-1}$$

```
Specific Heat of Water      Specific Heat of Ice      Latent Heat of Fusion
--------------------        --------------------      ---------------------
    c  ≡ 1                      c   ≡ .5                      L ≡ 80
     w                          i
Initial Values:
---------------
  Mass of Water      Temp. of Water        Mass of Ice       Temp. of Ice
  -------------      --------------        -----------       ------------
    m   := 200          T   := 20            m   := 20          T   := -30
     w                   w                    i                  i
        Final State Equation                                Condition
        --------------------                                ---------
```

$$T_1 := \frac{m_w \cdot c_w \cdot T_w + m_i \cdot c_i \cdot T_i + m_i \cdot L_w}{c_i \cdot \left[m_i + m_w\right]}$$

```
                                        All ice below 0 deg C
                                        ---------------------
```

$$x_w := \frac{-\left[m_w \cdot c_w \cdot T_w + m_i \cdot c_i \cdot T_i\right]}{L}$$

```
                                        T=0 deg C, Xw water freezes
                                        ---------------------------
```

$$x_i := \frac{m_w \cdot c_w \cdot T_w + m_i \cdot c_i \cdot T_i}{L}$$

```
                                        T=0 deg C, Xi ice melts
                                        -----------------------
```

$$T_2 := \frac{m_w \cdot c_w \cdot T_w + m_i \cdot c_i \cdot T_i - m_i \cdot L}{c_w \cdot \left[m_i + m_w\right]}$$

```
                                        All water above 0 deg C
                                        -----------------------
Results
-------
```

$T_1 := \text{if}\left[T_1 \leq 0, T_1, -9999\right]$ $T_1 := \text{if}\left[T_1 \geq T_i, T_1, -9999\right]$ $T_1 = -9999$

$x_w := \text{if}\left[x_w \geq 0, x_w, -9999\right]$ $x_w := \text{if}\left[x_w \leq m_w, x_w, -9999\right]$ $x_w = -9999$

$x_i := \text{if}\left[x_i \geq 0, x_i, -9999\right]$ $x_i := \text{if}\left[x_i \leq m_i, x_i, -9999\right]$ $x_i = -9999$

$T_2 := \text{if}\left[T_2 \geq 0, T_2, -9999\right]$ $T_2 := \text{if}\left[T_2 \leq T_w, T_2, -9999\right]$ $T_2 = 9.545$

WORKSHEET 5.10
Calorimetry.

    We begin by defining the calorimetric constants of water. We next assign the masses of ice and water (in grams) to be mixed and their initial temperatures (in degrees Celsius) as specified by the problem. The formulas for the four cases described are assigned.

    To determine which case applies, we use MathCAD's **if** function. If the solution is not physically acceptable, the result is modified to -9999. This arbitrary number is used to flag an unacceptable value. (Using the global format option, the exponential tolerance of the worksheet has been set as et=6. This keeps the number -9999 from being displayed in the exponential format.)

For the initial conditions given in the problem, the only acceptable answer is $T_2 = 9.5°$ C (Case IV). (The expressions for the other cases give values of -9999.) A sufficiently large quantity of water was mixed in to melt all the ice and to produce a single phase (water) at 9.5°.

If we keep the initial amount of water constant but increase the amount of ice from $m_i = 20$ to $m_i = 50$, we find that the only acceptable answer is provided by Case III. The result is $x_i = 40.6$, suggesting that this many grams melted and that the final state is a mixed phase of ice and water at T= 0°C. If we further increase the initial mass of ice to $m_i = 500$, the acceptable answer is given by Case II as $x_w = 43.8$. This indicates that some water froze but that the final state still consists of a mixture of ice and water at T= 0°C. Finally if we set $m_i = 1500$, the answer is given by Case I as $T_1 = -2.9°$C, indicating that there is only ice present at the sub-zero temperature.

HEAT TRANSFER

Heat naturally flows from hot to cold. The mode of transfer can be through matter (conduction or convection) or through empty space (radiation). Often more than one mode of transfer is involved in a heat-transfer process. Consider the following problem. A steel rod of length d and cross sectional area A is totally insulated on its side walls. One end face is blackened and inserted into an evacuated oven at 600 K. The other end face is immersed into ice water at 273 K. What is the temperature of the blackened end? At what rate is heat being transferred from the oven to the ice water?

Two modes of heat transfer are involved—*radiation* and *conduction*. Only radiative heat transfer (e.g., Watts or cal/s) occurs from the walls of the oven to the blackened end face of the rod. Since the oven is evacuated, there is no convection. Along the steel rod, heat transfer occurs by conduction. The transfer rates are given by the formulas,

$$H_{cond} = K_t \cdot [T - T_{ice}] \cdot A/d \qquad \text{(Conduction)}$$

and

$$H_{rad} = \sigma \cdot [T_{oven}^4 - T^4] \cdot A \qquad \text{(Radiation—\textit{Stefan's law})}$$

where

H = heat energy flow per unit time (W)
A = cross sectional area of rod (m^2)
K_t = thermal conductivity of the steel $(W \cdot m^{-1} \cdot K^{-1})$
T = temperature of blackened end face (K)
T_{ice} = temperature of the end immersed in ice water (K)
d = length of steel rod (m)
T_{oven} = is the temperature of the oven (K)
$\sigma = 5.67 \cdot 10^{-8} W \cdot m^{-2} \cdot K^{-4}$ (*Stefan-Boltzmann* constant).

In the steady state, the heat transfer from the oven to the rod must be equal to the heat transfer along the rod to the ice. The solution to the problem is therefore obtained by setting H_{rad} equal to H_{cond} or

$$K_t \cdot [T - T_{ice}] \cdot \frac{A}{d} = \sigma \cdot [T_{oven}^4 - T^4] \cdot A$$

This *nonlinear* equation must be solved for the unknown T. Once the value of T is found, it is substituted into either side of the equation to obtain the heat flow rate. The analysis of this heat flow problem is shown in Worksheet 5.11.

MathCAD solution: Worksheet 5.11. The basic units of the dimensions length, mass, and time are assigned in meters, kilograms, and seconds respectively. We define the joule, the calorie, and the watt. The ice point temperature is assigned in units of Kelvins. We treat temperature as a dimensionless quantity. The Stefan-Boltzmann constant has

```
Define Basic Units:      m ≡ 1L          kg ≡ 1M          s ≡ 1T      K ≡ 1
-------------------

Define Secondary Units:     The Joule        The Calorie        The Watt
----------------------      ---------        -----------        --------
                                 2
                                m                                       J
                        J ≡ kg ──          cal ≡ 4.186·J      W ≡ 1 · ─
                                 2                                      s
                                s
                                                                    -8   W
Ice Point:  T     ≡ 273    Stefan-Boltzmann Constant:      σ ≡ 5.67·10  · ─────
----------   ice           --------------------------                      2  4
                                                                          m ·K

   Oven Temp            Area of Rod         Length of Rod      Conductivity of Rod
   ---------            -----------         -------------      -------------------
                                 2                                          W
 T      := 600·K      A := .0001·m        d := 1·m          K     := 50 · ────
  oven                                                        t            m·K

   Law of Radiative Transfer                       Law of Conduction
   ------------------------                         -----------------
                                                              T - T
                           4     4                               ice
 H     (T) := σ· ⎡ T     - T  ⎤·A         H     (T) := K   · ───── ·A
  rad            ⎣  oven      ⎦            cond           t    d

Solution
--------
 Guess:   T := 400·K                      Set modes equal
 -----              Given                 ---------------
                                          H    (T) ≈ H     (T)
                                           rad        cond       T := Find(T)

Display Results
---------------
Temp. of black end                        Heat Transfer
------------------                        -------------
                                                                    cal
   T = 392.934·K          H    (T) = 0.6·W        H    (T) = 0.143·───
                           rad                     rad               s
                                                                    cal
                         H    (T) = 0.6·W        H    (T) = 0.143·───
                          cond                    cond              s
```

WORKSHEET 5.11
Heat transfer.

units of $W \cdot m^{-2} \cdot K^{-4}$. Next the parameters of the oven and the properties of the rod are assigned. The thermal conductivity K_t is expressed in $W \cdot m^{-1} \cdot K^{-1}$. Using the laws of radiation and conduction, H_{rad} and H_{cond} are expressed as functions of T. They are set equal to each other and solved for T in a **Given/Find** solve block. Finally, the temperature of the blackened side and the heat transfer rate are displayed—the latter in both Watts and calories per second. If we type **H.rad=**, we see,

$$\text{H}_{\text{rad}}= \ 0.6 \cdot \text{mass} \cdot \text{length}^2 \cdot \text{time}^{-3} \ \blacksquare$$

By filling the placeholder with **W** and then with **cal/s**, the heat transfer is displayed accordingly. Note that H_{rad} and H_{cond} give the same value, verifying the solution.

If we decrease the conductivity K_t of the rod (i.e., make it a better insulator), we observe an increase in temperature of the blackened side and a decrease in the heat transfer rate. If we increase the conductivity of the rod, the temperature of the blackened end face approaches that of the cold end face and the transfer rate increases.

COULOMB'S LAW

A positive point charge q will produce an electric field in space. The field vector is directed away from the charge and its magnitude varies according to Coulomb's Law,

$$E(r) = k \cdot \frac{q}{r^2}$$

where k is a universal constant whose numerical value depends on the choice of units being used, and r is the distance from the charge. For a collection of point charges, the resultant field is the sum of the individual field vectors produced by the charges. The components of the electric field at a point in space (x, y, z) are given by the formulas:

$$F_x(x, y, z) = k \cdot \sum_n q_n \cdot \frac{x - x_n}{\left[(x - x_n)^2 + (y - y_n)^2 + (z - z_n)^2\right]^{3/2}}$$

$$E_y(x, y, z) = k \cdot \sum_n q_n \cdot \frac{y - y_n}{\left[(x - x_n)^2 + (y - y_n)^2 + (z - z_n)^2\right]^{3/2}}$$

$$E_z(x, y, z) = k \cdot \sum_n q_n \cdot \frac{z - z_n}{\left[(x - x_n)^2 + (y - y_n)^2 + (z - z_n)^2\right]^{3/2}}$$

where q_n is the nth charge and (x_n, y_n, z_n) are its coordinates.

The electric field can also be calculated by first obtaining the electric *potential* (also called the voltage). Unlike the electric field which is a vector, the potential is a scalar and is easier to compute. The formula for the electric potential is given by,

$$V(x, y, z) = k \cdot \sum_n \frac{q_n}{[(x - x_n)^2 + (y - y_n)^2 + (z - z_n)^2]^{1/2}}$$

It can be shown that the electric field vector is obtained by taking the negative *gradient* of the potential function as,

$$\mathbf{E}(x, y, z) = -\nabla V(x, y, z)$$

or in component form as,

$$E_x = -\frac{\partial V(x, y, z)}{\partial x}, \qquad E_y = -\frac{\partial V(x, y, z)}{\partial y}, \qquad E_z = -\frac{\partial V(x, y, z)}{\partial z}$$

The magnitude of the field is given by,

$$E(x, y, z) = [E_x^2(x, y, z) + E_y^2(x, y, z) + E_z^2(x, y, z)]^{1/2}$$

In Worksheet 5.12, we compute the electric field produced by six point charges.

MathCAD solution: Worksheet 5.12. We choose a set of units in which $k = 1$ and create data tables for the magnitude of the charges and for the coordinates at which they are located. The table for the magnitude of the charges is created by typing the

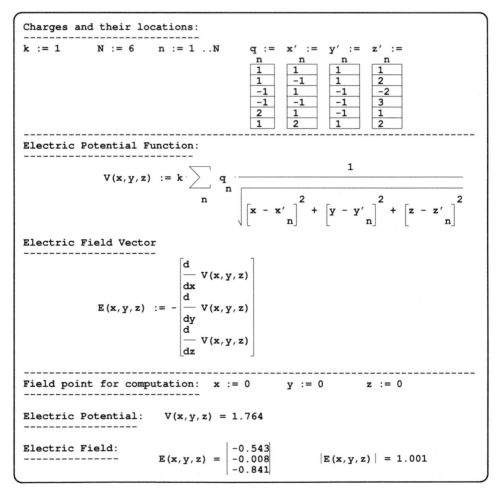

WORKSHEET 5.12
Coulomb's law.

key sequence: **q[n:1,1,-1,-1,2,1{Enter}**. The data table for x'_n is assigned by typing: **x'[n:1,-1,1,-1,1,2{Enter}**. Recall that to generate a prime, we use the backquote key.

Next we assign the function for the electric potential. Note that we use primes on the charge coordinates (x'_n, y'_n, z'_n) to distinguish them from the field coordinates (x, y, z). The electric field is computed by assigning a vector to it and filling the place-holders appropriately. We type **E(x,y,z):-{<Alt>M}3 0** and fill the upper placeholder with **x?V(x,y,z)**. We then fill the other placeholders with the corresponding derivatives.

Finally, an arbitrary point in space (0,0,0) is chosen and the electric potential, the components of the electric field and the magnitude of the electric field are evaluated. By changing the coordinates or magnitudes of the charges (in the data tables) or by changing the coordinates of the field point, we can see how the electric field changes. Note that if the field point is on any one of the charges, the electric field is undefined.

GAUSS' LAW

Computations with Coulomb's law are difficult to perform for continuously distributed source charges. If, however, the distribution has some spatial symmetry, it is often easier to compute the electric field using *Gauss' law*.

Gauss' law states that the net *electric flux* leaving any closed surface is proportional to the net charge *inside* the surface or,

$$\Phi = 4 \cdot \pi \cdot k \cdot q_{ins} \qquad \text{(Gauss' law)}$$

The flux leaving a closed surface is defined as,

$$\Phi = \int E_n \, dA \qquad \text{(definition of flux)}$$

where E_n is the component of the electric field **E** perpendicular to the surface element dA. The integral is taken over the closed surface.

Consider a sphere of radius R whose charge distribution is given by $\rho(r)$ where r is the distance from the center of the sphere. Because of the symmetric distribution of the charge, the electric field must be radially oriented. If we choose an arbitrary point r from the center, we find the following results,

$$\Phi(r) = E \cdot 4 \cdot \pi \cdot r^2$$

and

$$q_{ins}(r) = 4 \cdot \pi \cdot \int_0^r \rho(r') \cdot r'^2 \cdot dr'$$

Thus, according to Gauss' law, the magnitude of the electric field is given by,

$$E(r) = 4 \cdot \pi \cdot k \cdot \frac{\int_0^r \rho(r') \cdot r'^2 \cdot dr'}{r^2}$$

Since there is no charge outside the sphere, the upper limit on the above integral becomes R when $r > R$. Therefore, outside the sphere, the field can be written,

$$E(r) = k \cdot \frac{Q}{r^2}$$

where the total charge on the sphere is,

$$Q = 4 \cdot \pi \cdot \int_0^R \rho(r') \cdot r'^2 \cdot dr'$$

In Worksheet 5.13 we apply the above formula to compute the electric fields inside and outside of a sphere of radius R and density $\rho(r)$.

> **MathCAD solution: Worksheet 5.13.** We set k=1 and R=1. We consider the case of a sphere whose density is uniform ($\rho(r) = 1$). The total charge on the sphere in computed and displayed. Next the interior and exterior fields are computed using Gauss' law. Since there is no charge outside the sphere, the exterior field is computed as if all the charge were concentrated at the center.

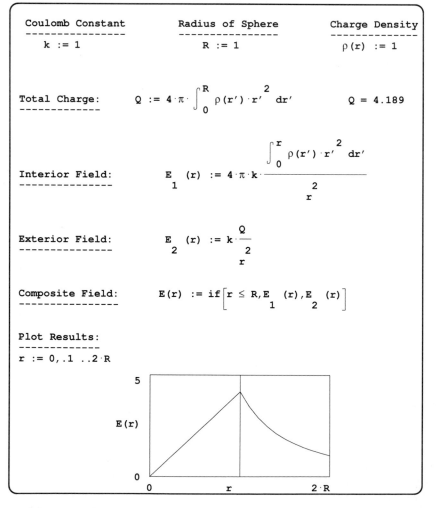

WORKSHEET 5.13
Gauss' law.

The electric fields are combined into a composite function using MathCad's `if` function. Finally the results are plotted from `r=0` to `r=2·R`. Note that the electric field inside the sphere increases *linearly* with `r` until `r=R`. Outside the sphere, the field decreases as `1/r²`. By changing $\rho(r)$ in the worksheet, we see how the fields change. Since there is no exterior charge, the exterior field always varies as `1/r²`. Try changing the density function of the sphere to $\rho(r)=r$.

DC NETWORKS

Consider a two-loop DC network as in Fig. 5.6. Each branch contains an EMF (battery) and a resistor. The right branch also contains a nonlinear (non-ohmic) device. A resistor is an ohmic or linear device because the voltage V across it is directly proportional to the current I through it. A resistor obeys Ohm's law,

$$V = R \cdot I$$

where the constant R is the resistance of the device. In contrast, an non-ohmic device may have a variable resistance in one direction and no resistance in the other. We consider a nonlinear element represented by,

$$V(I) = c \cdot I^2 \qquad \text{(for } I > 0\text{)}$$

$$V(I) = 0 \qquad \text{(for } I < 0\text{)}$$

The objective is to find the currents flowing in each branch of the circuit shown in Fig. 5.6.

To solve the problem, we use *Kirchoff's* rules, which are:

1. The net voltage drop around any loop is zero.
2. The net current leaving any junction (or node) is zero.

These rules lead to the following set of equations for the three unknown currents,

$$E_1 - R_1 \cdot I_1 - E_2 - R_2 \cdot E_2 = 0$$

$$E_3 - R_3 \cdot I_3 - V(I_3) - E_2 - R_2 \cdot I_2 = 0$$

$$I_1 + I_3 = I_2$$

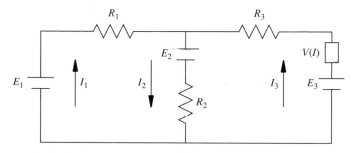

FIGURE 5.6

We are assuming current directions as in Fig. 5.6. The assumed direction of I_3 is taken to be positive for the behavior of the nonlinear element.

When Kirchoff's laws are applied to simple resistor networks, the branch currents are arbitrarily assigned a direction of flow. If the solution to any branch current is a negative number, the actual current flow is opposite to the assigned direction. Furthermore, if all the EMF's are reversed, each branch current reverses. However when a nonlinear device such as a diode is present in one of the branches, a negative result for a branch current needs a more careful analysis. This is because the voltage versus current function of a diode $V(I)$ depends on the direction of the current. In worksheet 5.14, we apply Kirchoff's laws to a dc network containing a nonlinear element.

> **MathCAD solution: Worksheet 5.14.** We assign the EMF's (E_1=10, E_2=3, E_3=6) and the resistances (R_1=3, R_2=1, R_3=2). Next we assign the parameter of the nonlinear element (c=1) discussed above and plot its characteristic V versus I relationship. We make a guess at the solution for the branch currents and set up the Kirchoff equations in a **Given/Find** solve block. The solutions for the branch currents are found and displayed as I_1=1.651, I_2=2.408, I_3=0.397.
>
> To appreciate the role of the nonlinear element, reverse the batteries by changing the signs of the EMFs. Note that the currents do not simply reverse as in a linear system. Next keep the batteries *reversed*, but remove the nonlinear element diode by setting c=0. Note that the results for the branch currents do not change. In the reverse direction, the nonlinear element offers no resistance and therefore cannot affect the currents regardless of the value of c.

AC CIRCUIT ANALYSIS

Consider a simple circuit consisting of a resistor R, a capacitor C, an inductor L, and an AC generator of peak voltage E_0 and frequency ω, as in Fig. 5.7. The generator is assumed to produce a voltage of the form,

$$E(t) = E_0 \cdot \cos(\omega \cdot t)$$

where ω is the frequency and E_0 is the amplitude.

The current in the circuit oscillates with the same frequency as the driving voltage, but its peak value is given by $I_0 = E_0/Z$. The quantity Z is called the *impedance* of the circuit and is given by

$$Z = [R^2 + (X_L - X_C)^2]^{1/2}$$

where

$$X_L = \omega \cdot L \qquad \text{(inductive reactance)}$$

$$X_C = \frac{1}{(\omega \cdot C)} \qquad \text{(capacitive reactance)}$$

Furthermore, there is a phase difference ϕ between the current and the driving voltage. At the resonant frequency $\omega_0 = 1/\sqrt{(L \cdot C)}$, the two reactances are equal and we

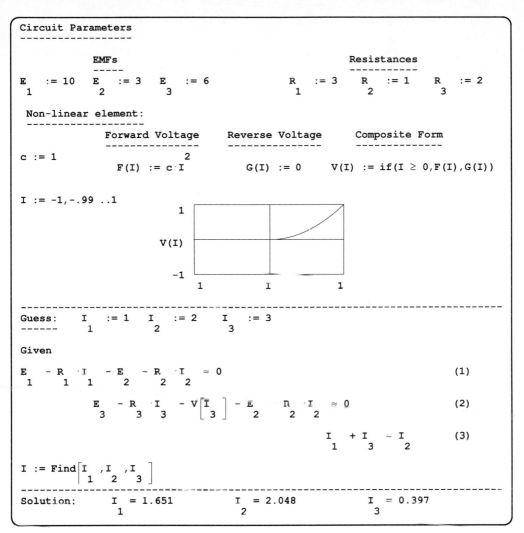

```
Circuit Parameters
------------------

          EMFs                                    Resistances
          ----                                    -----------
E    := 10    E    := 3    E    := 6        R    := 3    R    := 1    R    := 2
 1             2            3                 1            2            3

 Non-linear element:
 -------------------
               Forward Voltage      Reverse Voltage      Composite Form
               ---------------      ---------------      --------------
c := 1                      2
               F(I) := c·I              G(I) := 0     V(I) := if(I ≥ 0,F(I),G(I))


I := -1,-.99 ..1
```

```
Guess:    I   := 1    I   := 2    I   := 3
------     1           2           3

Given
```

$$E_1 - R_1 \cdot I_1 - E_2 - R_2 \cdot I_2 \approx 0 \qquad\qquad (1)$$

$$E_3 - R_3 \cdot I_3 - V\left[I_3\right] - E_2 - R_2 \cdot I_2 \approx 0 \qquad (2)$$

$$I_1 + I_3 \approx I_2 \qquad (3)$$

$$I := \text{Find}\left[I_1, I_2, I_3\right]$$

```
Solution:     I   = 1.651       I   = 2.048       I   = 0.397
               1                 2                 3
```

WORKSHEET 5.14
A DC network.

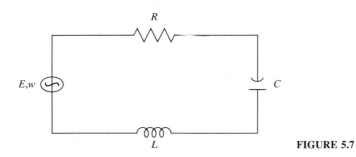

FIGURE 5.7

find $Z = R$. Since this gives the minimum value of Z, the current is largest at the resonant frequency.

The oscillating voltages across each of the three circuit elements have the same frequency as that of the driving voltage but have peak values given by,

$$V_{R0} = R \cdot I_0, \qquad V_{L0} = X_L \cdot I_0, \qquad \text{and} \qquad V_{C0} = X_C \cdot I_0$$

Each of these voltages is out of phase with the driving voltage.

A DIGRESSION ON COMPLEX NUMBERS. Any complex number can be written as $z = \alpha + \beta \cdot j$ where $j = \sqrt{-1}$. The numbers α and β represent the *real* and *imaginary* parts of z respectively. The *complex conjugate* of z is $z^* = \alpha - \beta \cdot j$. The quantity,

$$|z|^2 = z^* \cdot z = (\alpha - \beta \cdot j) \cdot (\alpha + \beta \cdot j) = \alpha^2 + \beta^2$$

is always real and positive. (Note: $j \cdot j = j^2 = -1$.)

A complex number can be represented in *polar* form as,

$$z = A \cdot e^{j \cdot \phi}$$

where A is the *modulus* (or absolute value) and ϕ is the *argument* (or phase) of the complex number z. The modulus and argument are related to α and β by

$$A = |z| = [\alpha^2 + \beta^2]^{1/2} \qquad \text{and} \qquad \tan(\phi) = \frac{\beta}{\alpha}$$

MathCAD handles complex number algebra in a straightforward manner. The following objects illustrate the basic operations:

```
    a := 1 + 2i          b := 2 - 3i

    a̅  = 1 - 2i          b̅  = 2 + 3i

  a + b = 3 - i        a - b = -1 + 5i

    a·b = 8 + i           a
                          ─  = -0.308 + 0.538i
                          b

    |a| = 2.346        arg(a) = 1.107
```

To enter the quantity $2i$, type **2i** (no asterisk in between). To enter the value i alone, you must type **1i**. To generate the complex conjugate of a, type **a"=**. (Within a mathematical object, the double quote generates the complex conjugate.) The complex conjugate is displayed with a "bar" over the variable. The modulus operation is the same as the absolute value and is obtained using the ¦ (pipe) key. The **arg** (argument) function returns an angle in radians. You may enter j instead of i as the imaginary unit. However all results will be displayed in terms of i unless the the im option is changed using the **{Esc} FORM** command.

To find the general form of the current and voltages, we use complex numbers. The reactances and the circuit impedance are written as complex quantities using,

$$X_C = -\frac{j}{(\omega \cdot C)}, \qquad X_L = j \cdot \omega \cdot L, \qquad \text{and} \qquad Z = R + X_L + X_C$$

The current and voltages are represented in complex form as,

$$I = \frac{E_0}{Z}, \qquad V_R = R \cdot I, \qquad V_C = X_C \cdot I, \qquad \text{and} \qquad V_L = X_L \cdot I$$

The peak values are derived by taking their absolute values as,

$$I_0 = |I|, \qquad V_{R0} = |V_R|, \qquad V_{C0} = |V_C|, \qquad \text{and} \qquad V_{L0} = |V_L|$$

The corresponding phases are,

$$\phi = \arg(I), \qquad \phi_R = \arg(V_R), \qquad \phi_C = \arg(V_C), \qquad \text{and} \qquad \phi_L = \arg(V_L)$$

Finally, the current and voltage forms are written as:

$$i(t) = I_0 \cdot \cos(\omega \cdot t + \phi), \qquad V_R(t) = V_{R0} \cdot \cos(\omega \cdot t + \phi_R)$$
$$V_C(t) = V_{C0} \cdot \cos(\omega \cdot t + \phi_C), \qquad V_L(t) = V_{L0} \cdot \cos(\omega \cdot t + \phi_L)$$

We examine the above circuit in Worksheet 5.15.

MathCAD solution: Worksheet 5.15. We assign the circuit parameters (R=2, C=1, L=1, E$_0$=1, ω=1.5). The driving voltage function is assigned and the *resonant frequency* is defined and displayed. We assign and display the reactances and circuit impedance using the symbol **j** for imaginary numbers.

   [Note: To use the letter **j** (instead of i) in the display format of imaginary numbers, make the global change by typing **{Esc} FORM**. When the prompt on the message line appears, change i to **j** in the im option.]

   To make the assignment for X$_C$, type **X.C:-1j/({<Alt>W}∗C)**. Similarly for the inductive reactance, type **X.L:1j∗{<Alt>W}∗L**. Note that **j** is always entered as **1j** with *no* multiplication operation between the two characters.

   The current and voltages are computed. In each case the peak values are obtained by computing the absolute value. For example to assign I$_0$,

type: **I.o: ¦ I**   and see: $I_0 := |I|$

To get the phases, use MathCAD's **arg** function. For the phase of the current,

type: **{<Alt>F}:arg(I)**   and see: $\phi := \arg(I)$

   The current and voltage functions are constructed using the computed absolute values and phases. The mathematical form of the current is expressed as,

$$i(t) = I_0 \cdot \cos(\omega \cdot t + \phi)$$

The voltage across each of the elements is expressed in a similar manner.

Finally, we plot the driving voltage (using dots) as well as the voltage on the three circuit elements (using solid lines). The plot range covers two cycles. Note that the voltages on the elements R, C, and L are phase-shifted relative to the driving voltage. When we change R, C, L, or the driving frequency ω, the peak values and phase shifts of the voltage forms change. Try changing the frequency so that it is equal to the resonant frequency ω_0. What happens to the peak current at resonance?

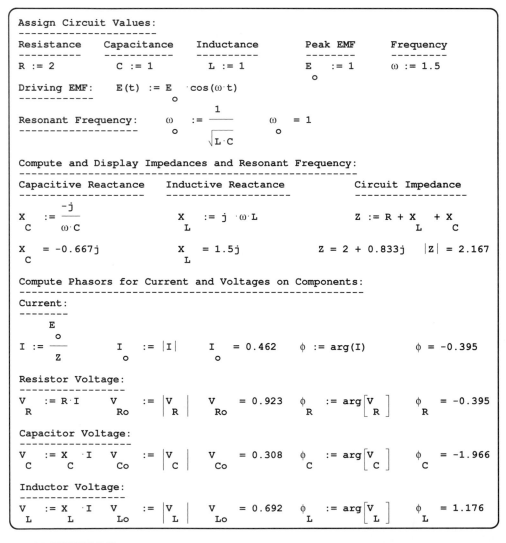

WORKSHEET 5.15

AC circuit analysis (*cont. below*).

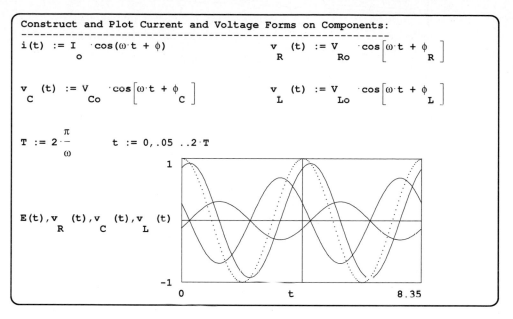

```
Construct and Plot Current and Voltage Forms on Components:
-----------------------------------------------------------
i(t)  := I   ·cos(ω·t + φ)              v  (t)  := V   ·cos[ω·t + φ  ]
          o                              R          Ro          [         R ]


v  (t)  := V   ·cos[ω·t + φ  ]          v  (t)  := V   ·cos[ω·t + φ  ]
 C          Co         [         C ]      L          Lo         [         L ]


      π
T := 2·—          t := 0,.05 ..2·T
      ω
```

WORKSHEET 5.15
(*cont.*)

NUCLEAR DECAY

The law of nuclear decay states that the rate at which a radioactive substance decays (i.e., the number of radioactive emissions per unit time) is proportional to the amount of the substance present at that time. According to the law, the decay rate is,

$$\frac{dN(t)}{dt} = -k \cdot N(t)$$

where $N(t)$ is the number of nuclei present at any given time and k is the *decay constant* of the substance. The decay constant is related to the following *time constants* by,

$$\tau = \frac{1}{k} \qquad \text{(mean life)}$$

$$T = \frac{\ln(2)}{k} = \frac{.693}{k} \qquad \text{(half life)}$$

After a time interval equal to the mean life, the substance is reduced by a factor of $1/e$. Similarly after a half life, it is reduced by one-half. The more radioactive a substance is, the larger its decay rate and the shorter its time constant. Using elementary integration techniques, it is possible to show that the solution to the decay equation is,

$$N(t) = N_0 \cdot e^{-k \cdot t}$$

where N_0 is the number of nuclei present at $t = 0$.

As is commonly the case, a radioactive element A decays into another radioactive element B which then decays further. The process can be represented by,

$$A \rightarrow B \rightarrow \text{ other substances}$$

The equations describing the decay of A and B are,

$$\frac{dA(t)}{dt} = -k_A \cdot A(t)$$

and

$$\frac{dB(t)}{dt} = -k_B \cdot B(t) + \frac{dA(t)}{dt}$$

where $A(t)$ and $B(t)$ represent the number of nuclei of each substance present at a time t and k_A and k_B are the respective decay constants. The decay process for substance B has two parts. The first term is due to the natural decay of B into other substances while the second is a *production* term due to the decay of A.

Using standard techniques found in texts on differential equations, we find the following solutions,

$$A(t) = A_0 \cdot \exp(-k_A \cdot t)$$

and

$$B(t) = [B_0 \cdot \exp(-k_B \cdot t)] + A_0 \cdot \left[\frac{k_A}{(k_B - k_A)} \right] \cdot [\exp(-k_A \cdot t) - \exp(-k_B \cdot t)]$$

$$(k_B \neq k_A)$$

where $\exp(u) = e^u$ and where A_0 and B_0 represent the number of nuclei of each substance present at $t = 0$.

By measuring the number of nuclei of each substance present at some time $t = 0$ and by knowing the decay constant of each element, we can predict the number of nuclei present at a later time. We examine the decay process of two elements in Worksheet 5.16.

MathCAD solution: Worksheet 5.16. The number of nuclei of each element present at $t = 0$ is assigned (A_0=100, B_0=0). Next, the half-lives are assigned (T_A=20, T_B=40) and the time constants computed. The equations of decay are defined and plotted. Note that since there is no production of element (A), the plot shows that it decays exponentially from its initial value to zero. Element (B), on the other hand, increases from its initial value of zero until it reaches a maximum. This is because B's rate of production (due to the decay of A) is greater than its rate of decay. After a maximum is reached, element B begins to decay. During this phase, the amount of element A has been reduced sufficiently so that element B's production rate is now smaller than its decay rate. Eventually, when the amount of element A is neglible, element B decays exponentially.

If the half-lives of the two elements are equal, element B will reach a maximum where the curves A(t) and B(t) intersect. Explain on physical grounds why this is so. Verify this in the worksheet by setting the half-lives approximately equal, e.g., T_A=40.0001, T_B=40. You cannot set T_A=T_B since the decay formula given for B(t) is not valid for this case.

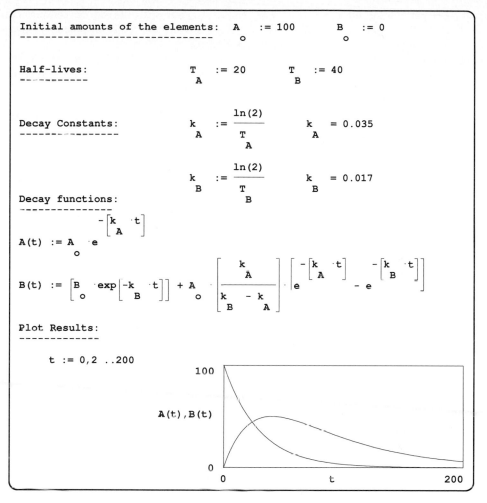

```
Initial amounts of the elements:   A    := 100        B    := 0
----------------------------------  o                 o


Half-lives:                     T    := 20       T    := 40
------------                    A                 B


                                     ln(2)
Decay Constants:                k    := -----     k    = 0.035
-----------------               A      T          A
                                       A

                                     ln(2)
                                k    := -----     k    = 0.017
                                B      T          B
Decay functions:                       B
----------------
                   -[k  ·t]
                     A
A(t) := A   e
         o

                                        [ k  ]  [-[k ·t]    -[k ·t]]
                                        [  A  ]  [   A          B   ]
B(t) := [B  ·exp[-k  ·t]] + A   --------- ·[e       - e          ]
         o        B          o  [k  - k  ]
                                [ B    A ]

Plot Results:
-------------

     t := 0,2 ..200
```

WORKSHEET 5.16
Decay of radioactive series $A \rightarrow B \rightarrow$.

PROBLEMS

1. A mass $M = 1$ g is accelerating at $a = 400$ cm $\cdot$ s^{-2} and has an instantaneous velocity of $v = 50$ cm $\cdot$ s^{-1}. The formulas for the force on the mass and the kinetic energy of the mass are,

$$F(\text{dynes}) = M(\text{g}) \cdot a(\text{cm} \cdot \text{s}^{-2})$$
$$F(\text{newtons}) = M(\text{kg}) \cdot a(\text{m} \cdot \text{s}^{-2})$$

and

$$KE(\text{ergs}) = \frac{1}{2} \cdot M(\text{g}) \cdot \left[v(\text{cm} \cdot \text{s}^{-1}) \right]^2$$
$$KE(\text{joules}) = \frac{1}{2} \cdot M(\text{kg}) \cdot \left[v(\text{m} \cdot \text{s}^{-1}) \right]^2$$

Using the basic dimensions $g \equiv 1M$, cm $\equiv 1L$, and s $\equiv 1T$ and the conversions m $\equiv 100 \cdot$ cm and kg $\equiv 1000 \cdot$ g, find the force in dynes and the kinetic energy in ergs and convert them to newtons and joules respectively.

2. The *equilibrant* **D** (i.e., the force needed to produce equilibrium) of a set of forces **A**, **B**, **C**, ... is defined by the relation $\mathbf{A} + \mathbf{B} + \mathbf{C} + \cdots + \mathbf{D} = 0$. Using a worksheet similar to Worksheet 5.2, find the equilibrant of the following three forces: $(30, 45°)$, $(20, 60°)$, and $(45, 160°)$. [Hint: The equilibrant points opposite to the resultant.]

3. An object is thrown with a horizontal velocity v from a cliff of height $h = 100$ m. On one graph, plot the trajectories for $v = 20$ m/s, $v = 50$ m/s, and $v = 100$ m/s. Determine the horizontal range in each case. [Assign the following: `g= -9.8, h= 100, n= 1 ..3, v`$_1$`= 20, v`$_2$`= 50, v`$_3$`= 100, x(v,t)= v·t, y(t)= (1/2)·g·t`^{2}`+ h, T= [- 2·h/g]`$^{1/2}$` , and R`$_n$`=v`$_n$`·T. Plot y(t),y(t),y(t)` versus `x(v`$_1$`,t), x(v`$_2$`,t), x(v`$_3$`,t)` using a plot range `t= 0,T/30 ..T`. To display the ranges, use `v`$_n$`= and R`$_n$`=.`]

4. Two vertically hanging masses m_1 and m_2 are attached by a string which passes over a pulley. The pulley is a solid wheel of mass M and radius R. If $m_2 = 20$ kg, $m_1 = 10$ kg, $M = 5$ kg, and $R = 0.1$ m, find the acceleration of the masses a, the tensions in the string supporting the masses T_2 and T_1, and the angular acceleration of the pulley α. Take the acceleration of gravity to be $g = 9.8$ m/s^2. Assume that the string does not slip on the pulley. [Hint: The four unknowns a, T_2, T_1, and α are determined from the following equations,

$$\left[\frac{1}{2} \cdot M \cdot R^2\right] \cdot \alpha = R \cdot [T_2 - T_1]$$

$$a = R \cdot \alpha$$

$$m_2 \cdot g - T_2 = m_2 \cdot a$$

$$T_1 - m_1 \cdot g = m_1 \cdot a$$

Use a **Given/Find** solve block to find the four unknowns.]

5. Two identical masses $m_1 = m_2 = 100$ gm resting side-by-side on a table are attached to two separate and parallel springs with elastic constants $k_1 = 1000$ d/cm and $k_2 = 4000$ d/cm. Each mass is at its equilibrium position. The first mass is displaced 50 cm to the right while the second is displaced 50 cm to the left. If they are released from rest, find the time and position where they first pass each other. [Hint: The equations of motion are $y_1(t) = 50 \cdot \cos(\omega_1 \cdot t)$ and $y_2(t) = -50 \cdot \cos(\omega_2 \cdot t)$ where $\omega_1 = [k_1/m_1]^{1/2}$ and $\omega_2 = [k_2/m_2]^{1/2}$. Plot both functions for $t > 0$ and estimate the time and position of the first intersection point. Use a **Given/Find** solve block to determine the precise time and position of intersection.]

6. The natural modes of a string are of the form,

$$y_n(x, t) = \cos(n \cdot \pi \cdot t) \cdot \sin(n \cdot \pi \cdot x) \qquad n = 1, 2, \ldots$$

Assume that the string is vibrating in a mixture of the lowest two modes and that the waveform can be represented by,

$$y(x, t) = 2 \cdot y_1(x, t) + y_2(x, t)$$

On a single graph, plot the shape of the string at $t = 0$, $t = .5$, and $t = 1$.

7. A parallel beam of coherent light of wavelength λ passes through a set of N slits spaced a distance d apart. The light spreads out and falls on a distant screen on the other side of

the slit system. In texts on optics, it is shown that the intensity pattern on the screen is given by,

$$I(\theta) = \left[\frac{\sin(N \cdot \Gamma(\theta))}{\sin(\Gamma(\theta))} \right]^2$$

where,

$$\Gamma(\theta) = \frac{\pi \cdot d \cdot \sin(\theta)}{\lambda}$$

Here θ represents the direction of travel of the light falling on the screen.

(a) Using $\lambda = 1$, $d = 2$, and $N = 4$, plot the function $I(\theta)$ for $-\pi/4 \le \theta \le \pi/4$. Estimate where the intensity is a maximum and where it is zero.

(b) Change the number of slits to $N = 3$. How does the pattern change?

8. (a) A 300 g block of aluminum at a temperature T_{al} is dropped into 300 g of water at $50C°$. Following the procedure in Worksheet 5.10, determine the final state of the system when $T_{al} = 200C°$ and when $T_{al} = 400C°$. Assume that the final state is either all water or a mixture of steam and water.

(b) Repeat part (a) if the mass of the aluminum is increased to 500 g.

$$c_{al} = 0.22 \text{ cal} \cdot (C°)^{-1} \cdot g^{-1} \qquad c_{water} = 1 \text{ cal} \cdot (C°)^{-1} \cdot g^{-1}$$

$$L_{water-steam} = 540 \text{ cal} \cdot g^{-1} \qquad T_{boiling} = 100°C$$

9. An exterior wall of a room has a thickness $L = 20$ cm and a thermal conductivity $k = 0.002 \text{ cal} \cdot s^{-1} \cdot cm^{-1} \cdot (C°)^{-1}$. The inside and outside air temperatures are $T_i = 25 \text{ C°}$ and $T_o = -15 \text{ C°}$ respectively. The natural convection parameter for a vertical wall is $h = 0.424 \cdot 10^{-4} \text{ cal} \cdot s^{-1} \cdot cm^{-2} \cdot (C°)^{-5/4}$. Find the interior and exterior surface temperatures of the wall and determine the heat flux through the wall. [Hint: Call T_2 and T_1 the interior and exterior surface temperatures of the wall and Q (cal· $s^{-1} \cdot cm^{-2}$) the heat flux. The values of the three unknowns are determined from the equations,

$$k \cdot \frac{T_2 - T_1}{L} = Q \qquad \text{(conduction through wall)}$$

$$h \cdot [T_i - T_2]^{5/4} = Q \qquad \text{(convection from room air to interior wall)}$$

$$h \cdot [T_1 - T_o]^{5/4} = Q \qquad \text{(convection to exterior wall to outside air)}$$

Set up a **Given/Find** solve block to find T_1, T_2, and Q.]

10. Following Worksheet 5.13, use Gauss' law to compute the electric field $E(r)$ both inside and outside of an infinitely long cylinder of radius R. Assume that the interior of the cylinder is uniformly charged with a density $\rho(r)$.

11. A battery of emf $E = 12$ volts is in a circuit with a resistor of $R = 100\Omega$, a capacitor $C = 10^{-11}$ F, and a double-throw switch (see Fig. 5.8).

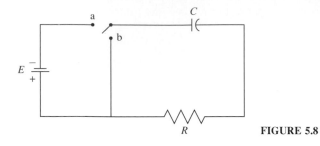

FIGURE 5.8

At $t = 0$, the switch is set to position **a** to charge the capacitor. At $t = t_0 = 0.5 \cdot 10^{-8}$ s, it is thrown to position **b** to allow the capacitor to discharge. It can be shown that the voltage on the capacitor varies with time according to the following equations:

$$V(t) = E \cdot \left(1 - \exp\left(-\frac{t}{\tau}\right)\right) \qquad\qquad \text{(for } t \le t_0\text{)}$$

$$= E \cdot \left[1 - \exp\left(-\frac{t_0}{\tau}\right)\right] \cdot \left[\exp\left\{\frac{(t_0 - t)}{\tau}\right\}\right] \qquad \text{(for } t > t_0\text{)}$$

where $\tau = R \cdot C$ is the *time constant* of the circuit.

(a) Using MathCAD's **if** function, plot $V(t)$ over the interval $[0, 2 \cdot t_0]$.

(b) Repeat (a) for $R = 10\Omega$ and for $R = 1000\Omega$.

12. A single-loop dc circuit consists of a battery $E = 12V$, a resistor $R = 3\Omega$, and a nonlinear element whose I versus V relationship is $I(V) = 0.05 \cdot V^{3/2}$. Find the current in the circuit I_0, the voltage on the resistor V_r, and the voltage on the nonlinear element V_{nl}. [Hint: The three unknowns satisfy the following equations,

$$0.05 \cdot V_{nl}^{3/2} = I_0, \qquad \frac{V_r}{R} = I_0, \qquad \text{and} \qquad V_r + V_{nl} = E$$

Set up a **Given/Find** solve block to find V_{nl}, V_r, and I_0.]

13. Consider a single-loop ac circuit consisting of a resistor ($R = 1\Omega$), an inductor ($L = 1H$), a capacitor ($C = 1F$), and a generator whose voltage varies as $E(t) = E_0 \cdot \cos(\omega \cdot t)$. Suppose the amplitude of the generator is fixed at $E_0 = 1$ V but its frequency can be varied. Plot the current in the circuit $I(\omega)$ versus ω using a plot range of $\omega = 0.001, 0.2 \ .. 10$. Where does the current peak? Why does the current fall off at both very high and very low frequencies? What happens to the curve as R is decreased? [Hint: The current can be expressed as a function of ω using,

$$I(\omega) = \frac{E_0}{Z(\omega)},$$

where,

$$Z(\omega) = [R^2 + \{X_L(\omega) - X_C(\omega)\}^2]^{1/2}$$

and where,

$$X_L(\omega) = \omega \cdot L, \qquad \text{and} \qquad X_C(\omega) = \frac{1}{(\omega \cdot C)}$$

REFERENCES

Bueche, F.: *Principles of Physics*, McGraw-Hill, New York, 1988.
Halliday, D. and R. Resnick: *Fundamentals of Physics*, Wiley, New York, 1990.

Ohanian, H. C.: *Physics*, Norton, New York, 1989.

Sears, F. W., M. W. Zemansky, and H. D. Young: *University Physics*, Addison-Wesley, Reading, Mass., 1988.

Serway, R. A.: *Physics for Scientists and Engineers*, Saunders, Philadelphia, Pa., 1987.

Tipler, P. A.: *Physics*, Worth, New York, 1990.

DIFFERENTIAL EQUATIONS AND SPECIAL FUNCTIONS

In this chapter, we deal with the solutions to ordinary differential equations of the first and second order. We begin by applying the Euler-Heun and Runge-Kutta numerical methods to linear and nonlinear differential equations. We then apply analytical methods to both homogeneous and non-homogeneous linear differential equations with constant coefficients. We continue with applications of Laplace transforms and Fourier series to differential equations.

In the last sections of this chapter, we consider some built-in MathCAD functions—the Bessel functions, the gamma function, the error function, and the cumulative normal distribution function.

NUMERICAL SOLUTION OF FIRST-ORDER DIFFERENTIAL EQUATIONS

Consider a first-order differential equation of the form,

$$\frac{dy}{dx} = y' = f(x, y)$$

As the initial condition, we require that the solution $y(x)$ pass through the point (x_0, y_0). We assume that the function $y' = f(x, y)$ is defined everywhere on an interval $[x_0, x_f]$. To develop a numerical solution, we divide the interval into N subintervals each of width $h = [x_f - x_0]/N$. Using the method of differentials, the value of $y_1 = y(x_1)$ where $x_1 = x_0 + h$ is approximately,

$$y_1 = y_0 + h \cdot \frac{dy}{dx}$$

or,

$$y_1 = y_0 + h \cdot f(x_0, y_0)$$

The process can be generalized for y_{n+1} as,

$$y_{n+1} = y_n + h \cdot f(x_n, y_n)$$

By iterating the equation, we obtain the solution y_n for the points $x_n = x_0 + n \cdot h$. The smaller we make the value of h (i.e., the larger the number of subintervals N), the more accurate the results become.

The above process is called a *predictor* method because it attempts in each step to predict y_{n+1} from the previous value y_n. This process can be improved upon by using the above result only as a first-order estimate. The estimate is then used in a correction formula to recompute a more accurate value. The process is called a *predictor-corrector* method. Adding a single correction makes the process a *second-order* method.

The Euler-Heun method is an example of a second-order, predictor-corrector method. The equation above is modified to,

$$y_{n+1} = y_n + h \cdot \frac{f(x_n, y_n) + f(x_{n+1}, y_{n+1}^*)}{2}$$

where,

$$y_{n+1}^* = y_n + h \cdot f(x_n, y_n)$$

Combining the above equations into a single equation we obtain,

$$y_{n+1} = y_n + \left[\frac{h}{2}\right] \cdot [f(x_n, y_n) + f(x_{n+1}, \{y_n + h \cdot f(x_n, y_n)\})]$$

We consider the following first-order differential equation,

$$y' = f(x, y) = x + y$$

with the initial condition,

$$y_0 = y(0) = 0 \qquad (x_0 = 0)$$

Applying the theory of differential equations, the analytical solution is,

$$y(x) = e^x - x - 1$$

Direct substitution into the differential equation verifies that this is a solution. The function $y(x)$ also satisfies the initial condition $y(0) = 0$.

In Worksheet 6.1, we apply the Euler-Heun method to the above differential equation and compare the analytical and numerical solutions.

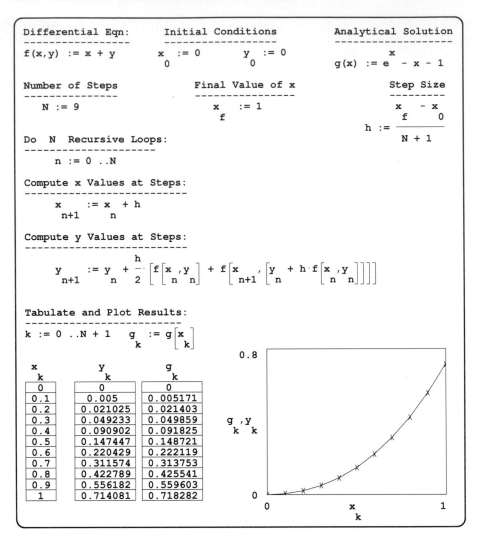

WORKSHEET 6.1
Euler-Heun method for first-order differential equations.

MathCAD solution: Worksheet 6.1. We assign the differential equation function $f(x, y) = x + y$, the initial conditions (x_0, y_0), and the analytical solution $g(x)$. (We use e^x for the exponential function; the form exp(x) can also be used.) The number of steps N, the end of the interval x_f, and the step size h are also assigned. The range variable for the number of loops n is defined and the Euler-Heun method is applied. MathCAD computes the values of x_n and y_n recursively.

The numerical and analytical solutions to the differential equation are displayed and plotted. The tables for y_n and g_n are displayed to six decimal places. (To adjust the local display format, place the cursor in each table and type **f**. On the message line, set pr=6.) The numerical results are plotted using exes. Note how well the numerical results agree with the theory. Vary N to see how the accuracy is affected.

NUMERICAL SOLUTION OF SECOND-ORDER DIFFERENTIAL EQUATIONS

We consider next the numerical solution of second-order differential equations using the *Runge-Kutta-Nyström* method. This method is a predictor-corrector method of the fourth order. To apply the method, we express the second derivative in terms of the first derivative y', the function y, and the independent variable x as,

$$y'' = f(y', y, x)$$

where $f(y', y, x)$ is defined on some interval $[x_0, x_f]$. For example, for the differential equation,

$$y'' + x^2 \cdot y'^2 + \cos(x) \cdot y = \sin(y)$$

solving for y'' gives,

$$y'' = f(y', y, x) = \sin(y) - x^2 \cdot y'^2 - \cos(x) \cdot y$$

To make the solution unique, we specify a set of initial conditions in the form,

$$y_0 = y(0) \qquad \text{and} \qquad y_0' = y'(0) \qquad (x_0 = 0)$$

To apply the Runge-Kutta-Nyström method on the interval $[x_0, x_f]$, we break up the interval into N subintervals each having a width $h = (x_f - x_0)/N$. The coordinate points at the left of each of the N subintervals are labeled x_0, x_1, ..x_n, ...x_{N-1}, where $x_n = x_0 + n \cdot h$. We proceed with the following steps:

Step I. Set $n = 0$. Specify x_0, y_0, and y_0'.

Step II. Compute the following constants:

a. $k_1 = \frac{1}{2} \cdot h \cdot f(x_n, y_n', y_n)$

b. $k_2 = \frac{1}{2} \cdot h \cdot f(x_n + \frac{1}{2} h, y_n + K, y_n' + k_1)$, where $K = \frac{1}{2} \cdot h \cdot (y_n' + \frac{1}{2} \cdot k_1)$

c. $k_3 = \frac{1}{2} \cdot h \cdot f(x_n + \frac{1}{2} \cdot h, y_n + K, y_n' + k_2)$

d. $k_4 = \frac{1}{2} \cdot h \cdot f(x_n + h, y_n + L, y_n' + 2 \cdot k_3)$, where $L = h \cdot (y_n' + k_3)$

Step III. Compute the coordinates of the next point:

$$x_{n+1} = x_n + h$$

$$y_{n+1} = y_n + h \cdot \left[y_n' + \frac{(k_1 + k_2 + k_3)}{3} \right]$$

Step IV. Compute the derivative at the next point:

$$y_{n+1}' = y_n' + \frac{k_1 + 2 \cdot k_2 + 2 \cdot k_3 + k_4}{3}$$

Step V. If $n = N - 1$ then exit to Step VI; else increment n by one (i.e., set $n = n + 1$) and loop to Step II.

Step VI. End.

The computed values of y_n and y'_n represent the solution and its derivative at the points x_n.

A DIGRESSION ON LOOP ITERATION. Note that the Runge-Kutta-Nyström method involves loop iteration. The computation deals with two unknowns (y and y') which depend on each other. Both must computed at the nth point before proceeding to the $n + 1$th point. The computation can be easily accomplished with most programming languages using a `DO/LOOP`, `WHILE/WEND`, or `FOR/NEXT` type of procedure according to the syntax of the language. For example, consider the following `FOR/NEXT` loop in QuickBASIC:

```
'************************************
a(0)=1 : b(0)=1
FOR n=0 to 3
        a(n+1) = a(n) + b(n)
        b(n+1) = a(n)^2 + b(n)^2
NEXT n
'************************************
```

The first line initializes the values of $a_0=1$ and $b_0=1$. The `FOR/NEXT` loop performs the required iteration. The results after each loop are as follows:

$$n=0: \; a_1 = a_0 + b_0 = 1 + 1 = 2 \qquad b_1 = a_0^2 + b_0^2 = 1 + 1 = 2$$

$$n=1: \; a_2 = a_1 + b_1 = 2 + 2 = 4 \qquad b_2 = a_1^2 + b_1^2 = 4 + 4 = 8$$

$$n=2: \; a_3 = a_2 + b_2 = 4 + 8 = 12 \qquad b_3 = a_2^2 + b_2^2 = 16 + 64 = 80$$

Note that *before* the a_{n+1} (and b_{n+1}) can be evaluated, *both* a_n and b_n must be computed.

MathCAD does not have `DO/LOOP`, `WHILE/WEND`, or `FOR/NEXT` procedures. It can, however, perform loop iteration using a rather clever but subtle technique. Suppose we try to perform the above loop iteration with the following MathCAD objects:

```
a0    := 1      b0     :=1      n := 0 ..3
an+1  := an + bn                bn+1  := an^2 + bn^2
         |                               |
  index out of bounds            index out of bounds
```

As indicated by the errors, this will not accomplish loop iteration since MathCAD tries to compute each equation separately for all n. In the first recursive operation, the values of a_{n+1} are computed assuming that the previous values of b_n have already been assigned (which they have not).

The trick in performing iteration is to place the iterated equations into a vector structure. Consider the following objects:

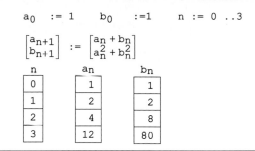

$$a_0 := 1 \qquad b_0 := 1 \qquad n := 0 \ .. \ 3$$

$$\begin{bmatrix} a_{n+1} \\ b_{n+1} \end{bmatrix} := \begin{bmatrix} a_n + b_n \\ a_n^2 + b_n^2 \end{bmatrix}$$

n	an	bn
0	1	1
1	2	2
2	4	8
3	12	80

The keystrokes for the vector assignment are:

{<Alt>M} 2 0 {Enter}: {<Alt>M} 2 0 {Enter}

[After each **{<Alt>M}**, the message line prompts for rows and columns. Make sure the response is **2 0** or simply **2**.] The following template will appear:

Fill the placeholders accordingly. To display the tables, type **n=**, **a[n=**, and **b[n=**.

Note that the iteration process works on the components of the vector in sequence during each loop. Thus a_{n+1} and b_{n+1} are derived from the previous values of a_n and b_n.

We consider the following second-order differential equation,

$$y'' - \tan^2(x) - y^3 = 0$$

with the initial conditions,

$$y(0) = 1 \qquad \text{and} \qquad y'(0) = 0$$

A *nonlinear* differential equation of this type is generally difficult to solve. The analytical solution is $y = \sec(x)$, as direct substitution verifies. The solution also satisfies the initial conditions $y(0) = 1$ and $y'(0) = 0$. In Worksheet 6.2, we apply the Runge-Kutta-Nyström method to the equation and compare the numerical and analytical solutions.

MathCAD solution: Worksheet 6.2. We express the differential equation in the form,

$$y'' = f(x, y, y') = \tan^2(x) + y^3$$

The interval for the calculation is $[0, 1]$. The initial conditions are assigned as $y_0 = y(0) = 1$ and $y'_0 = y'(0) = 0$. [Note that the initial values are assigned using literal and not numerical subscripts, that is, **y.o** and **y'.o**.] Next the number of subintervals $N = 100$ is assigned and the increment h is computed. The values of x_n for the points of compu-

```
Define the function  y"=f(x,y,y'):    f(x,y,y') := tan(x)²  + y³
---------------------------------

      Define x interval              Choose initial conditions
      -----------------              -------------------------
start_x := 0      end_x := 1           y  := 1        y'  := 0
                                        o              o

                     Runge-Kutta Calculation
                     =======================
Intervals:    N := 100                          end_x - start_x
----------                                   h := ---------------
                            Increment:              N
                            ----------

Compute points on x-axis:
-------------------------
x  := start_x          n := 0 ..N - 1          x    := x  + h
 0                                              n+1     n

Define Runge-Kutta functions:
-----------------------------
k1(x,y,y') := .5·h·f(x,y,y')


k2(x,y,y') := .5·h·f(x + .5·h,y + .5·h·(y' + .5·k1(x,y,y')),y' + k1(x,y,y'))


k3(x,y,y') := .5·h·f(x + .5·h,y + .5·h·(y' + .5·k1(x,y,y')),y' + k2(x,y,y'))


k4(x,y,y') := .5·h·f(x + h,y + h·(y' + k3(x,y,y')),y' + 2·k3(x,y,y'))
```

$$Y(x,y,y') := h \cdot \left[y' + \frac{k1(x,y,y') + k2(x,y,y') + k3(x,y,y')}{3} \right]$$

$$Y'(x,y,y') := \frac{k1(x,y,y') + 2 \cdot k2(x,y,y') + 2 \cdot k3(x,y,y') + k4(x,y,y')}{3}$$

WORKSHEET 6.2
Numerical solution of a second-order differential equation (*cont. below*).

tation are assigned. The Runge-Kutta-Nyström equations are then assigned according to the theory presented above.

The initial values y_0 and y_0' are seeded into y_0 and y_0' for loop iteration. The iteration is performed N-1 times using the vector structure outlined above. The solution to the differential equation and its derivative at the points x_n are given by y_n and y'_n. The results are plotted and compared to the exact solution v(u)=sec(x) We use a plot format of type=ol.

As we increase the number of points N, the results become more accurate but the computation takes longer. Decrease the number of points to N=10 and note the reduction in accuracy.

In the next sections we will study second-order linear differential equations with constant coefficients. Solutions will be developed analytically. Numerical methods can be used to verify the results.

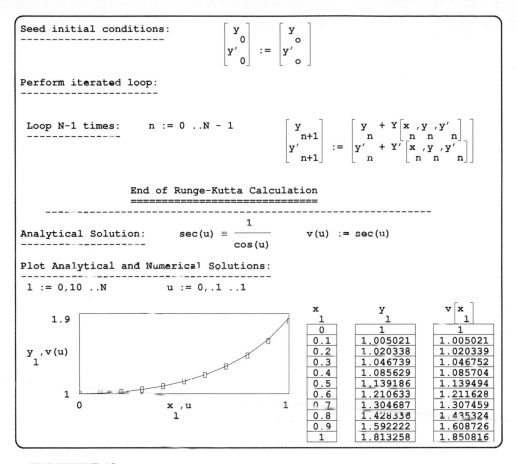

WORKSHEET 6.2
(*cont.*)

SECOND-ORDER LINEAR DIFFERENTIAL EQUATIONS

We consider a differential equation of the form:

$$a \cdot y'' + b \cdot y' + c \cdot y = f(t)$$

Note that since the following applications deal with variations with respect to time, we have changed the independent variable from x to t. This equation is classified as a *nonhomogeneous*, second-order linear differential equation with *constant* coefficients. If the right-hand side is zero (i.e., $f(t) = 0$), the equation is termed *homogeneous*. The general solution to the equation can be written as

$$y = y_c(t) + y_p(t)$$

where $y_c(t)$ is the general solution to the homogeneous equation. The function $y_c(t)$ is called the *complementary* solution. The particular solution $y_p(t)$ is *any* solution to the nonhomogeneous equation. Methods for finding a particular solution can be found in standard texts on differential equations.

Homogeneous Case

We first consider the solution of the homogeneous equation:

$$a \cdot y'' + b \cdot y' + c \cdot y = 0$$

The form of the general solution to this equation is determined by the roots of the *auxiliary* equation

$$a \cdot m^2 + b \cdot m + c = 0$$

which, according to the quadratic formula, are:

$$m_1 = \frac{-b + \{b^2 - 4 \cdot a \cdot c\}^{1/2}}{2 \cdot a}$$

and

$$m_2 = \frac{-b - \{b^2 - 4 \cdot a \cdot c\}^{1/2}}{2 \cdot a}$$

We express the roots as $m_1 = \alpha + \beta$ and $m_2 = \alpha - \beta$, where

$$\alpha = \frac{-b}{2 \cdot a} \qquad \text{and} \qquad \beta = \frac{[b^2 - 4 \cdot a \cdot c]^{1/2}}{2 \cdot a}$$

The general solution to the homogeneous differential equation can be expressed either in terms of m_1 and m_2 or in terms of α and β as:

$$y(t) = A \cdot e^{m_1 \cdot t} + B \cdot e^{m_2 \cdot t} \qquad (\text{if } m_1 \neq m_2)$$

or

$$y(t) = A \cdot e^{(\alpha+\beta) \cdot t} + B \cdot e^{(\alpha-\beta) \cdot t} \qquad (\text{if } \beta \neq 0)$$

and

$$y = e^{m \cdot t} \cdot (A \cdot t + B) \qquad (\text{if } m = m_1 = m_2)$$

or

$$y = e^{\alpha \cdot t} \cdot (A \cdot t + B) \qquad (\text{if } \beta = 0)$$

The *initial value* coefficients A and B are derived from the initial conditions $y(0)$ and $y'(0)$. If the solution $y(t)$ represents a physical phenomenon, it must be a real quantity. Thus if the roots m_1 and m_2 are real, then A and B must also be real.

If the roots of the auxiliary equation are a complex conjugate pair, they may be expressed as,

$$m_1 = \alpha + j \cdot \omega \qquad m_2 = \alpha - j \cdot \omega$$

where

$$\alpha = \frac{-b}{2 \cdot a} \qquad \text{and} \qquad \omega = \frac{[4 \cdot a \cdot c - b^2]^{1/2}}{2 \cdot a}$$

For complex roots $(4 \cdot a \cdot c > b^2)$, the above solution may be written as,

$$y(t) = e^{\alpha t} \cdot A \cdot e^{j \cdot \omega \cdot t} + B \cdot e^{-j \cdot \omega \cdot t}$$

Since the left-hand side must be real and the right-hand side has terms with imaginary exponents, the coefficients A and B must be complex quantities. The complex form of the solution can be expressed in terms of real quantities [using the Euler identity: $e^{\pm j \cdot \omega \cdot t} = \cos(\omega \cdot t) \pm j \cdot \sin(\omega \cdot t)$] as:

$$y(t) = e^{\alpha t} \cdot [A' \cdot \cos(\omega \cdot t) + B' \cdot \sin(\omega \cdot t)]$$

where A' and B' are both real. Hence, when the roots m_1 and m_2 are complex, the solution is oscillatory.

In summary, we have three cases of solutions:

Case I (Overdamped Motion). m_1 and m_2 are real and distinct.

Solution.

$$y = A \cdot e^{(\alpha + \beta) \cdot t} + B \cdot e^{(\alpha - \beta) \cdot t}$$

$$\alpha = \frac{-b}{2 \cdot a} \qquad \text{and} \qquad \beta = \frac{[b^2 - 4 \cdot a \cdot c]^{1/2}}{2 \cdot a}$$

Case II (Underdamped Motion). m_1 and m_2 form a complex conjugate pair.

Solution.

$$y = e^{\alpha t} \cdot [A \cdot e^{j \cdot \omega \cdot t} + B \cdot e^{-j \cdot \omega \cdot t}]$$

or

$$y = e^{\alpha \cdot t} \cdot [A' \cdot \cos(\omega \cdot t) + B' \cdot \sin(\omega \cdot t)]$$

$$\alpha = \frac{-b}{2 \cdot a} \qquad \text{and} \qquad \omega = \frac{[4 \cdot a \cdot c - b^2]^{1/2}}{2 \cdot a}$$

Case III (Critically Damped Motion). $m_1 = m_2 = m$ are equal.

Solution.

$$y = e^{\alpha \cdot t} \cdot (A \cdot t + B)$$

$$\alpha = \frac{-b}{2 \cdot a}$$

The form of the solution is determined by the value of the *discriminant* D defined as $D = [b^2 - 4 \cdot a \cdot c]$. We have overdamped, underdamped or critically damped motion according to whether D is positive, negative, or zero.

The *arbitrary* constants A and B are determined by the *initial* conditions $y_0 = y(0)$ and $y_0' = y'(0)$. The connection is,

$$A = \frac{(1 - \alpha/\beta) \cdot y_0 + y_0'/\beta}{2}$$

and

$$B = \frac{(1 + \alpha/\beta) \cdot y_0 - y_0'/\beta}{2}$$

While the constants A and B may be either real (if β is real) or complex conjugates of each other (if β is imaginary), the solution for $y(t)$ must be real. Note that the constants A and B are undefined for $\beta = 0$; the form of our solution is therefore not valid for the case of critical damping. However, the solution for critical damping can still be obtained by considering the limit of the overdamped solution as $\beta \to 0$. We examine the solution for all three cases in Worksheet 6.3.

> **MathCAD solution: Worksheet 6.3.** We assign the format parameters as `zt=5` (zero tolerance) and `im=j` (imaginary unit). All number less than 10^{-5} display as zero and all complex numbers display using the letter `j`. We next assign the differential equation coefficients (`a=1, b=.5, c=1`) and the initial values (`y`$_0$`=3, y'`$_0$`=0`). The vibrational parameters α and β are computed. Using MathCAD's **if** function, we modify the β=0 case (critical damping) to a negligibly small value (ϵ=10^{-4}). This is done to avoid difficulties with the mathematical form of the arbitrary constants A and B, which, as noted above, become undefined if β=0. The results still accurately describe critically damped motion. Note that we have set ω equal to the imaginary part of β using MathCAD's **Im** function. [If we want to extract the real part of a complex number, we use the **Re** function.] If β is real (overdamping), then ω=0; otherwise, we have β= $\omega \cdot$`j`.
>
> Finally, the solution and its derivative are constructed and plotted for $0 \leq$`t`$\leq$10 in steps of 0.05. The x-axis (`y=0`) is plotted for reference. The plot format uses `type=1dl`. This graphs the solution `y(t)` with a solid line, the derivative `y'(t)` with dots, and the "zero" line (i.e., the x-axis) with a solid line. The vibrational parameters (α, β, and ω) and arbitrary constants (A and B) are displayed. In this example, we have the case of underdamping (β imaginary). The solution oscillates but is damped. Note that the initial conditions are satisfied (i.e., `y`$_0$`=3, y'`$_0$`=0`).
>
> If we change the damping coefficient to `b= 2`, we have β=0 (critically damped motion). (Actually, the **if** function makes the reassignment β=`.000001`; since the zero tolerance was set to `zt=5`, β displays as zero.). The motion decays rapidly and `y(t)` approaches zero asymptotically without becoming negative. If we increase the value of the damping parameter to `b= 3`, we have overdamped motion (β real). Note that the motion is nonoscillatory but decays more slowly than in the critically damped case.
>
> Can the critically damped or overdamped solutions ever cross the t-axis? Set `b=2`, `y`$_0$`=3` and `y'`$_0$`=-10` and see what happens.

Nonhomogeneous Case

We now return to the nonhomogeneous equation,

$$a \cdot y'' + b \cdot y' + c \cdot y = f(t)$$

In engineering applications, the term on the right $f(t)$ is called the *driving* term. As we have seen above, the general solution to the nonhomogeneous equation is

$$y(t) = y_c(t) + y_p(t)$$

where $y_c(t)$ is the complementary solution and $y_p(t)$ is a particular solution. Using the results of the previous section for $y_c(t)$, the general solution can be written,

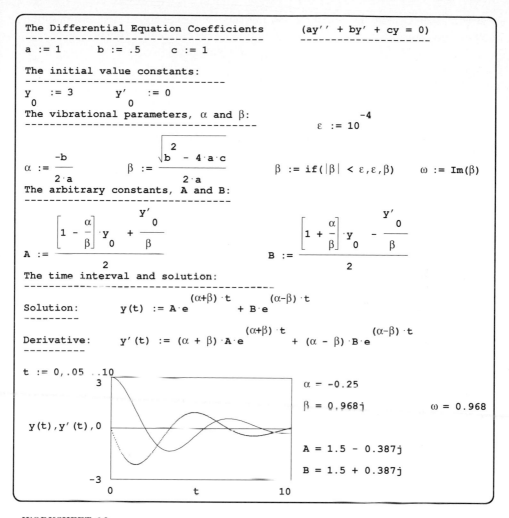

WORKSHEET 6.3
Damped vibrations.

$$y(t) = A \cdot e^{(\alpha+\beta) \cdot t} + B \cdot e^{(\alpha-\beta) \cdot t} + y_p(t) \qquad \text{(overdamped or underdamped)}$$
$$y(t) = e^{\alpha \cdot t} \cdot (A \cdot t + B) + y_p(t) \qquad \text{(critically damped)}$$

where $y_p(t)$ is *any* solution to the nonhomogeneous equation. The arbitrary constants A and B are determined from the initial conditions. In most physical situations, α is a negative number. This means that as t becomes sufficiently large, the complementary solution $y_c(t)$ damps out leaving only the particular solution $y_p(t)$. For this reason, $y_c(t)$ is also called the *transient* solution and $y_p(t)$ the *steady-state* solution.

We consider the effect of a harmonic driving term of the form,

$$f(t) = F_0 \cdot \cos(\omega_0 \cdot t)$$

where F_0 and ω_0 are the amplitude and frequency respectively. It is shown in differential equations texts that a particular solution to the differential equation is

$$y_p(t) = C \cdot \cos(\omega_0 \cdot t - \phi)$$

where,

$$C = \frac{F_0}{[(c - a \cdot \omega_0^2)^2 + (b \cdot \omega_0)^2]^{1/2}} \qquad \text{and} \qquad \phi = \tan^{-1}\left[\frac{(b \cdot \omega_0)}{(c - a \cdot \omega_0^2)}\right]$$

The arbitrary constants of the general solution, A and B, are found from the initial conditions by solving the following:

$$y(0) = y_0 \qquad \text{or} \qquad A + B + y_p(0) = y_0$$

and

$$y'(0) = y_0' \qquad \text{or} \qquad (\alpha + \beta) \cdot A + (\alpha - \beta) \cdot B + y_p'(0) = y_0'$$

In Worksheet 6.4, we analyze this problem.

MathCAD solution: Worksheet 6.4. We assign the coefficients of the equation along with the amplitude and frequency of the driving term. We next fix the initial conditions

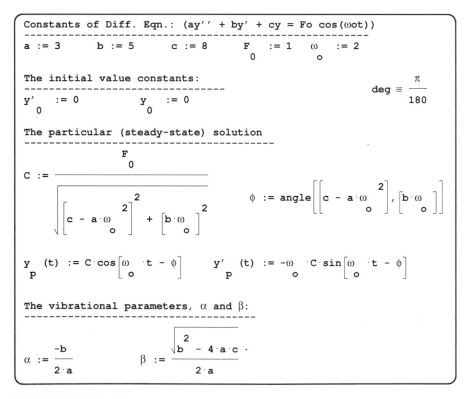

WORKSHEET 6.4
Forced vibrations (*cont. below*).

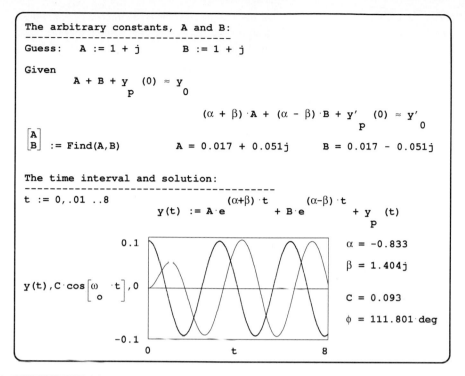

The arbitrary constants, A and B:
```
--------------------------------
```
Guess: A := 1 + j   B := 1 + j

Given
$$A + B + y_p(0) \approx y_0$$

$$(\alpha + \beta) \cdot A + (\alpha - \beta) \cdot B + y'_p(0) \approx y'_0$$

$\begin{bmatrix} A \\ B \end{bmatrix}$:= Find(A, B)   A = 0.017 + 0.051j   B = 0.017 - 0.051j

The time interval and solution:
```
-------------------------------------
```
t := 0, .01 .. 8
$$y(t) := A \cdot e^{(\alpha + \beta) \cdot t} + B \cdot e^{(\alpha - \beta) \cdot t} + y_p(t)$$

$\alpha = -0.833$

$\beta = 1.404j$

$C = 0.093$

$\phi = 111.801 \cdot deg$

WORKSHEET 6.4
(*cont.*)

$y_0 = 0$ and $y'_0 = 0$. The amplitude and phase are computed and the particular solution y_p and its derivative are constructed. Note that when the denominator approaches zero (resonance), the argument of the arctan function approaches infinity and the phase angle approaches $\pi/2$. MathCAD will give a "singularity" error for this case. To circumvent the problem, we use MathCAD's **angle** function. This function is actually a two-argument arctan function. It not only avoids the singularity error associated with the arctan, but it also automatically places the phase angle in the correct quadrant.

The vibrational parameters α and β are computed next. To determine the arbitrary constants, the relevant relational conditions are constructed and solved with a **Given/Find** solve block. The constants are assigned to a MathCAD vector and are displayed. The vector assignment is accomplished by typing {<Alt>M}2 0{Enter}:Find(A,B) and filling the placeholders with A and B. We could have solved for A and B using analytical methods but chose the **Given/Find** solve block to make our work easier.

Finally, we plot the solution y (t), the driving term C·cos (ω_0·t), and the x-axis (i.e., y=0). We format the graph using type=1dl. The solution will be plotted with a solid line, the driving term with dots, and the x-axis with a solid line.

Note that near the origin, the transient component is present. As t (time) increases, the transient disappears and the steady-state solution remains. The steady-state is a harmonic form of the same frequency as the driving term. However, the two waveforms are out of phase by ϕ ($\phi=-111.8°$). This mathematical result explains the phase difference between the steady-state current and the driving voltage in a simple ac circuit.

Change either the frequency of the driving term or the coefficients of the differential equation and observe the behavior of the steady-state amplitude C and the phase ϕ. If necessary, extend the plot range on the t-axis to observe the steady state.

LAPLACE TRANSFORMS

Let us reconsider the nonhomogeneous differential equation,

$$y'' + b \cdot y' + c \cdot y = f(t)$$

We set the coefficient $a = 1$. This poses no loss in generality since the original equation can be divided through by a. The objective is to find a solution to the differential equation subject to the initial conditions $y(0) = y_0$ and $y'(0) = y_0'$.

A powerful way to solve the above equation is with *Laplace transforms*. The Laplace transform $Y(s)$ of a function $y(t)$ is defined as,

$$L\{y(t)\} = Y(s) = \int_0^\infty e^{-s \cdot t} \cdot y(t) \; dt$$

The *inverse* Laplace transform $y(t) = L^{-1}\{Y(s)\}$ is computed from a complex contour integral. However both the Laplace transform and its inverse are usually obtained from a table.

MathCAD cannot compute a Laplace transform or its inverse. However, if we provide the analytical solution, it can perform the numerical calculations and answer the "what-if" question. The reader should consult a text on applied engineering analysis for details on Laplace transforms. We merely outline the approach.

Step I. Take the Laplace transform of the equation. This is written as,

$$L\{y''(t) + b \cdot y'(t) + c \cdot y(t)\} = L\{f(t)\}$$

$$[s^2 \cdot Y(s) - s \cdot y_0 - y_0'] + b \cdot [s \cdot Y(s) - y_0] + c \cdot Y(s) = F(s)$$

where $Y(s)$ and $F(s)$ are the Laplace transforms of the solution and the driving term respectively.

Step II. Solve algebraically for $Y(s)$. This gives:

$$Y(s) = \frac{A \cdot s}{(s - m_1) \cdot (s - m_2)} + \frac{B}{(s - m_1) \cdot (s - m_2)]} + \frac{F(s)}{(s - m_1) \cdot (s - m_2)}$$

where $A = y_0$ and $B = b \cdot y_0 + y_0'$. The constants m_1 and m_2 are the roots of the auxiliary equation given by,

$$m_1 = \frac{-b + \{b^2 - 4 \cdot c\}^{1/2}}{2}$$

and

$$m_2 = \frac{-b - \{b^2 - 4 \cdot c\}^{1/2}}{2}$$

Step III. Take the inverse Laplace transform of $Y(s)$. The solution takes the form,

$$y(t) = y_c(t) + y_p(t)$$

where

$$y_c(t) = -\left[\frac{B + m_1 \cdot A}{m_2 - m_1}\right] \cdot e^{m_1 \cdot t} + \left[\frac{B + m_2 \cdot A}{m_2 - m_1}\right] \cdot e^{m_2 \cdot t}$$

and

$$y_p(t) = \left[\frac{1}{m_2 - m_1}\right] \int_0^t [e^{m_2 \cdot (t-\tau)} - e^{m_1 \cdot (t-\tau)}] \cdot f(\tau)d\tau$$

[Note that the above solution is not valid for the case $m_1 = m_2$ (i.e., critical damping).]

When the constants A and B are expressed in terms of the initial conditions y_0 and y_0', the solution for the transient component $y_c(t)$ is identical to the form developed in the previous section. The steady-state response $y_p(t)$ can be determined for any driving term $f(t)$ provided the integral can be evaluated. The integral is simple to compute if $f(t)$ is a pulse, that is, it turns on at some time t_1 and turns off at a later time t_2.

Suppose that the driving term is of the form,

$$f(t) = F_0 \cdot \delta(t - t_0)$$

where $\delta(t - t_0)$ is the *Dirac delta function*. This unusual function is zero everywhere except at the point t_0 where it becomes infinite. Nevertheless, the area under the delta function is equal to one. The delta function may be viewed as the limiting form of a rectangular pulse whose area remains fixed while its width d approaches zero and its height h approaches infinity. The delta function is an abstraction of a spike or impulse; in fact, it is commonly called an *impulse* function. In engineering analysis, the homogeneous part of the differential equation can represent a system in which a mass attached to a spring moves in a viscous medium (mechanical analog) or it can represent an L-R-C circuit (electrical analog). The Dirac delta function simulates striking the mass with a hammer or applying a voltage spike to the circuit at $t = t_0$.

The delta function has the following properties.

$$\int_a^b \delta(t - t_0) \cdot dt = 1 \qquad (a \le t_0 \le b)$$

$$= 0 \qquad \text{(otherwise)}$$

and

$$\int_a^b \delta(t - t_0) \cdot f(t) \cdot dt = f(t_0) \qquad (a \le t_0 \le b)$$

$$= 0 \qquad \text{(otherwise)}$$

Using the second property, the Laplace transform solution given above becomes,

$$y_p(t) = \left[\frac{F_0}{m_2 - m_1}\right] \cdot [e^{m_2 \cdot (t-t_0)} - e^{m_1 \cdot (t-t_0)}] \cdot \Phi(t - t_0)$$

where $\Phi(t - t_0)$ is the Heaviside or step function defined as,

$$\Phi(t - t_0) = 0 \qquad (t < t_0)$$

$$= 1 \qquad (t \ge t_0)$$

In Worksheet 6.5, we study the solution to the differential equation where the driving term is a Dirac delta function.

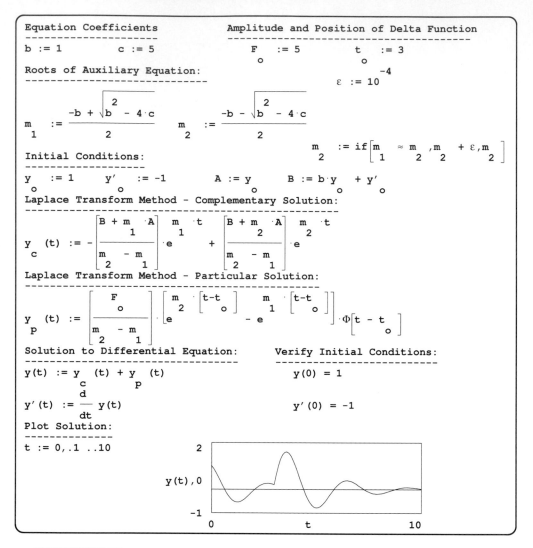

WORKSHEET 6.5

Laplace transform solution to a differential equation.

MathCAD solution: Worksheet 6.5. We assign the coefficients of the differential equation (b=1 and c=5) and the parameters of the delta function $F_0 \cdot \delta(t-t_0)$. The roots of the auxiliary equation m_1 and m_2 are computed. Note that since the solutions for y_c and y_p are not valid for equal roots (critical damping), we make an adjustment for the case $m_1 = m_2$. Using MathCAD's **if** function, the second root is displaced from the first by $\epsilon = 10^{-4}$.

The initial conditions $y_0=1$ and $y'_0=-1$ are assigned and the constants A and B are computed. Using the formulas given above, the general solution is constructed. Note the use of MathCAD's Heaviside function Φ. The solution and its derivative are evaluated at t=0 and verified to be consistent with the initial conditions. Finally, the solution is plotted from t=0 to t=10. The solution begins as a typical underdamped oscillation. At t=t$_0$ (t$_0$=3), the response function y(t) is "re-excited" by the impulse of the delta function and undergoes a sudden change. After the impulse, it proceeds to oscillate in the underdamped mode.

Turn off the delta function (i.e., by setting F$_0$=0) and see if reexcitation disappears. Vary F$_0$ and t$_0$ and note the changes in the response. Finally, determine how an impulse affects overdamped motion by adjusting the coefficients of the equation accordingly.

FOURIER SERIES

If the driving term in the differential equation is periodic, the solution can be found using the method of Fourier series. We therefore digress to review Fourier series.

A function which is periodic with a period T has the mathematical property $y(t) = y(t + T)$, that is, it repeats itself after a period T. It can be shown that as long as the function is piecewise continuous and has both a left-hand and a right-hand derivative everywhere on the interval, it can be represented as an infinite series of sine and cosine functions (harmonics). Such a series is called a *Fourier* series and is written as:

$$f(t) = a_0 + \sum_{n=1}^{\infty} a_n \cdot \cos\left(\frac{n \cdot 2 \cdot \pi \cdot t}{T}\right) + \sum_{n=1}^{\infty} b_n \cdot \sin\left(\frac{n \cdot 2 \cdot \pi \cdot t}{T}\right)$$

For the proper choice of the coefficients a_n and b_n, the series converges to $f(t)$ everywhere except at a discontinuity. At such a point, the series converges to a value equal to the average of the left-hand and right-hand values of the function. The coefficients of the Fourier series are given by the formulas:

$$a_0 = \left[\frac{1}{T}\right] \cdot \int_0^T f(t) \cdot dt, \qquad a_n = \left[\frac{2}{T}\right] \int_0^T f(t) \cdot \cos\left(\frac{n \cdot 2 \cdot \pi \cdot t}{T}\right) \cdot dt$$

and

$$b_n = \left[\frac{2}{T}\right] \cdot \int_0^T f(t) \cdot \sin\left(\frac{n \cdot 2 \cdot \pi \cdot t}{T}\right) \cdot dt$$

The interval of integration need not be from zero to T, but can be over any interval whose size is T (e.g., from $-T/2$ to $T/2$).

Thus a periodic function can be decomposed into its component Fourier harmonics which can then be used to resynthesize the function. In practice, a function is approximated using only a finite number of harmonics. The number of terms that are included depends on the accuracy required and on the nature of the function itself. Often the symmetry of the function reduces the number of coefficients to be computed. For an even function (i.e., $f(-t) = f(t)$), all $b_n = 0$ while for an odd function (i.e., $f(-t) = -f(t)$), all $a_n = 0$.

In Worksheet 6.6, we consider the Fourier analysis of a square wave of period $T = 2 \cdot L$, defined as,

$$y(t) = -1 \qquad (-L \leq t < 0)$$

$$y(t) = +1 \qquad (0 \leq t < L)$$

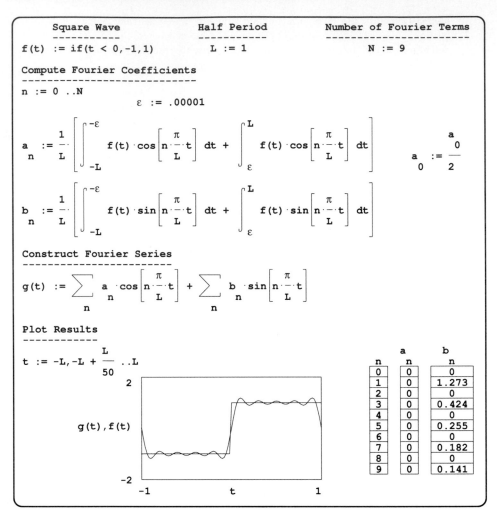

WORKSHEET 6.6

Fourier series.

and

$$y(t + 2 \cdot L) = y(t)$$

The quantity L represents the "half-period" of the square wave.

> **MathCAD solution: Worksheet 6.6.** We begin by defining the parameters of the square wave and the number of Fourier terms (N=9) to be included in the analysis. The Fourier coefficients are computed. Note that the square wave is discontinuous at t=0. The algorithm used by MathCAD in computing integrals sometimes presents a problem if the integrand is discontinuous. The computation may take a long time or MathCAD may return an `integral not converging` error. To circumvent this problem, we break the integral into two smaller integrals and exclude a small interval $(2 \cdot \epsilon)$ about the

discontinuity. If ϵ is small enough, the error in the result is negligible. The coefficient a$_0$ is obtained by setting n=0 in the general equation for a$_n$ and then taking one-half of the result.

We next construct the Fourier series. (Recall that to generate the summation template, type **$**.) Finally we plot the function f(t) and its Fourier sum g(t) over the period of definition. The coefficients are listed in tabular form by typing **n=**, **a$_n$=**, **b$_n$=**. We set the global zero tolerance to zt=3, so that all values smaller than 10^{-3} will display as zero.

Since our square wave is an odd function, all a$_n$=0. Computation shows that the alternating b coefficients also vanish. Hence we are actually synthesizing the square wave using only five nonzero terms. From the plot, it can be seen how the series of harmonics simulates the square wave. Note that the series gives g(0)=0 which is the average of the left-hand and right-hand values of f(t) at t=0.

Making N large increases the computation time of the worksheet. This time can be reduced dramatically if we replace the MathCAD integrals with analytically derived coefficients. For the above square wave the analytical coefficients are:

$$a_n = 0,$$

$$b_n = 0 \qquad (n \text{ even})$$

and

$$b_n = \frac{4}{n \cdot \pi} \qquad (n \text{ odd})$$

To decrease computation time, change the summation range to **n:1,3;N** (i.e., n=1, 3, . .N) and replace the integral representations of the coefficients with the assignments **a$_n$:=0** and **b$_n$:=4/(n·π)**.

To observe the Fourier analysis of a saw tooth wave and a triangle wave, use the following functions to compute the Fourier coefficients,

$$f(t) = t \qquad (\text{saw tooth wave})$$

and

$$f(t) = \mathbf{if}(t < 0, t + 1, 1 - t) \qquad (\text{triangle wave})$$

Using Fourier Series to Solve Differential Equations

Consider the following differential equation,[1]

$$a \cdot y'' + b \cdot y' + c \cdot y = f(t)$$

where $f(t)$ is a periodic driving term. We use the method of Fourier series to find the steady state solution $y_p(t)$. As shown earlier, the response to a harmonic driving term $f(t) = F_0 \cdot \cos(\omega_0 \cdot t)$ is,

$$y_p(t) = F_0 \cdot \beta \cdot \cos(\omega_0 \cdot t - \phi)$$

---

[1] In order to maintain consistency with the section on harmonic driving terms, we return to using the constant a in the differential equation.

where,

$$\beta = \frac{1}{[(c - a \cdot \omega_0^2)^2 + (b \cdot \omega_0)^2]^{1/2}}$$

and

$$\phi = \tan^{-1}\left[\frac{b \cdot \omega_0}{c - a \cdot \omega_0^2}\right]$$

It seems plausible that if the driving term has a Fourier representation of,

$$f(t) = \sum_{n=0}^{\infty} A_n \cdot \cos(\omega_n \cdot t) + \sum_{n=1}^{\infty} B_n \cdot \sin(\omega_n \cdot t), \qquad \left(\omega_n = n \cdot 2 \cdot \pi \cdot \frac{t}{T}\right)$$

then the steady-state response should be of the form,

$$f(t) = \sum_{n=0}^{\infty} A_n \cdot \beta_n \cdot \cos(\omega_n \cdot t - \phi_n) + \sum_{n=1}^{\infty} B_n \cdot \beta_n \cdot \sin(\omega_n \cdot t - \phi_n)$$

Assume that the driving term is a square wave. As noted in the previous section, a square wave of amplitude F_0 and period T can be decomposed into a Fourier series of the form,

$$f(t) = \sum_{\substack{n=1 \\ (n\ \text{odd})}}^{\infty} [B_n \cdot \sin(\omega_n \cdot t)$$

where,

$$B_n = \left(\frac{4}{n} \cdot \pi\right) \cdot F_0 \qquad \text{and} \qquad \omega_n = \frac{(2 \cdot \pi \cdot n)}{T}$$

It is not surprising then that the steady-state response to this square wave is,

$$y_p(t) = \sum_{\substack{n=1 \\ (n\ \text{odd})}}^{\infty} [B_n \cdot \beta_n \cdot \sin(\omega_n \cdot t - \phi_n)$$

where

$$\beta_n = \frac{1}{[(c - a \cdot \omega_n^2)^2 + (b \cdot \omega_n)^2]^{1/2}}$$

and

$$\phi_n = \tan^{-1}\left[\frac{b \cdot \omega_n}{(c - a \cdot \omega_n^2)}\right]$$

In Worksheet 6.7, we apply these formulas to construct the steady-state solution when the driving term is a periodic square wave.

> **MathCAD solution: Worksheet 6.7.** We assign the number of Fourier terms (N=19) to be used in the computation, the coefficients of the differential equation (a=1, b=.5, c=1), and the period of the square wave (T=π). The harmonic frequencies ω_n, are assigned and the response amplitudes β_n and phases ϕ_n computed. Resonance occurs

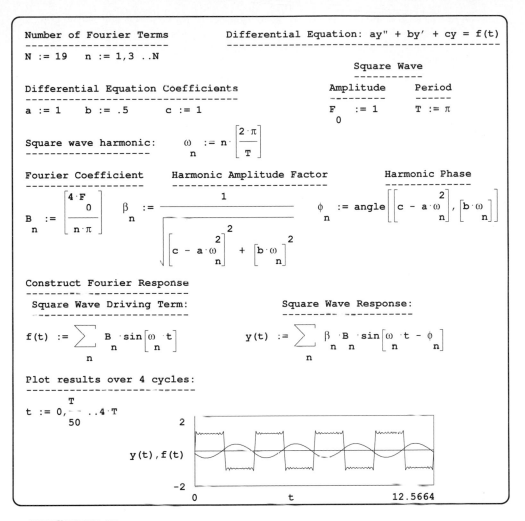

Number of Fourier Terms

N := 19   n := 1,3 ..N

Differential Equation: ay" + by' + cy = f(t)

Square Wave

Differential Equation Coefficients

a := 1   b := .5   c := 1

Amplitude   Period

F_0 := 1   T := π

Square wave harmonic: $\omega_n := n \cdot \left[\dfrac{2 \cdot \pi}{T}\right]$

Fourier Coefficient

$B_n := \left[\dfrac{4 \cdot F_0}{n \cdot \pi}\right]$

Harmonic Amplitude Factor

$\beta_n := \dfrac{1}{\sqrt{\left[c - a \cdot \omega_n^2\right]^2 + \left[b \cdot \omega_n\right]^2}}$

Harmonic Phase

$\phi_n := \text{angle}\left[\left[c - a \cdot \omega_n^2\right], \left[b \cdot \omega_n\right]\right]$

Construct Fourier Response

Square Wave Driving Term:

$f(t) := \displaystyle\sum_n B_n \cdot \sin\left[\omega_n \cdot t\right]$

Square Wave Response:

$y(t) := \displaystyle\sum_n \beta_n \cdot B_n \cdot \sin\left[\omega_n \cdot t - \phi_n\right]$

Plot results over 4 cycles:

$t := 0, \dfrac{T}{50} \ ..4 \cdot T$

y(t),f(t)

2

-2

0   t   12.5664

WORKSHEET 6.7
Steady-state response to a square wave using Fourier series.

whenever any of the harmonic frequencies satisfies $\omega_n = \sqrt{c/a}$. Since the argument of the arctan function involves division by zero, MathCAD gives a singularity error. Actually, as $x \to \pm\infty$, arctan (x) $\to \pm\pi/2$. To circumvent this problem and set the phases in the proper quadrants, we use MathCAD's **angle** function, as was done in Worksheet 6.4.

Finally, the square wave and response functions are constructed and plotted over four cycles. While the response function looks like a sine or cosine (it is not) and has the same period as the square wave, its peak is approximately one-half that of the square wave.

Change the coefficients of the equation and the period of the square wave. In particular, see what happens when a=1, b=.5, c=1 and the square wave period is T=2·π. Since $\omega_1 = \sqrt{c/a} = 1$, the first harmonic component of the square wave generates a resonance condition. Note that the peak value of the response function is now greater than that of the square wave. The worksheet takes a long time to compute. To speed up the process, reduce the number of Fourier terms in the sum and decrease the number of points plotted.

To see the response when the driving term is a triangle wave, use the representation,

$$f(t) \approx \sum_{\substack{n=1 \\ (n \text{ odd})}}^{N} \frac{4}{(n^2 \cdot \pi)} \cdot \cos(\omega_n \cdot t) \qquad (N = 19)$$

A BOUNDARY VALUE PROBLEM—THE VIBRATING STRING

Consider a string of length L fixed at both ends. Suppose that the string has a linear mass density μ and is under a tension T. Transverse waves travel back and forth along the string with a velocity $v = \sqrt{(T/\mu)}$. As was shown in Chapter 5, there exists a set of natural modes of vibration for the string represented by,

$$y_n(x, t) = A_n \cdot \cos(\omega_n \cdot t) \cdot \sin(k_n \cdot x) \qquad (n = 1, 2, \ldots)$$

where

$$k_n = n \cdot \frac{\pi}{L} \qquad \text{(wave number)}$$

and

$$\omega_n = v \cdot k_n \qquad \text{(frequency)}$$

We add an (arbitrary) amplitude A_n to the mode. The velocity v relates the wavenumber to the frequency of the mode.

If the string is initially deformed into any one of the natural modes $A_n \cdot \sin(k_n \cdot x)$ and released, it vibrates in that mode with the frequency ω_n and has a time factor $\cos(\omega_n \cdot t)$ (see Chapter 5). If, however, the string is deformed in an arbitrary shape $y_0(x)$ and then released, it vibrates in a more complicated manner. The vibrational pattern is actually a mixture of the natural modes, with each mode having its own amplitude. The amplitudes are determined by the Fourier decomposition of the initial deformation into the natural modes. The vibration of the string can then be represented as,

$$y(x, t) = \sum_{n=1}^{\infty} A_n \cdot \cos(\omega_n \cdot t) \cdot \sin(k_n \cdot x)$$

where

$$A_n = \left[\frac{2}{L}\right] \cdot \int_0^L y_0(x) \cdot \sin(k_n \cdot x) \cdot dx$$

Thus by knowing the initial deformation $y_0(x)$, we can compute the coefficients A_n and construct the solution $y(x, t)$ for the configuration of the string at later times. In theory, an infinite number of Fourier terms is required to reproduce the exact solution. In practice, a finite number of terms usually yields a satisfactory approximation.

Consider a string of length L that is plucked at its center to form a triangle and is then released. Let the displacement at the center be Y_0. The initial deformation is represented by,

$$y_0(x) = 2 \cdot Y_0 \cdot \frac{x}{L} \qquad \left(0 \leq x < \frac{L}{2}\right)$$

$$y_0(x) = 2 \cdot Y_0 \cdot \frac{L - x}{L} \qquad \left(\frac{L}{2} \leq x < L\right)$$

We describe the subsequent motion of the string in Worksheet 6.8.

MathCAD solution: Worksheet 6.8. We assign the length of the string and the amplitude of the deformation. We next construct and plot the initial configuration of the string.

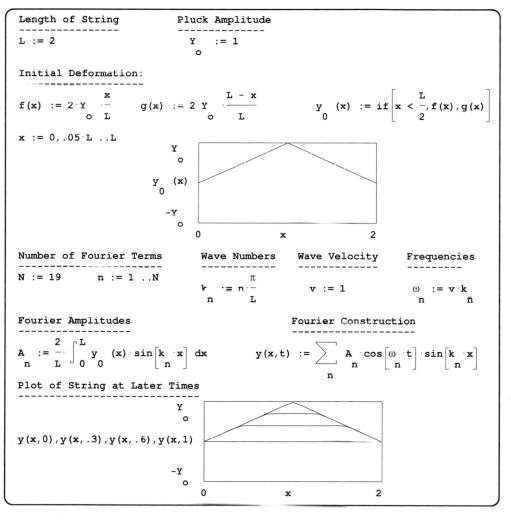

WORKSHEET 6.8
The plucked string.

Note that at `t=0`, the string is in the shape of a triangle. We then assign the number of modes and their wave numbers. The velocity of transverse waves on the string is assumed to be one.

Using Fourier's formula, we compute the mode amplitudes and construct the Fourier series for the string's displacement function `y(x,t)`. The string's shape is plotted for four different times. Note that soon after release, the string forms a "flat" spot which grows until the string becomes straight. By plotting the function at later times, it is observed that the displacement becomes negative and the flat spot gradually shrinks until a triangle is formed on the lower side. The string then begins to move upward in a similar fashion. It eventually returns to its initial deformation and the cycle begins again.

Try different initial deformations and observe the motion. [Note: Since the string is fixed at both ends, all deformations must satisfy: $y_0(0) = y_0(L) = 0$.] In particular, pluck the string at $x = L/4$. To do this, make the replacements,

$$f(x) = 4 \cdot Y_0 \cdot \frac{x}{L}$$

$$g(x) = \left[\frac{4}{3}\right] \cdot Y_0 \cdot \frac{L-x}{L}$$

and

$$y_0(x) = if\left(x < \frac{L}{4}, f(x),\ g(x)\right)$$

BESSEL FUNCTIONS

The Bessel function of order n, written $J_n(x)$, is a solution to Bessel's differential equation,

$$x^2 \cdot y'' + x \cdot y' + (x^2 - n^2) \cdot y = 0$$

While Bessel's equation is linear, it cannot be solved with the methods presented above because the coefficients are *not* constants. Using analytical techniques, it is possible to find a pair of linearly independent solutions which are written,

$J_n(x)$ Bessel function of the *first* kind (Bessel function)

and

$Y_n(x)$ Bessel function of the *second* kind (Neumann function)

At $x = 0$, the Bessel function remains finite while the Neumann function becomes infinite.

MathCAD generates these built-in functions as follows:

For $J_n(x)$, type: **Jn(n,x)**.
For $Y_n(x)$, type: **Yn(n,x)**.

For $n = 0$ and $n = 1$, MathCAD also allows the following syntax:

For $J_0(x)$, type: **J0(x)**; for $J_1(x)$, type: **J1(x)**.
For $Y_0(x)$, type: **Y0(x)**; for $Y_1(x)$, type: **Y1(x)**.

While Bessel and Neumann functions also exist for noninteger n, MathCAD only generates the functions for orders $n = 0, 1, 2, \ldots$.. In Worksheet 6.9, we examine some Bessel functions.

MathCAD solution: Worksheet 6.9. We plot the first three orders of the Bessel and Neumann functions. Note that all Bessel functions are zero at the origin except J_0 (x) which is one. The Neumann functions all approach negative infinity as x approaches zero. To plot these functions, we avoid the origin by setting x= 0.1, 0.2 ..10. Furthermore, the scale on the y-axis is manually set to range from y=−1 to y=+1. The left placeholder on the x-axis is set to x=0.

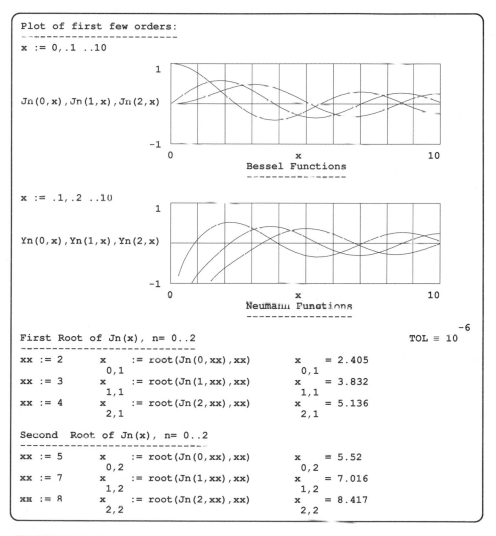

```
Plot of first few orders:
--------------------------
x := 0,.1 ..10
```

Bessel Functions

```
x := .1,.2 ..10
```

Neumann Functions

```
                                                                  -6
First Root of Jn(x), n= 0..2                          TOL ≡ 10
---------------------------
xx := 2      x     := root(Jn(0,xx),xx)      x     = 2.405
              0,1                             0,1
xx := 3      x     := root(Jn(1,xx),xx)      x     = 3.832
              1,1                             1,1
xx := 4      x     := root(Jn(2,xx),xx)      x     = 5.136
              2,1                             2,1


Second Root of Jn(x), n= 0..2
-----------------------------
xx := 5      x     := root(Jn(0,xx),xx)      x     = 5.52
              0,2                             0,2
xx := 7      x     := root(Jn(1,xx),xx)      x     = 7.016
              1,2                             1,2
xx := 8      x     := root(Jn(2,xx),xx)      x     = 8.417
              2,2                             2,2
```

WORKSHEET 6.9
Bessel functions.

Note that each of the functions has its own set of roots where it crosses the x-axis. The first two roots of $J_0(x)$, $J_1(x)$, and $J_2(x)$ are computed using MathCAD's **root** function. Each root is stored in a doubly subscripted variable $x_{m,n}$ which represents the mth root of the nth order Bessel function. For example, to assign $x_{0,1}$, type **x[(0,1):** and see $x_{0,1} :=$.

GAMMA, ERROR, AND CUMULATIVE NORMAL DISTRIBUTION FUNCTIONS

The *gamma function* extends the definition of the factorial operation to nonintegers. It is defined by the integral,

$$\Gamma(z) = \int_0^\infty e^{-t} \cdot t^{z-1} dt \qquad (Re(z) > 0)$$

Using integration by parts, the following property can be established,

$$\Gamma(z + 1) = z \cdot \Gamma(z)$$

For nonnegative integers n, this leads to the rule:

$$\Gamma(n + 1) = n! \qquad (n = 0, 1, 2, \ldots)$$

The gamma function is used to extend the definition of the factorial not only to fractions but also to complex numbers. To generate the gamma function with MathCAD, type **{<Alt>G}** and see Γ. *If you are using the gamma function, do not use the Greek letter Γ for any other purpose in the worksheet!*

The *error function* is defined by the integral:

$$\text{erf}(x) = \left[\frac{2}{\sqrt{\pi}} \right] \cdot \int_0^x e^{-t^2} dt$$

It is used in statistics since it represents the area between zero and x under the bell-shaped Gaussian curve,

$$y(t) = \left[\frac{2}{\sqrt{\pi}} \right] \cdot e^{-t^2}$$

As x approaches infinity, the area and therefore $\text{erf}(x)$ approach one. To use Math-CAD's built-in error function, type **erf(x)**. While the integral definition of $\text{erf}(z)$ is valid for complex arguments, MathCAD will only allow real values.

The *cumulative (standardized) normal distribution function* is similar to the error function and is defined by the integral:

$$\text{cnorm}(x) = \left[\frac{1}{\sqrt{2 \cdot \pi}} \right] \cdot \int_{-\infty}^x e^{-t^2/2} dt$$

To use this MathCAD function, type **cnorm(x)**. MathCAD only allows real arguments. The built-in function **cnorm** is actually unnecessary since it can be generated from the **erf** function using:

$$\text{cnorm}(x) = \frac{1}{2} \left[1 + \text{erf} \left(\frac{x}{\sqrt{2}} \right) \right]$$

We illustrate some properties of $\Gamma(x)$, $\text{erf}(x)$, and $\text{cnorm}(x)$ in Worksheet 6.10.

MathCAD solution: Worksheet 6.10. The global zero tolerance is set to zt=6. We list the gamma function for some positive integers and for some positive and negative half-integers. We verify the relation $\Gamma(x+1)=x!$ for integers and the more general recursive form $\Gamma(x+1)=x\cdot\Gamma(x)$ for nonintegers. We show that $\Gamma(1/2)=\sqrt{\pi}$. We do this by displaying $\Gamma(1/2)$ (by typing **{<Alt>G}(1/2)=**). We then fill the placeholder with $\sqrt{\pi}$ (by typing **\{<Alt>P}**).

The error function is plotted and tabulated for $-2\leq x\leq 2$ in steps of 0.5. Finally, we plot and tabulate cnorm(x) and compare it to an expression containing erf(x) which we call y(x). Note that y(x) is plotted using rectangles. The equivalence of cnorm(x) and y(x) is evident from both the graph and the tables.

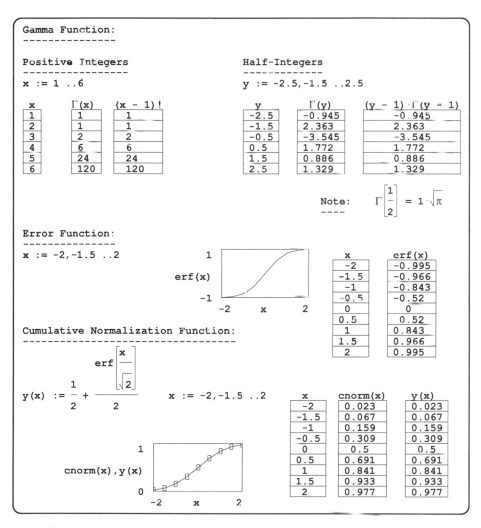

Gamma Function:

Positive Integers
----

x := 1 ..6

x	$\Gamma(x)$	(x - 1)!
1	1	1
2	1	1
3	2	2
4	6	6
5	24	24
6	120	120

Half-Integers
----

y := -2.5,-1.5 ..2.5

y	$\Gamma(y)$	$(y - 1)\cdot\Gamma(y - 1)$
-2.5	-0.945	-0.945
-1.5	2.363	2.363
-0.5	-3.545	-3.545
0.5	1.772	1.772
1.5	0.886	0.886
2.5	1.329	1.329

Note: $\Gamma\left[\dfrac{1}{2}\right] = 1\cdot\sqrt{\pi}$

Error Function:
----

x := -2,-1.5 ..2

x	erf(x)
-2	-0.995
-1.5	-0.966
-1	-0.843
-0.5	-0.52
0	0
0.5	0.52
1	0.843
1.5	0.966
2	0.995

Cumulative Normalization Function:

$$y(x) := \frac{1}{2} + \frac{\mathrm{erf}\left[\dfrac{x}{\sqrt{2}}\right]}{2}$$

x := -2,-1.5 ..2

x	cnorm(x)	y(x)
-2	0.023	0.023
-1.5	0.067	0.067
-1	0.159	0.159
-0.5	0.309	0.309
0	0.5	0.5
0.5	0.691	0.691
1	0.841	0.841
1.5	0.933	0.933
2	0.977	0.977

WORKSHEET 6.10
Statistical functions.

In the next chapter we will use MathCAD to solve problems dealing with matrices. We will also consider topics in complex variables.

PROBLEMS

1. Given the differential equation,

$$y'' + 2 \cdot y = 0 \qquad \text{with} \qquad x_0 = 0 \qquad \text{and} \qquad y(x_0) = 2$$

   (a) Use the Euler-Heun method to develop a solution on the interval $[0, 2]$. Set the number of subintervals to $N = 10$.
   (b) Using both a table and a plot, compare the result in part (a) with the analytical result $y(x) = 2 \cdot e^{-2 \cdot x}$. Use a global display format of pr=8.
   (c) Repeat parts (a) and (b) using $N = 20$. [See Worksheet 6.1.]

2. Consider the second-order differential equation,

$$2 \cdot y'' - y' - y = x + 2$$

   with

$$x_0 = 0, \qquad y_0 = 0, \qquad \text{and} \qquad y_0' = 0$$

   (a) Use the Runge-Kutta-Nyström method to develop a solution on the interval $[0, 1]$. Set the number of subintervals to $N = 5$.
   (b) Using both a table and a plot, compare the result in part (a) with the analytical result $y(x) = e^x - x - 1$. Use a global display format of pr=8.
   (c) Repeat parts (a) and (b) using $N = 10$. [See Worksheet 6.2.]

3. A series ac circuit consists of an inductor $L = 1H$, a resistor $R = .1\Omega$, a capacitor $C = 4F$, and a switch. The switch is opened and the capacitor is charged with $Q_0 = 3$ Coulombs. At $t = 0$ the switch is closed.
   (a) Following Worksheet 6.3, solve the equation and plot both the charge on the capacitor $Q(t)$ and the current in the circuit $I(t)$. [Hint: The differential equation is,

$$L \cdot Q''(t) + R \cdot Q'(t) + \frac{Q(t)}{C} = 0 \qquad \text{with} \qquad Q_0 = 3 \qquad \text{and} \qquad Q_0' = 0$$

   The current in the circuit is obtained using $I(t) = Q'(t)$.]
   (b) Solve the differential equation using the Runge-Kutta-Nyström method and compare the result with part (a).

4. (a) Show that for the critically damped case ($\beta = 0$), the correct analytical solution to the equation $a \cdot y'' + b \cdot y' + c \cdot y = 0$ is:

$$y(t) = e^{\alpha \cdot t} \cdot (A + B \cdot t) \qquad \left(\alpha = \frac{-b}{2 \cdot a} \right)$$

   where the initial value constants are,

$$A = y_0 \qquad \text{and} \qquad B = y_0' - \alpha \cdot y_0$$

   (b) Using Worksheet 6.3, examine the error involved when the overdamped case with $\beta = 10^{-4}$ is used to approximate critical damping.

5. Given the following differential equation,

$$y''(t) + \omega^2 \cdot y(t) = A \cdot \cos(\omega \cdot t) \qquad \text{with} \qquad y(0) = 0 \qquad \text{and} \qquad y'(0) = 0$$

   (a) Show by direct substitution that a particular solution to this equation is,

$$y_p(t) = \frac{t \cdot A \cdot \sin(\omega \cdot t)}{2 \cdot \omega}$$

(b) Find the complementary solution $y_c(t)$ and the general solution $y(t)$.

(c) Using a `Given/Find` solve block, find the arbitrary coefficients for the given initial conditions and plot the solution.

(d) Solve the differential equation using the Runge-Kutta-Nyström method and compare the result with part (c).

6. Solve the problem studied in Worksheet 6.4 using the Runge-Kutta-Nyström method.

7. Consider the differential equation,

$$y'' + y' + 5 \cdot y = F(t) \qquad \text{with} \qquad y_0 = 1 \qquad \text{and} \qquad y_0' = -1$$

Let $F(t)$ be a rectangular unit pulse turning on at $t = t_0$ and turning off at $t = t_0 + 1$. This function can be written as,

$$F(t) = [\Phi(t - t_0) - \Phi(t - \{t_0 + 1\})]$$

where Φ is the Heaviside function.

(a) Setting $t_0 = 6$, find the solution over the interval $[0, 16]$ using the Runge-Kutta-Nyström method with $N = 50$.

(b) If we narrow the pulse and increase its height while keeping the area equal to one, the function $F(t)$ approaches a Dirac delta function. The Runge-Kutta solution for this case will give inaccurate results. Why?

8. Following Worksheet 6.6, show that the analytical form of the odd Fourier sine coefficients of a square wave are of the form $b_n = 4/[n \cdot \pi]$. Display the coefficients by entering `b[n· n·π =`.

9. Following Worksheet 6.7, find the steady-state response of the differential equation,

$$y'' + 0.5 \cdot y' + y = f(t)$$

where $f(t)$ is a triangle wave. For a triangle wave, use the representation,

$$f(t) = \sum_{\substack{m=1 \\ (n=\text{odd})}}^{19} \left[\frac{4}{(n^2 \cdot \pi)} \cdot \cos(\omega_n \cdot t) \right]$$

10. The motion of a string fixed at both ends was studied in Worksheet 6.8. Find the motion when the string is plucked at $x = L/4$. To do this, set the initial deformation of the string equal to:

$$y_0(x) = 4 \cdot Y_0 \cdot \frac{x}{L} \qquad\qquad \left(0 \le x \le \frac{L}{4} \right)$$

$$y_0(x) = \left[\frac{4}{3} \right] \cdot Y_0 \cdot \frac{L - x}{L}, \qquad \left(\frac{L}{4} < x \le L \right)$$

11. Verify the following recursion relation for Bessel functions,

$$J_{n+2}(x) = 2 \cdot (n + 1) \cdot \frac{J_{n+1}(x)}{x} - J_n(x)$$

for the cases $n = 0$ and $n = 1$. [Hint: Construct the functions $f(x) = 2 \cdot J_1(x)/x - J_0(x)$ and $g(x) = 4 \cdot J_2(x)/x - J_1(x)$. Using plots, compare $f(x)$ with $J_2(x)$ and $g(x)$ with $J_3(x)$.]

12. (*a*) The asymptotic form of the **erf** function for large x is given by,

$$\text{erf}(x) \approx f(x) = 1 - \frac{\exp(-x^2)}{\sqrt{\pi} \cdot x} \qquad (x \gg 1)$$

Verify this by plotting and tabulating $f(x)$ and $\text{erf}(x)$ over the interval $[1, 2]$.

(*b*) The asymptotic form of the gamma function $\Gamma(x)$ is given by,

$$\Gamma(x + 1) \approx f(x) = \left[\sqrt{(2 \cdot \pi \cdot x)} \right] \cdot \left[\frac{x}{e} \right]^x \qquad (x \gg 1)$$

Verify this by plotting and tabulating $f(x)$ and $\Gamma(x + 1)$ over the interval $[0, 3]$.

REFERENCES

Boas, M. L.: *Mathematical Methods in the Physical Sciences*, Wiley, New York, 1966.

Bradbury, T. C.: *Mathematical Methods*, Wiley, New York, 1984.

Chapra, S. C. and R. P. Canale: *Numerical Methods for Engineers*, McGraw-Hill, New York, 1985.

Churchill, R. V.: *Fourier Series and Boundary Value Problems*, McGraw-Hill, New York, 1941.

Ford, L. R.: *Differential Equations*, McGraw-Hill, New York, 1955.

Giordano, F. R. and M. D. Weir: *Differential Equations—Modeling Approach*, Addison-Wesley, Reading, Mass., 1990.

Kreyzig, E.: *Advanced Engineering Mathematics*, Wiley, New York, 1988.

Marcus, D. A.: *Differential Equations—An Introduction*, W. C. Brown, Dubuque, Iowa, 1991.

Ross, S. L.: *Introduction to Ordinary Differential Equations*, Wiley, New York, 1989.

CHAPTER 7

MATRICES
AND
COMPLEX
VARIABLES

MATRICES

A matrix is an array of numbers arranged in rows and columns. An $m \times n$ matrix is one with m rows and n columns. If $m = 1$ $(n > 1)$, then the matrix is a *row* matrix; if $n = 1$ $(m > 1)$, it is a *column* matrix. A column (or row) matrix is also called a *vector* and its elements are referenced by a single subscript. The elements of a general matrix $(n > 1$ and $m > 1)$ have two subscripts. A *square* matrix is one in which $n = m$.

Note: MathCAD's ORIGIN refers to the subscript value of the first element of a vector or a matrix. By convention, the element in the first row and column of a matrix is referenced by the subscripts $(1, 1)$. However, MathCAD's default value is *zero. Therefore when working with matrices, you should change the* ORIGIN *from zero to one.* Do this by typing **{Esc} SET**. Then choose ORIGIN and set it equal to one. You can also enter ORIGIN≡1 directly into the worksheet. After this change is made, the elements of a matrix **M** will be represented by M_{mn} where the subscripts m and n are positive integers (i.e., $m = 1, 2, ..$ and $n = 1, 2 ..$).

Matrix Algebra

The following rules of algebra apply to matrices:

1. Only matrices with the same $m \times n$ structure can be added or subtracted. The elements of the resulting matrix are obtained by adding or subtracting the corresponding elements of the original matrices. The sum or difference is also an $m \times n$ matrix. Addition and subtraction of matrices **A**, **B**, and **C** obey the associative and commutative laws, that is,

$$(\mathbf{A} + \mathbf{B}) + \mathbf{C} = \mathbf{A} + (\mathbf{B} + \mathbf{C}) = \mathbf{A} + \mathbf{B} + \mathbf{C} = \mathbf{A} + \mathbf{C} + \mathbf{B}$$

2. A matrix **A** may be multiplied by a matrix **B** to form another matrix **C**, which we write as,

$$\mathbf{C} = \mathbf{A} \cdot \mathbf{B}$$

provided that the number of columns in **A** matches the number of rows in **B**. The matrix **C** has the same number of rows as in **A** and columns as in **B**. The elements of **C** are determined by the rule:

$$C_{ij} = \sum_k A_{ik} \cdot B_{kj}$$

3. Matrix multiplication obeys the associative and distributive laws but *not* the commutative law. Thus we have:

$$\mathbf{A} \cdot (\mathbf{B} \cdot \mathbf{C}) = (\mathbf{A} \cdot \mathbf{B}) \cdot \mathbf{C}$$

and

$$\mathbf{A} \cdot (\mathbf{B} + \mathbf{C}) = \mathbf{A} \cdot \mathbf{B} + \mathbf{A} \cdot \mathbf{C}$$

but

$$\mathbf{A} \cdot \mathbf{B} \neq \mathbf{B} \cdot \mathbf{A}$$

The parentheses in the triple product above are therefore unnecessary.

4. A matrix **A** can be multiplied by a number b. The result is a matrix with the same structure as **A** but with each element multiplied by b.

5. The transpose of a matrix **A** is written $\mathbf{A}^T$. Its elements are obtained by interchanging rows and columns. If **A** is an $m \times n$ matrix, then $\mathbf{A}^T$ is an $n \times m$ matrix.

6. The matrix generated by *augmenting* two matrices is formed by placing the matrices side-by-side. It is written:

$$\mathbf{C} = \text{augment}(\mathbf{A}, \mathbf{B})$$

The matrices **A** and **B** must have the same number of rows.

Items 7–11 apply only to square matrices (i.e., $n = m$):

7. The main diagonal of a matrix runs from the upper left to the lower right corner. The *trace* of a matrix **A** is the sum of the elements on the main diagonal and is written tr(**A**).

8. The *determinant* of a matrix **A** is defined as the determinant of its elements and is written det(**A**) or |**A**|.

9. The *identity* or *unit* matrix is a square matrix with ones down the main diagonal and zeros elsewhere. It is commonly denoted by **E**, **I** or **1**.

10. The *Kronecker delta* δ_{ij} is equal to one when $i = j$ and equal to zero when $i \neq j$. The elements of the identity matrix defined above can be represented by the Kronecker delta.

11. The *inverse* of a matrix, written $\mathbf{A}^{-1}$, is the matrix which when multiplied with **A** gives the identity matrix or,

$$\mathbf{A}^{-1} \cdot \mathbf{A} = \mathbf{I}$$

If |**A**| = 0, then $\mathbf{A}^{-1}$ does *not* exist. A matrix whose determinant is zero (and thus has no inverse) is called *singular*.

The *Levi-Civita density* ϵ_{ijk} is often used in matrix algebra. It is defined as follows:

$$\epsilon_{ijk} = 1 \qquad \text{for } i, j, k \text{ different and an even permutation of 123}$$

$$= 1 \qquad \text{for } i, j, k \text{ different and an odd permutation of 123}$$

$$= 0 \qquad \text{for any two (or all three) of } i, j, k \text{ equal}$$

where $i, j, k = 1 ..3$. For example $\epsilon_{123} = +1$, $\epsilon_{312} = +1$, $\epsilon_{132} = -1$, $\epsilon_{112} = 0$. The Levi-Civita density is known in mathematical physics as an *antisymmetric tensor of the third rank*. It is also called the *permutation symbol*, the *alternating tensor*, or the *isotropic tensor*. Since its elements are triply subscripted, it cannot be displayed as a matrix.

Assigning an $m \times n$ Matrix A

Type **A:{<Alt>M}**. A message line prompt will appear as follows:

no file	Array size (rows columns):	9	10	auto

in version 2.0, and

Array size (rows columns):	9	10	auto

in version 2.5. Enter the matrix row and column parameters with **m n** (separated by a space) and type **{Enter}**. When the matrix template appears, fill in the placeholders. You may use the arrow keys to position the cursor within the matrix. You may also use **{Tab}** to move sequentially forward through the placeholders or **{<Shift>Tab}** to move backward. Typical matrix templates look like:

Inserting and Deleting Rows or Columns in an Existing Matrix A

Place the cursor on a reference matrix element. This element defines the row and column where you want the insertion or deletion to take effect. Type **{<Alt>M}** and the message line will indicate Insert/delete (+/-) rows cols:. Type two numbers **m n** separated by a space. The first number represents the number of rows and the second the number of columns to be inserted or deleted. Entering positive numbers inserts rows and/or columns; entering negative numbers deletes them. Insertion occurs *below* the reference row and to the *right* of the reference column. Deletion occurs *below* (and includes) the reference row. Similarly, deletion occurs to the *right* of (and includes) the reference column. If you want to alter only rows, you may type a single digit. If you want to alter only columns, you must enter a zero for the rows (e.g., 0 2).

Addition and Subtraction

Addition and subtraction of matrices are performed using the usual keystrokes: **+** and **-**. Since matrix addition and subtraction obey the associative and commutative laws, parentheses are unnecessary. You *cannot* add or subtract matrices of *different* sizes. If you try, MathCAD will give an array size mismatch error.

Multiplication

The dot symbol (type *****) is used to multiply matrices. (You *cannot* divide matrices.) When multiplying two matrices, the one on the left must have the same number of *columns* as the one on the right has *rows*. If you violate this rule, MathCAD will give an array size mismatch error.[1] Multiplication of three matrices obeys the associative law and so parentheses are unnecessary.

Matrix multiplication is not commutative, that is, $\mathbf{A} \cdot \mathbf{B} \neq \mathbf{B} \cdot \mathbf{A}$. The commuted (reversed) product of two matrices may not even exist. For example if $\mathbf{A}$ is a 3×3 matrix and $\mathbf{B}$ is a 3×2 matrix, the product $\mathbf{A} \cdot \mathbf{B}$ exists and is 3×2 matrix. However,

---

[1] The one exception to this rule is the multiplication of two column matrices of the same length, e.g., $\mathbf{a} \cdot \mathbf{b}$. Clearly the first matrix has only one column while the second has more than one row. MathCAD assumes that this operation will represent the *dot* product of the two vectors and generates a scalar. The scalar is the sum of the products of the corresponding components.

since **B** has 2 columns and **A** has 3 rows, the commuted product **B** · **A** does not exist. On the other hand, if **A** is a 2 × 3 matrix and **B** is a 3 × 2 matrix, then the product **A** · **B** exists and is a 2 × 2 matrix. The commuted product **B** · **A** also exists, but is a 3 × 3 matrix so that **A** · **B** ≠ **B** · **A**. Product commutation is possible only for square matrices of the same size.

Using matrix multiplication, we can *define* an operation in which a square matrix is raised to a positive integer power. The definition is,

$$\mathbf{C}^n \equiv \mathbf{C} \cdot \mathbf{C} \cdot \mathbf{C} \ldots \qquad (n \text{ times})$$

We may therefore construct a matrix *polynomial* using,

$$\mathbf{C} = a \cdot \mathbf{A}^2 + b \cdot \mathbf{B}^3$$

where a and b are scalars.

MathCAD supports matrix polynomial forms; however it does *not* support other forms such as transcendental matrix functions. You *cannot* compute sin(**A**), where **A** is a matrix, with MathCAD. However, MathCAD does allow the elements of a matrix to be functions. For example, you can make the assignment,

$$A(\theta) = \begin{bmatrix} \cos(\theta) & -\sin(\theta) & 0 \\ \sin(\theta) & \cos(\theta) & 0 \\ 0 & 0 & 1 \end{bmatrix}$$

The Transpose of a Matrix

Consider the following 3 × 3 matrix **A**,

$$\mathbf{A} = \begin{bmatrix} 2 & 2 & 3 \\ 1 & 4 & 2 \\ 1 & -1 & 3 \end{bmatrix}$$

To create the transpose of this matrix, which is written $\mathbf{A}^T$, type **A{<Alt>!}**. For example, if we type **D:A{<Alt>!}** and **B=**, we see:

$$\mathbf{B} := \mathbf{A}^T \qquad \mathbf{B} = \begin{bmatrix} 2 & 1 & 1 \\ 2 & 4 & -1 \\ 3 & 2 & 3 \end{bmatrix}$$

Note that the *transpose* of **A** is obtained by interchanging the rows and columns of **A**.

Augmenting Matrices

Two matrices **A** and **B** may be augmented (linked) to form a single matrix by using MathCAD's **augment** function. To augment the above matrices, type: **C:augment(A,B)** and **C=** and see:

$$\mathbf{C} := \text{augment}(\mathbf{A}, \mathbf{B}) \qquad \mathbf{C} = \begin{bmatrix} 2 & 2 & 3 & 2 & 1 & 1 \\ 1 & 4 & 2 & 2 & 4 & -1 \\ 1 & -1 & 3 & 3 & 2 & 3 \end{bmatrix}$$

If the matrices being augmented do not have the same number of rows, MathCAD gives an `array size mismatch` error. Note that the order of the matrices in the augmentation process *is* important.

The Trace and Determinant of a Square Matrix

The trace of a square matrix is the sum of the elements along the main diagonal. We generate it using MathCAD's **tr** function. The determinant of a square matrix is the determinant of its elements and is obtained using MathCAD's absolute value operation ¦. For the matrix **A** above, we type **A=**, **tr(A)=**, and ¦**A=** and see:

$$A = \begin{bmatrix} 2 & 2 & 3 \\ 1 & 4 & 2 \\ 1 & -1 & 3 \end{bmatrix} \qquad \mathrm{tr}(A) = 9 \qquad |A| = 11$$

The Identity Matrix and the Kronecker Delta

The identity or unit matrix is a square matrix with ones down the main diagonal and zeros elsewhere. To create the identity matrix of size $n \times n$, use MathCAD's **identity(n)** function. The Kronecker delta δ_{ij} is equal to one when $i = j$ and equal to zero when $i \neq j$. It is generated using the Greek letter δ (**{<Alt>D}**) as $\delta(i,j)$. (If you are using the Kronecker delta, do not use the Greek letter δ for any other purpose in the worksheet!)

Below we show two ways of creating the 3×3 identity matrix:

```
ORIGIN≡1

A := identity(3)      A =  ⎡1 0 0⎤        (matrix method)
                           ⎢0 1 0⎥
                           ⎣0 0 1⎦

i := 1 ..3    j := 1 ..3
B_i,j := δ(i,j)
                      B =  ⎡1 0 0⎤        (subscript method)
                           ⎢0 1 0⎥
                           ⎣0 0 1⎦
```

To assign the elements of **B**, type: **B[(i,j):{<Alt>D}(i,j)**.

The Inverse of a Square Matrix

The inverse of a matrix **A**, if it exists (i.e., $|A| \neq 0$), is written A^{-1}. It satisfies the equation: $A^{-1} \cdot A = A \cdot A^{-1} = I$ where **I** is the identity matrix. To display the inverse of **A** with MathCAD, simply add the exponent -1 after the matrix by typing **A^-1=**. If the inverse does not exist, MathCAD gives a `singularity` error. The following objects illustrate the inverse:

$$A := \begin{bmatrix} 1 & -1 & 2 \\ 1 & 1 & 2 \\ 2 & 3 & 3 \end{bmatrix} \qquad B := A^{-1} \qquad B = \begin{bmatrix} 1.5 & -4.5 & 2 \\ -0.5 & 0.5 & 0 \\ -0.5 & 2.5 & -1 \end{bmatrix}$$

$$|A| = -2 \qquad B \cdot A = \begin{bmatrix} 1 & 0 & 0 \\ 0 & 1 & 0 \\ 0 & 0 & 1 \end{bmatrix} \qquad A \cdot B = \begin{bmatrix} 1 & 0 & 0 \\ 0 & 1 & 0 \\ 0 & 0 & 1 \end{bmatrix}$$

Extracting a Column (Vector) from a Matrix

If we are given any $m \times n$ matrix A and wish to extract the kth column, we use the *matrix superscript* operation by typing: **A{<Alt>^}k**, where $1 \le k \le n$. The keystroke **{<Alt>^}** generates the matrix superscript. The following objects illustrate column extraction:

ORIGIN≡1

$$A := \begin{bmatrix} 1 & -1 & 2 \\ 1 & 1 & 2 \\ 2 & 3 & 3 \end{bmatrix} \qquad B := A^{<2>} \qquad B = \begin{bmatrix} -1 \\ 1 \\ 3 \end{bmatrix}$$

The vector B is derived by extracting the second column of the matrix A.

The Levi-Civita Density

The Levi-Civita density is generated using MathCAD's Greek letter ϵ (**{<Alt>E}**) as $\epsilon(i,j,k)$. Although the Levi-Civita density is actually a *triply* subscripted variable and written mathematically as ϵ_{ijk}, it is treated by MathCAD as a function. MathCAD does not support variables with more than two subscripts. The three integer arguments are restricted to $1 \le i,j,k \le 3$. The following objects illustrate an application of the Levi-Civita density to the vector cross product:

ORIGIN ≡ 1

$$a := \begin{bmatrix} 2 \\ 3 \\ 4 \end{bmatrix} \qquad b := \begin{bmatrix} 1 \\ 3 \\ 2 \end{bmatrix} \qquad c := a \times b \qquad c = \begin{bmatrix} -6 \\ 0 \\ 3 \end{bmatrix}$$

$$i := 1 \, ..3 \qquad j := 1 \, ..3 \qquad k := 1 \, ..3$$

$$d_i := \sum_j \sum_k \epsilon(i,j,k) \cdot a_j \cdot b_k \qquad d = \begin{bmatrix} -6 \\ 0 \\ 3 \end{bmatrix}$$

The first row computes the cross product of two vectors (column matrices) in the conventional way. The computation is then repeated in a more sophisticated way using ϵ_{ijk}. Note: With ORIGIN≡1, the arguments of $\epsilon(i,j,k)$ can only be $1, 2$ or 3. If you violate this rule or if you forget to change MathCAD's subscript ORIGIN to one, you will get a domain error.

In Worksheet 7.1, we examine the fundamental properties of matrices.

MathCAD solution: Worksheet 7.1. The subscript origin has been changed from zero to one. [Enter ORIGIN≡1 into the worksheet or use the **{<Esc>} SET** command.]

Assigned Matrices and Scalars   ORIGIN ≡ 1

$$A := \begin{bmatrix} 2 & 2 \\ 1 & 1 \\ 3 & 3 \end{bmatrix} \quad B := \begin{bmatrix} 1 & 3 & 2 \\ 2 & 1 & 3 \end{bmatrix} \quad C := \begin{bmatrix} 1 & 3 & 2 \\ 3 & 4 & 5 \\ 2 & 3 & 2 \end{bmatrix} \quad D := \begin{bmatrix} 1 & 4 & 2 \\ 2 & 3 & 1 \\ 3 & 3 & 4 \end{bmatrix} \quad E := \begin{bmatrix} 1 \\ 2 \\ 3 \end{bmatrix}$$

Addition and Subtraction   a := 2   b := 3

$$C + D = \begin{bmatrix} 2 & 7 & 4 \\ 5 & 7 & 6 \\ 5 & 6 & 6 \end{bmatrix} \qquad C - D = \begin{bmatrix} 0 & -1 & 0 \\ 1 & 1 & 4 \\ -1 & 0 & -2 \end{bmatrix} \qquad A + B = \blacklozenge$$

> array size mismatch

Multiplication

$$A \cdot B = \begin{bmatrix} 6 & 8 & 10 \\ 3 & 4 & 5 \\ 9 & 12 & 15 \end{bmatrix} \qquad B \cdot C = \begin{bmatrix} 14 & 21 & 21 \\ 11 & 19 & 15 \end{bmatrix} \qquad A \cdot C = \blacklozenge$$

> array size mismatch

Associative Law for Mutiplication

$$B \cdot (C \cdot D) = \begin{bmatrix} 119 & 182 & 133 \\ 94 & 146 & 101 \end{bmatrix} \qquad\qquad B \cdot C \cdot D = \begin{bmatrix} 119 & 182 & 133 \\ 94 & 146 & 101 \end{bmatrix}$$

$$(B \cdot C) \cdot D = \begin{bmatrix} 119 & 182 & 133 \\ 94 & 146 & 101 \end{bmatrix}$$

Commuted Products

$$A \cdot B = \begin{bmatrix} 6 & 8 & 10 \\ 3 & 4 & 5 \\ 9 & 12 & 15 \end{bmatrix} \quad B \cdot A = \begin{bmatrix} 11 & 11 \\ 14 & 14 \end{bmatrix} \quad C \cdot D = \begin{bmatrix} 13 & 19 & 13 \\ 26 & 39 & 30 \\ 14 & 23 & 15 \end{bmatrix} \quad D \cdot C = \begin{bmatrix} 17 & 25 & 26 \\ 13 & 21 & 21 \\ 20 & 33 & 29 \end{bmatrix}$$

Matrix Polynomials

$$C^2 = \begin{bmatrix} 14 & 21 & 21 \\ 25 & 40 & 36 \\ 15 & 24 & 23 \end{bmatrix} \qquad D^3 = \begin{bmatrix} 101 & 168 & 108 \\ 84 & 137 & 86 \\ 162 & 258 & 175 \end{bmatrix} \qquad a \cdot C^2 + b \cdot D^3 = \begin{bmatrix} 331 & 546 & 366 \\ 302 & 491 & 330 \\ 516 & 822 & 571 \end{bmatrix}$$

Augmenting Matrices

$$\mathrm{augment}(A, C) = \begin{bmatrix} 2 & 2 & 1 & 3 & 2 \\ 1 & 1 & 3 & 4 & 5 \\ 3 & 3 & 2 & 3 & 2 \end{bmatrix} \qquad\qquad \mathrm{augment}(A, B) = \blacklozenge\ \blacklozenge$$

> array size mismatch

WORKSHEET 7.1
Fundamentals of matrices (*cont. below*).

We assign four matrices and two scalars. We next display addition and subtraction and demonstrate that **A** + **B** is an invalid operation. We continue with multiplication and illustrate the associative law. Note that **A** · **C** cannot be computed. We verify that matrix multiplication is not necessarily commutative even for square matrices.

We then demonstrate how MathCAD computes a matrix polynomial. The augmenting of matrices is shown. Note that two matrices with different numbers of rows cannot be augmented. The transpose, trace, and determinant of a matrix are then computed. Note that the trace and determinant apply only to square matrices. Note also that a matrix and its transpose have the same trace and determinant.

Transpose of a Matrix

$A^T = \begin{vmatrix} 2 & 1 & 3 \\ 2 & 1 & 3 \end{vmatrix}$ $B^T = \begin{vmatrix} 1 & 2 \\ 3 & 1 \\ 2 & 3 \end{vmatrix}$ $C^T = \begin{vmatrix} 1 & 3 & 2 \\ 3 & 4 & 3 \\ 2 & 5 & 2 \end{vmatrix}$ $D^T = \begin{vmatrix} 1 & 2 & 3 \\ 4 & 3 & 3 \\ 2 & 1 & 4 \end{vmatrix}$ $E^T = (1 \quad 2 \quad 3)$

Trace and Determinant of Square Matrices

$\text{tr}(C) = 7$ $\text{tr}(D) = 8$ $|C| = 7$ $|D| = -17$ $|C^T| = 7$ $\text{tr}(C^T) = 7$

$\text{tr}(A) = \blacklozenge$ $|A| = \blacklozenge$ $|D^T| = -17$ $\text{tr}(D^T) = 8$

| must be square | | must be square |

Inverse of a Square Matrix

$C^{-1} = \begin{vmatrix} -1 & 0 & 1 \\ 0.571 & -0.286 & 0.143 \\ 0.143 & 0.429 & -0.714 \end{vmatrix}$ $D^{-1} = \begin{vmatrix} -0.529 & 0.588 & 0.118 \\ 0.294 & 0.118 & -0.176 \\ 0.176 & -0.529 & 0.294 \end{vmatrix}$

Confirmation of Inverse

$C^{-1} \cdot C = \begin{vmatrix} 1 & 0 & 0 \\ 0 & 1 & 0 \\ 0 & 0 & 1 \end{vmatrix}$ $C \cdot C^{-1} = \begin{vmatrix} 1 & 0 & 0 \\ 0 & 1 & 0 \\ 0 & 0 & 1 \end{vmatrix}$ $D^{-1} \cdot D = \begin{vmatrix} 1 & 0 & 0 \\ 0 & 1 & 0 \\ 0 & 0 & 1 \end{vmatrix}$ $\begin{vmatrix} C^{-1} \end{vmatrix} = 0.143$

$\begin{vmatrix} D^{-1} \end{vmatrix} = -0.059$

Kronecker Delta

$j := 1 ..3$ $i := 1$ $\delta(i,j)$ $i := 2$ $\delta(i,j)$ $i := 3$ $\delta(i,j)$

1		0		0
0		1		0
0		0		1

$i := 1 ..3$

$I_{i,j} := \delta(i,j)$ $I = \begin{vmatrix} 1 & 0 & 0 \\ 0 & 1 & 0 \\ 0 & 0 & 1 \end{vmatrix}$ $\text{identity}(3) = \begin{vmatrix} 1 & 0 & 0 \\ 0 & 1 & 0 \\ 0 & 0 & 1 \end{vmatrix}$

Levi-Civita Density

$i := 1 ..3$ $j := 1 ..3$ $k := 1 ..3$

$u := \begin{vmatrix} 2 \\ 3 \\ 4 \end{vmatrix}$ $v := \begin{vmatrix} 1 \\ 3 \\ 2 \end{vmatrix}$ $u \times v = \begin{vmatrix} -6 \\ 0 \\ 3 \end{vmatrix}$ $d := \displaystyle\sum_i \sum_j \sum_k \varepsilon(i,j,k) \cdot u_j \cdot v_k$ $d = \begin{vmatrix} -6 \\ 0 \\ 3 \end{vmatrix}$

WORKSHEET 7.1
(*cont.*)

We next compute the inverse of each of the square matrices and confirm that a matrix multiplied by its inverse gives the identity matrix. Note that the determinant of a matrix is equal to the reciprocal of the determinant of its inverse.

We complete the worksheet by displaying some properties of the Kronecker delta and the Levi-Civita density. Recall that the vector cross product is generated using the {**<Alt>***} key.

Change the elements of the matrix **C** to:

$$C = \begin{bmatrix} 1 & 3 & 2 \\ 3 & 4 & 6 \\ 2 & 3 & 4 \end{bmatrix}$$

What does MathCAD give for the inverse C^{-1}? For the determinant $|C|$?

Solving Linear Equations with Matrices

Matrix methods are often used in solving a set of simultaneous linear algebraic equations. Consider the following system of linear equations:

$$a_{11} \cdot x + a_{12} \cdot y + a_{13} \cdot z = b_1$$

$$a_{21} \cdot x + a_{22} \cdot y + a_{23} \cdot z = b_2$$

$$a_{31} \cdot x + a_{32} \cdot y + a_{33} \cdot z = b_3$$

The 12 constants (nine a's and three b's) are all known; x, y, and z represent the unknowns. To solve for the unknowns using matrices, we write the equation set as:

$$\begin{bmatrix} a_{11} & a_{12} & a_{13} \\ a_{21} & a_{22} & a_{23} \\ a_{31} & a_{32} & a_{33} \end{bmatrix} \cdot \begin{bmatrix} x \\ y \\ z \end{bmatrix} = \begin{bmatrix} b_1 \\ b_2 \\ b_3 \end{bmatrix}$$

or symbolically as,

$$\mathbf{A} \cdot \mathbf{r} = \mathbf{b}$$

The components of the vector $\mathbf{r}$ represent the unknowns x, y, and z.

To solve the problem, we compute the inverse $\mathbf{A}^{-1}$ and write the solution as,

$$\mathbf{r} = \mathbf{A}^{-1} \cdot \mathbf{b}$$

If the matrix is singular, the inverse cannot be constructed and a unique solution does not exist. Computing the inverse of a matrix with pencil and paper is tedious; with MathCAD the inversion process is simple and quick.

In engineering applications, the constants and unknowns of a linear system of equations may be complex numbers. We demonstrate this by applying the above matrix procedure to a two-loop ac circuit (see Fig. 7.1). Each branch has an impedance (Z) consisting of an inductor (L), a capacitor (C), and a resistor (R) in series. Each branch also has an ac generator. All the generators have the same frequency (ω) and phase ($\phi = 0$) but different peak voltages (E). The impedance of each branch is represented by a complex phasor. For example, the first branch has:

$$Z1 = R1 + j \cdot \left(\omega \cdot L1 - \frac{1}{\omega \cdot C1} \right)$$

and

$$E1(t) = E1 \cdot \cos(\omega \cdot t)$$

Using Kirchoff rules (see the solution of the DC circuit in Chapter 5), we find that the unknown branch currents satisfy the following system of linear equations,

$$Z1 \cdot I_1 + Z2 \cdot I_2 + 0 = E1 - E2$$

$$0 + Z2 \cdot I_2 + Z3 \cdot I_3 = E3 - E2$$

$$I_1 - I_2 + I_3 = 0$$

which can be written in matrix form as,

$$\begin{bmatrix} Z1 & Z2 & 0 \\ 0 & Z2 & Z3 \\ 1 & -1 & 1 \end{bmatrix} \cdot \begin{bmatrix} I_1 \\ I_2 \\ I_3 \end{bmatrix} = \begin{bmatrix} E1 & - & E2 \\ E3 & - & E2 \\ & 0 & \end{bmatrix}$$

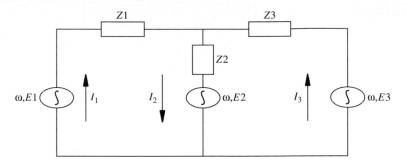

FIGURE 7.1

or

$$A \cdot I = b$$

The solution is written as,

$$I = A^{-1} \cdot b$$

The three components of the column matrix I represent the unknown branch currents I_1, I_2, and I_3. Each current is a complex number whose modulus (absolute value) is the magnitude of the current $|I|$ and whose argument is the phase ϕ. For example, the solution for the first branch current is written as,

$$I_1(t) = |I_1| \cdot \cos(\omega \cdot t + \phi_1)$$

The solution to the circuit in Fig. 7.1 is given in Worksheet 7.2.

> **MathCAD solution: Worksheet 7.2.** The subscript origin has been set to one. Complex numbers will be displayed using the imaginary unit j by invoking the **<Esc> FORM** command and setting im=j. The amplitudes and the frequency of the generators are assigned. The impedance function $Z(R, L, C)$ is defined. Using the values of the circuit elements, each branch impedance phasor is computed and then displayed. The magnitude and phase of each complex current are also displayed. MathCAD's **arg** function extracts the phase from a complex number. [Setting C1=∞ ({**<Alt>I**}) and L3=0 gives each a zero impedance and effectively removes them from the circuit.[2]]
>
> The (square) **A**-matrix and the (column) **b**-matrix, corresponding to the linear system of equations, are assigned. The inverse is computed and the (column) **I**-matrix found. The individual branch currents are given by the components of **I**. Each is displayed in complex form. The magnitude and phase of each current are also displayed.
> The actual branch currents are given by:
>
> $$I(t) = Re(I \cdot e^{j \cdot \omega \cdot t})$$

---

[2]Infinity should be used with care. Since it is MathCAD's largest number (i.e., 10^{307}), $3 \cdot \infty$, or ∞^2 will give an *overflow* error. Similarly $1/\infty$ will give an *underflow* error. In problems that do not normally deal with very large or very small numbers, we can reduce the value of infinity by redefining it. For example, we can reassign $\infty \equiv 10^{100}$ in the worksheet. If the zero tolerance has been set to zt=15, then $1/\infty$ will display as zero.

```
Generator Parameters                              ORIGIN ≡ 1
--------------------
          Amplitudes              Driving Frequency  and Voltage Form
          ----------             -----------------------------------
E1 := 6      E2 := 1    E3 := 2    ω := .1   E(t) := cos(ω·t)

Define Impedance Phasor Function
--------------------------------
                        1                                        π
Z(R,L,C) := R + │ω·L - ─── │·j                        deg ≡  ───
                │      ω·C │                                    180

Fix Circuit Parameters and compute impedances
---------------------------------------------
R1 := 3     L1 := 1    C1 := ∞          Z1 := Z(R1,L1,C1)

R2 := 1     L2 := 4    C2 := 3          Z2 := Z(R2,L2,C2)

R3 := 2     L3 := 0    C3 := 8          Z3 := Z(R3,L3,C3)

Display Branch Impedance Phasors
--------------------------------
Z1 = 3 + 0.1j            Z2 = 1 - 2.933j            Z3 = 2 - 1.25j

│Z1│ = 3.002            │Z2│ = 3.099            │Z3│ = 2.358

arg(Z1) = 1.909·deg     arg(Z2) = -71.175·deg     arg(Z3) = -32.005·deg


Find Branch Currents:
---------------------
                       ┌Z1  Z2   0 ┐        ┌3 + 0.1j  1 - 2.933j          0 ┐
   A-Matrix:"   A :=   │ 0  Z2  Z3 │   A =   │     0    1 - 2.933j  2 - 1.25j │
   ---------           │ 1  -1   1 │        │     1        -1             1 │
                       └           ┘        └                               ┘
                       ┌E1 - E2┐            ┌5┐
   b-Matrix:    b :=   │E3 - E2│      b =   │1│
   ---------           │   0   │            │0│
                       └       ┘            └ ┘
                             -1                ┌ 1.05 + 0.303j┐
Solution Matrix:   I := A  ·b         I =     │ 0.505 + 0.469j│
---------------                               │-0.544 + 0.166j│
                                              └               ┘
```

WORKSHEET 7.2
Matrix methods for AC circuit loop analysis (*cont. below*).

Each current is plotted over two cycles. The form of a generator $(\cos(\omega \cdot t))$ is plotted (using dots) for referencing the phases of the currents.

Change the original circuit values (the E's, R's, C's and L's) or the frequency of the system (ω) and observe the effect on the branch currents.

The Eigenvalue Problem

Consider the following system of linear equations:

$$\mathbf{A} \cdot \mathbf{r} = \lambda \cdot \mathbf{r}$$

$$\begin{bmatrix} a_{11} & a_{12} & a_{13} \\ a_{21} & a_{22} & a_{23} \\ a_{31} & a_{32} & a_{33} \end{bmatrix} \cdot \begin{bmatrix} x \\ y \\ z \end{bmatrix} = \lambda \cdot \begin{bmatrix} x \\ y \\ z \end{bmatrix}$$

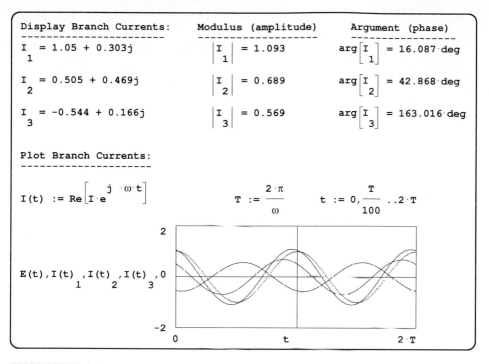

```
Display Branch Currents:        Modulus (amplitude)        Argument (phase)
------------------------        -------------------        ----------------
I  = 1.05 + 0.303j              |I | = 1.093              arg⎡I ⎤ = 16.087·deg
 1                                | 1|                        ⎣ 1⎦

I  = 0.505 + 0.469j             |I | = 0.689              arg⎡I ⎤ = 42.868·deg
 2                                | 2|                        ⎣ 2⎦

I  = -0.544 + 0.166j            |I | = 0.569              arg⎡I ⎤ = 163.016·deg
 3                                | 3|                        ⎣ 3⎦


Plot Branch Currents:
---------------------

                 ⎡   j ·ω·t⎤                2·π                  T
I(t) := Re⎢I·e      ⎥          T := ───          t := 0,─── ..2·T
                 ⎣         ⎦                 ω                  100
```

WORKSHEET 7.2
(*cont.*)

where λ is a constant. By transposing the right-hand side to the left, we obtain:

$$\begin{bmatrix} a_{11} - \lambda & a_{12} & a_{13} \\ a_{21} & a_{22} - \lambda & a_{23} \\ a_{31} & a_{32} & a_{33} - \lambda \end{bmatrix} \cdot \begin{bmatrix} x \\ y \\ z \end{bmatrix} = 0$$

This equation set is called *homogeneous* because every term in the set contains one of the unknowns x, y, or z. Since we have three equations and three unknowns, we might expect that a solution always exists. Note that the *trivial* solution $x = 0$, $y = 0$, and $z = 0$ always exists. However, a nontrivial solution exists if and only if the following determinant vanishes:

$$\begin{vmatrix} a_{11} - \lambda & a_{12} & a_{13} \\ a_{21} & a_{22} - \lambda & a_{23} \\ a_{31} & a_{32} & a_{33} - \lambda \end{vmatrix} = 0$$

or

$$D(\lambda) = |\mathbf{A} - \lambda\mathbf{E}| = 0$$

where $\mathbf{E}$ is the identity matrix. This determinant is called the *characteristic* or *secular* determinant of the homogeneous equation set. The left-hand side of the equation $D(\lambda)$ is actually a third-degree polynomial of the variable λ, called the *characteristic* or *secular* polynomial. The equation is therefore an algebraic equation (called the *characteristic* or *secular* equation) to be solved for the unknown parameter λ.

For a system of n equations, the characteristic equation is an nth-degree algebraic equation.

For the above equation set, the characteristic equation is a cubic equation. Let us assume, for the moment, that it has three distinct real roots λ_1, λ_2, and λ_3. Then, only for these values does a nontrivial solution to the original set of equations exist. When we substitute λ_1 back into the set, we find one solution x_1, y_1, and z_1. We get the other two solutions by substituting λ_2 and λ_3. The three scalars λ_1, λ_2, and λ_3 are called the *eigenvalues* of the matrix $\mathbf{A}$. The vectors (x_1, y_1, z_1), (x_2, y_2, z_2) and (x_3, y_3, z_3) are the corresponding *eigenvectors*.

The solution to the equation set can now be written:

$$
\begin{bmatrix} a_{11} & a_{12} & a_{13} \\ a_{21} & a_{22} & a_{23} \\ a_{31} & a_{32} & a_{33} \end{bmatrix} \cdot \begin{bmatrix} x_i \\ y_i \\ z_i \end{bmatrix} = \lambda_i \cdot \begin{bmatrix} x_i \\ y_i \\ z_i \end{bmatrix}
$$

or in matrix form,

$$
\mathbf{A} \cdot \mathbf{r}_i = \lambda_i \cdot \mathbf{r}_i \qquad (i = 1..3)
$$

It should be pointed out that the components of the eigenvectors are not completely fixed by this eigenvalue equation. We can still require that each of the eigenvectors be *normalized*, that is, each be of unit length, or,

$$
[x_i^2 + y_i^2 + z_i^2]^{\frac{1}{2}} = |\mathbf{r}_i| = 1 \qquad (i = 1..3).
$$

Definition. A matrix which is equal to its own transpose (i.e., $\mathbf{A}^T = \mathbf{A}$) is called *symmetric*. Interchanging the rows and columns of a symmetric matrix leaves it unchanged.

Theorem 7.1. The eigenvalues (and eigenvectors) of a real, symmetric matrix are real.

Definition. If the eigenvalues of a matrix are distinct (i.e., no two are equal), then the matrix is called *nondegenerate*; otherwise it is *degenerate*.

Theorem 7.2. The eigenvectors of a real, symmetric, nondegenerate matrix are mutually orthogonal (perpendicular), that is, the dot product (see Chapter 3) of any two different vectors gives $\mathbf{r}_i \cdot \mathbf{r}_j = 0$ $(i \neq j)$. If they have also been normalized (i.e, $\mathbf{r}_i \cdot \mathbf{r}_i = 1$), we may write $\mathbf{r}_i \cdot \mathbf{r}_j = \delta_{ij}$.

In Worksheet 7.3, we illustrate how to compute the eigenvalues and eigenvectors of a real, symmetric, nondegenerate 3×3 matrix. We also demonstrate the above two theorems.

MathCAD solution: Worksheet 7.3. The subscript origin has been set to one. We assign a *real, symmetric* matrix $\mathbf{A}$ whose eigenvalues we seek. The identity matrix $\mathbf{E}$ and the characteristic polynomial $D(\lambda)$ are defined. We use λ_i to represent the eigenvalues which are to be determined from the roots of the characteristic equation $D(\lambda) = 0$.

MathCAD's **root** function is used to find these roots. We assign the original characteristic polynomial to a new variable DD (λ). The first root is found to be

ORIGIN ≡ 1

Define matrix A, unit matrix E, and Characteristic Polynomial, D(λ):

$$A := \begin{bmatrix} 2 & 1 & 2 \\ 1 & 5 & 1 \\ 2 & 1 & 3 \end{bmatrix} \qquad E := identity(3) \qquad D(\lambda) := |A - \lambda \cdot E|$$

Find eigenvalues from roots of Characteristic Eqn: TOL ≡ .0001

Left most start for root search -> λ := -100   Eigenvalues

$DD(\lambda) := D(\lambda)$ $\lambda_1 := root(DD(\lambda), \lambda)$ $\lambda_1 = 0.431$

$DD(\lambda) := \dfrac{D(\lambda)}{\lambda - \lambda_1}$ $\lambda_2 := root(DD(\lambda), \lambda)$ $\lambda_2 = 3.364$

$DD(\lambda) := \dfrac{DD(\lambda)}{\lambda - \lambda_2}$ $\lambda_3 := root(DD(\lambda), \lambda)$ $\lambda_3 = 6.204$

Plot Characteristic Polynomial:

$\lambda_\alpha := \lambda_1 - .2 \qquad \lambda_\beta := \lambda_3 + .2$

$\lambda := \lambda_\alpha, \lambda_\alpha + .1 .. \lambda_\beta$ Eigenvalues
                                                                          ----

	Eigenvalues
10	$\lambda_1 = 0.431$
$D(\lambda), 0$	$\lambda_2 = 3.364$
-10	$\lambda_3 = 6.204$
0.23115 λ 6.33115	

WORKSHEET 7.3
Finding the eigenvalues and eigenvectors of a real, symmetric, nondegenerate 3 × 3 matrix (*cont. below*).

λ_1=0.431. We next reduce the degree of the cubic polynomial to a quadratic by dividing it by $(\lambda - \lambda_1)$. The two roots of the resulting quadratic, DD(λ) =DD(λ) / $(\lambda - \lambda_1)$, contain the remaining two roots of the characteristic equation. One root is found to be λ_2=3.362. The process is repeated to reduce the quadratic to a linear function by dividing it by $(\lambda - \lambda_2)$. The remaining root is found to be λ_3=6.204. Note that all three roots are real as required by Theorem 7.1. The characteristic polynomial is plotted showing the roots. Because the eigenvalues are distinct, the matrix **A** is called nondegenerate.

To obtain the corresponding eigenvectors, we use the following method. The characteristic equation can be written, in terms of its roots, as $(\lambda - \lambda_1) \cdot (\lambda - \lambda_2) \cdot (\lambda - \lambda_3) = 0$. It can be verified that the matrix **A** also satisfies this equation, or,

$$(A - \lambda_1 \cdot E) \cdot (A - \lambda_2 \cdot E) \cdot (A - \lambda_3 \cdot E) = 0$$

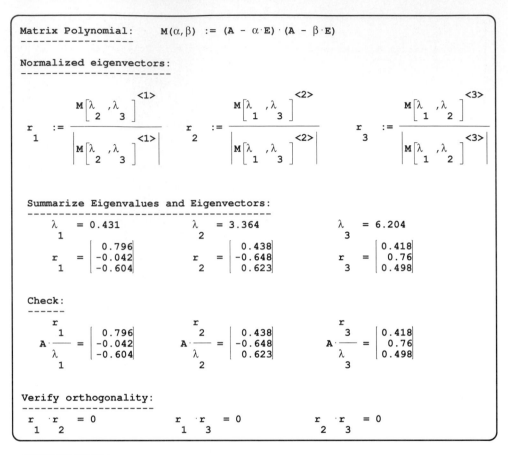

WORKSHEET 7.3
(*cont.*)

This can be written as,

$$(\mathbf{A} - \lambda_1 \cdot \mathbf{E}) \cdot \mathbf{M}(\lambda_2, \lambda_3) = 0$$

where

$$\mathbf{M}(\lambda_2, \lambda_3) = (\mathbf{A} - \lambda_2 \cdot \mathbf{E}) \cdot (\mathbf{A} - \lambda_3 \cdot \mathbf{E})$$

By examining the matrix relation above, it follows that *any* column of the matrix $\mathbf{M}(\lambda_2, \lambda_3)$ could be an eigenvector of the matrix $\mathbf{A}$ corresponding to the eigenvalue λ_1. The other two eigenvectors are generated by permuting the indices.

Following this approach, we define a quadratic matrix function $\mathbf{M}(\alpha, \beta)$. The first normalized eigenvector $\mathbf{r}_1$ is constructed from $\mathbf{M}(\lambda_2, \lambda_3)$ by extracting the first column. We do this using the matrix superscript operation $\mathbf{M}(\alpha, \beta)^{<1>}$. We type: **M({<Alt>A},{<Alt>B}){<Alt>^}1**. The first eigenvector is therefore written as,

$$\mathbf{r}_1 = \frac{\mathbf{M}(\lambda_2, \lambda_3)^{<1>}}{|\mathbf{M}(\lambda_2, \lambda_3)^{<1>}|}$$

where the denominator serves to normalize the eigenvector, that is, make it of unit length. By permuting the indices, the remaining eigenvectors are constructed.

We check the results by observing that the eigenvalues and eigenvectors do indeed satisfy the original matrix eigenvalue equation $\mathbf{A} \cdot \mathbf{r}_i = \lambda_i \cdot \mathbf{r}_i$. If the test fails on any one of the eigenvectors, then try extracting a different column. For example, if $\mathbf{r}_1$ fails the test, then try extracting the *second* column of the matrix, i.e., $\mathbf{r}_1 = \mathbf{M}(\lambda_2, \lambda_3)^{<2>}$. Finally, we verify Theorem II by confirming that the eigenvectors are mutually orthogonal.

Change the elements of the matrix but maintain its symmetry. Note that the eigenvalues remain real. Note also that if the matrix is nondegenerate, the eigenvectors remain mutually orthogonal. Next make the matrix nonsymmetric and use as an initial guess for the roots $\lambda = 100 + 100j$. The roots may now be complex.

Change the original symmetric matrix so that $a_{12}=j$ and $a_{21}=-j$. This complex matrix is not symmetric but has the property $\mathbf{A} = \mathbf{A}^{T*}$, where the asterisk means take the complex conjugate. Such a matrix is called *self-adjoint* or *Hermitian*. Note the eigenvalues. Like a real, symmetric matrix, the eigenvalues of a Hermitian matrix must be real.

The Eigenvalue Problem and Coupled Vibrations

Consider a mass (m) suspended from the ceiling by a spring (k). Suppose that a second mass (M) is suspended from the first by second spring (K) (see Fig. 7.2). The upper mass (1) is displaced downward an amount y_{1_0} while the lower mass (2) is displaced downward an amount y_{2_0}. Both masses are released with respective velocities v_{1_0} and v_{2_0}. We seek the equations of motion for the two masses $y_1(t)$ and $y_2(t)$. We take the downward direction as positive.

Applying Newton's law ($\mathbf{F} = m \cdot \mathbf{a}$) to each mass, we obtain the following differential equations,

$$m \cdot y_1'' = -k \cdot y_1 + K \cdot (y_2 - y_1)$$

$$M \cdot y_2'' = -K \cdot (y_2 - y_1)$$

After some algebra this can be simplified to,

$$y_1'' = a_{11} \cdot y_1 + a_{12} \cdot y_2$$

$$y_2'' = a_{21} \cdot y_1 + a_{22} \cdot y_2$$

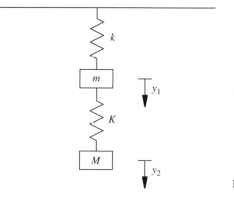

FIGURE 7.2

where

$$a_{11} = -\frac{(k+K)}{m} \qquad a_{12} = \frac{K}{m}$$

$$a_{21} = \frac{K}{M} \qquad a_{22} = -\frac{K}{M}$$

These equations form a set of *coupled*, linear, homogeneous, second-order, differential equations with constant coefficients. We assume that the solution for the motion of the masses has the oscillatory form:

$$y_1(t) = A \cdot e^{j \cdot \omega \cdot t} \qquad y_2(t) = B \cdot e^{j \cdot \omega \cdot t}$$

where the frequency (ω) and the amplitudes (A and B) are to be determined. If we substitute these solutions back into the differential equation set, we obtain the *algebraic* equation set,

$$-\omega^2 \cdot A = a_{11} \cdot A + a_{12} \cdot B$$

$$-\omega^2 \cdot B = a_{21} \cdot A + a_{22} \cdot B$$

which can be written in matrix form as,

$$\mathbf{a} \cdot \mathbf{r} = \lambda \cdot \mathbf{r}$$

where,

$$\lambda = -\omega^2 \qquad \text{and} \qquad r = \begin{bmatrix} A \\ B \end{bmatrix}$$

This two-dimensional, matrix eigenvalue equation has two eigenvalues and two eigen-vectors. Consequently there are only two frequencies for which the masses can oscillate in simple harmonic motion. These so-called *eigenfrequencies* (or natural frequencies) are related to the eigenvalues by:

$$\omega_1 = \sqrt{-\lambda_1} \qquad \text{and} \qquad \omega_2 = \sqrt{-\lambda_2}$$

We state without proof that the eigenvalues λ_1 and λ_2 are real and *negative* for all values of m, M, k, and K. Thus the frequencies are always real quantities. For each frequency there is an eigenvector given by:

$$r_1 = \begin{bmatrix} A_1 \\ B_1 \end{bmatrix} \qquad \text{and} \qquad r_2 = \begin{bmatrix} A_2 \\ B_2 \end{bmatrix}$$

The two linearly independent solutions (natural modes) to our original problem are,

Mode 1:

$$y_1(t) = A_1 \cdot e^{\pm j \cdot \omega_1 \cdot t}$$

$$y_2(t) = B_1 \cdot e^{\pm j \cdot \omega_1 \cdot t}$$

Mode 2:

$$y_1(t) = A_2 \cdot e^{\pm j \cdot \omega_2 \cdot t}$$

$$y_2(t) = B_2 \cdot e^{\pm j \cdot \omega_2 \cdot t}$$

The general solution to our problem is constructed from a mixture of the natural modes and can be written in real form as,

$$y_1(t) = A_1 \cdot [\alpha_1 \cdot \cos(\omega_1 \cdot t) + \beta_1 \cdot \sin(\omega_1 \cdot t)] + A_2 \cdot [\alpha_2 \cdot \cos(\omega_2 \cdot t) + \beta_2 \cdot \sin(\omega_2 \cdot t)]$$

$$y_2(t) = B_1 \cdot [\alpha_1 \cdot \cos(\omega_1 \cdot t) + \beta_1 \cdot \sin(\omega_1 \cdot t)] + B_2 \cdot [\alpha_2 \cdot \cos(\omega_2 \cdot t) + \beta_2 \cdot \sin(\omega_2 \cdot t)]$$

The arbitrary constants α_1, β_1, α_2, and β_2 are determined from the initial conditions, $y_1(0) = y_{1_0}$, $y_2(0) = y_{2_0}$, $y_1'(0) = v_{1_0}$, and $y_2'(0) = v_{2_0}$, using:

$$\alpha_1 = \frac{B_2 \cdot y_{1_0} - A_2 \cdot y_{2_0}}{A_1 \cdot B_2 - A_2 \cdot B_1}$$

$$\alpha_2 = \frac{B_1 \cdot y_{1_0} - A_1 \cdot y_{2_0}}{B_1 \cdot A_2 - A_1 \cdot B_2}$$

and

$$\beta_1 = \frac{B_2 \cdot v_{1_0} - A_2 \cdot v_{2_0}}{\omega_1 \cdot (A_1 \cdot B_2 - A_2 \cdot B_1)}$$

$$\beta_2 = \frac{B_1 \cdot v_{1_0} - A_1 \cdot v_{2_0}}{\omega_2 \cdot (B_1 \cdot A_2 - A_1 \cdot B_2)}$$

Summary. To solve the coupled mass problem:

1. Set up the differential equations in the form,

$$y_1'' = a_{11} \cdot y_1 + a_{12} \cdot y_2$$

$$y_2'' = a_{21} \cdot y1 + a_{22} \cdot y_2$$

2. Find the eigenvalues λ_1 and λ_2 and the corresponding eigenvectors $\mathbf{r}_1$ and $\mathbf{r}_2$. From these, compute the frequencies $\omega_1 = \sqrt{-\lambda_1}$ and $\omega_2 = \sqrt{\lambda_2}$ and the amplitudes A_1, B_1, A_2, and B_2,

3. Compute the initial value constants α_1, α_2, β_1, and β_2 from the initial conditions.

4. Construct the solutions for $y_1(y)$ and $y_2(t)$.

We illustrate the solution to the above problem in Worksheet 7.4.

MathCAD solution: Worksheet 7.4. Note: This worksheet extends beyond the two-page limit of the student edition of MathCAD. If you are using this edition, the last objects will not appear in the worksheet when you load it. Delete the expository text (use {**F3**}) and "repack" the worksheet deleting blank lines (use {**<Ctrl>F10**}). When the worksheet has been tightly packed, the remaining objects will appear at the bottom.

We assign the masses and spring constants and construct both the **a**-matrix and the identity matrix **E**. Applying the techniques of Worksheet 7.3, we determine the eigenvalues and eigenvectors from which we derive ω_1, ω_2, A_1, A_2, B_1, and B_2. We next choose initial conditions for the masses and compute the initial value constants α_1, α_2, β_1, and β_2. We construct the solutions $y_1(t)$ and $y_2(t)$. Using MathCAD's derivative

Equation set: $y_1'' = -[(k+K)/m]\, y_1 + [K/m]\, y_2$ ORIGIN $\equiv 1$

$y_2'' = [K/M]\, y_1 + [-K/M]\, y_2$

Masses and Spring Constants

---

m := 1   k := 3   M := 1   K := 2

Construct A matrix and Identity Matrix

$a_{1,1} := -\left[\dfrac{k+K}{m}\right]$ $a_{1,2} := \dfrac{K}{m}$ $a_{2,1} := \dfrac{K}{M}$ $a_{2,2} := \dfrac{-K}{M}$ E := identity(2)

Display Matrices:

$a = \begin{vmatrix} -5 & 2 \\ 2 & -2 \end{vmatrix}$ $E = \begin{vmatrix} 1 & 0 \\ 0 & 1 \end{vmatrix}$

Find Roots (Eigenvalues) of Characteristic Polynomial

Characteristic Polynomial: $D(x) := |a - x \cdot E|$ Guess: x := -100

First Root: $DD(x) := D(x)$ $\lambda_1 := \text{root}(DD(x), x)$ $\lambda_1 = -6$

Second Root: $DD(x) := \dfrac{D(x)}{x - \lambda_1}$ $\lambda_2 := \text{root}(DD(x), x)$ $\lambda_2 = -1$

Eigenfrequencies:

$\omega_1 := \sqrt{-\lambda_1}$ $\omega_1 = 2.449$ $\omega_2 := \sqrt{-\lambda_2}$ $\omega_2 = 1$

WORKSHEET 7.4
The eigenvalue problem and coupled vibrations (*cont. below*).

operation, we obtain the velocity functions $v_1(t)$ and $v_2(t)$. The results are plotted using a solid line for $y_1(t)$ and dots for $y_2(t)$. The initial conditions are verified.

Note that although we are dealing with masses and springs, the motions of the coupled system are *not* simple harmonic. The motions appear to be quite irregular. Actually they are superpositions of the two natural modes of the system. For the masses to vibrate in only one of these modes, we must choose special initial conditions. For example, try the following initial conditions,

$$y_{1_0} = 1, \quad y_{2_0} = \frac{B_2}{A_2}, \quad v_{1_0} = 0, \quad \text{and} \quad v_{2_0} = 0$$

Since the only nonzero arbitrary constant is α_2, both masses move in simple harmonic motion in mode 2 at a frequency ω_2. If we set,

$$y_{1_0} = 1, \quad y_{2_0} = \frac{B_1}{A_1}, \quad v_{1_0} = 0, \quad \text{and} \quad v_{2_0} = 0$$

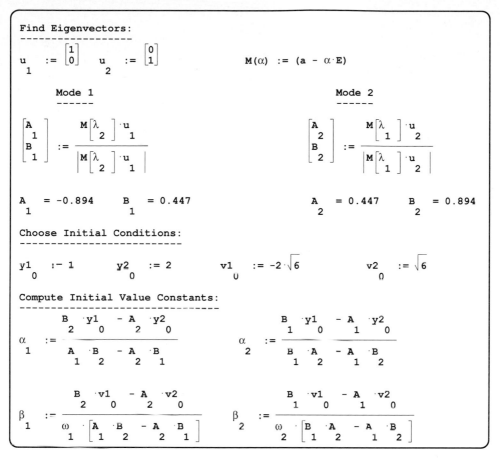

```
Find Eigenvectors:
------------------
        ⎡1⎤              ⎡0⎤
u    := ⎢0⎥      u   := ⎢1⎥          M(α)  := (a - α·E)
 1      ⎣ ⎦       2     ⎣ ⎦
 1               2

        Mode 1                              Mode 2
        ------                              ------

⎡A ⎤      M⎡λ ⎤ ·u                 ⎡A ⎤      M⎡λ ⎤ ·u
⎢ 1⎥       ⎣ 2⎦  1                 ⎢ 2⎥       ⎣ 1⎦  2
⎢B ⎥  := ───────────              ⎢B ⎥  := ───────────
⎣ 1⎦     |M⎡λ ⎤ ·u |              ⎣ 2⎦     |M⎡λ ⎤ ·u |
            ⎣ 2⎦  1                          ⎣ 1⎦  2

A   = -0.894    B   = 0.447        A   = 0.447    B   = 0.894
 1               1                  2              2
```

Choose Initial Conditions:

$$y1_0 := -1 \qquad y2_0 := 2 \qquad v1_0 := -2\sqrt{6} \qquad v2_0 := \sqrt{6}$$

Compute Initial Value Constants:

$$\alpha_1 := \frac{B_2 \cdot y1_0 - A_2 \cdot y2_0}{A_1 \cdot B_2 - A_2 \cdot B_1} \qquad \alpha_2 := \frac{B_1 \cdot y1_0 - A_1 \cdot y2_0}{B_1 \cdot A_2 - A_1 \cdot B_2}$$

$$\beta_1 := \frac{B_2 \cdot v1_0 - A_2 \cdot v2_0}{\omega_1 \cdot \left[A_1 \cdot B_2 - A_2 \cdot B_1\right]} \qquad \beta_2 := \frac{B_1 \cdot v1_0 - A_1 \cdot v2_0}{\omega_2 \cdot \left[B_1 \cdot A_2 - A_1 \cdot B_2\right]}$$

WORKSHEET 7 4
(*cont. below*)

we observe only mode 1 and both masses exhibit simple harmonic motion at a frequency ω_1. Note also that in the "low frequency" mode 2, the masses vibrate harmonically *in phase* whereas in the "high frequency" mode 1, they vibrate *out of phase*.

COMPLEX VARIABLES

A complex number z can be written in terms of two real variables x and y as:

$$z = x + i \cdot y$$

where x and y represent the real and imaginary parts of z respectively. To plot a given point, we require a two-dimensional space containing an x-axis and a y-axis, called the *z-plane*. Every complex number is represented by a *point* in this plane.

A function of a complex variable $w(z)$ produces a new complex number for every value of z. This number can be written as;

$$w = u(x, y) + i \cdot v(x, y)$$

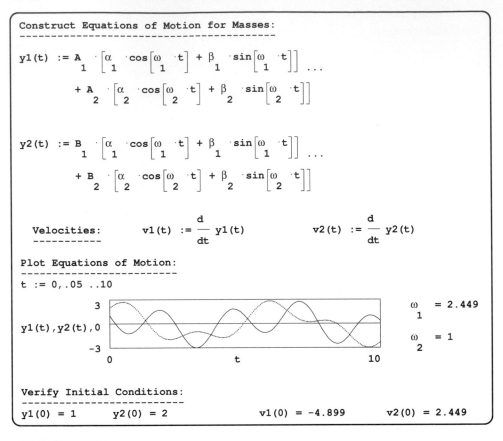

WORKSHEET 7.4
(*cont.*)

where $u(x, y)$ and $v(x, y)$ are the real and imaginary parts of w respectively. For example, consider the function $w = z^2$. This function may be simplified as,

$$w = z^2 = (x + i \cdot y)^2 = (x + i \cdot y) \cdot (x + i \cdot y) = (x^2 - y^2) + i \cdot (2 \cdot x \cdot y),$$

from which it follows that,

$$u(x, y) = x^2 - y^2 \qquad \text{and} \qquad v(x, y) = 2 \cdot x \cdot y$$

For a point in the z-plane $z = z_i(x = x_i, y = y_i)$, the function produces a corresponding point $w_i(u_i = u(x_i, y_i), v_i = v(x_i, y_i))$ in the *w-plane*. Thus a complex function $w(z)$ can be represented by a *pair* of real functions $u(x, y)$ and $v(x, y)$. The function is said to "map" a set of points in the z-plane into another set of points in the *w*-plane.

If a complex function is defined and differentiable in a domain, it is said to be *analytic* there. A necessary condition for a function to be analytic is that it obey the Cauchy-Riemann equations:

$$\frac{\partial u}{\partial x} = \frac{\partial v}{\partial y} \quad \text{and} \quad \frac{\partial u}{\partial y} = \frac{-\partial v}{\partial x}$$

or

$$u_x = v_y \quad \text{and} \quad u_y = -v_x$$

The function $w = z^2$ is analytic. Its real and imaginary parts are given by,

$$u(x, y) = x^2 - y^2 \quad \text{and} \quad v(x, y) = 2 \cdot x \cdot y$$

with derivatives,

$$u_x = 2 \cdot x, \qquad u_y = -2 \cdot y \quad \text{and} \quad v_x = 2 \cdot y, \qquad v_y = 2 \cdot x$$

Since $u_x = v_y$ and $u_y = -v_x$ the Cauchy-Riemann equations are satisfied.

In Worksheet 7.5, we illustrate how an analytic function maps points. We also verify that an analytic function satisfies the Cauchy-Riemann equations.

```
Define Complex Variable, z:            Choose Complex Function, w(z):
---------------------------            -----------------------------
z(x,y) := x + i ·y                                          2
                                       w(x,y) := z(x,y)


Assign Real (u) and Imaginary (v) Parts of w:
---------------------------------------------------
u(x,y) := Re(w(x,y))                   v(x,y) := Im(w(x,y))


Take First Partials of u(x,y) amd v(x,y):
-----------------------------------------
          d                                      d
u  (x,y) := ── u(x,y)          u  (x,y) := ── u(x,y)
 x          dx                  y          dy

          d                                      d
v  (x,y) := ── v(x,y)          v  (x,y) := ── v(x,y)
 x          dx                  y          dy

Compute Cauchy-Riemann Difference Functions:
--------------------------------------------
F(x,y) := u  (x,y) - v  (x,y)      G(x,y) := u  (x,y) + v  (x,y)
           x          y                      y          x

Evaluate Variables at Fixed Points
----------------------------------
i := 1 ..5

Entered Points:                Computed Values of u and v:
---------------                ---------------------------
x :=    y :=          u   := u⎡x ,y ⎤      u        v   := v⎡x ,y ⎤      v
 i       i             i     ⎣ i  i⎦        i        i      ⎣ i  i⎦        i
```

x_i	y_i		u_i			v_i
1	2		-3			4
2	3		-5			12
3	4		-7			24
4	5		-9			40
5	6		-11			60

WORKSHEET 7.5
Analytic functions—the Cauchy-Riemann equations (*cont. below*).

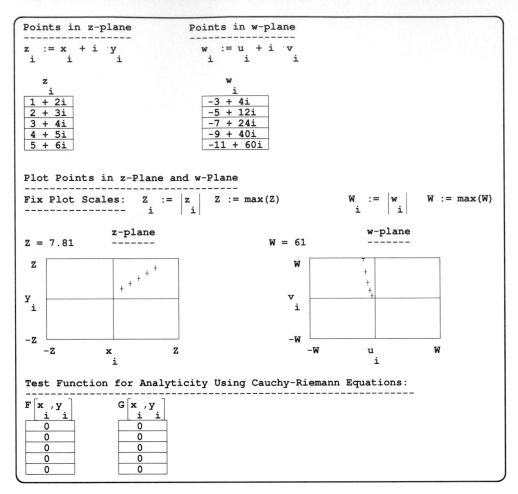

WORKSHEET 7.5
(*cont.*)

MathCAD solution: Worksheet 7.5. We assign the complex variable z and the complex function $w(z) = z^2$. We assign the functions $u(x,y)$ and $v(x,y)$ and then construct the four partial derivatives. The functions

$$F(x,y) = u_x(x,y) - v_y(x,y)$$

and

$$G(x,y) = u_y(x,y) + v_x(x,y)$$

test the validity of the Cauchy-Riemann equations. If they vanish, the Cauchy-Riemann equations are satisfied.

We examine five arbitrary points in the z-plane and plot them using type=p. The tabular entry is made for x_i and y_i separately. The functions $u(x,y)$ and $v(x,y)$ are evaluated at these points and plotted in the w-plane. The maximum modulus of the points in the z-plane (Z) and in the w-plane (W) are determined. These are used to manually set the scale for the plots. Finally, we verify that the function obeys the Cauchy-Riemann equations at all five points.

Check if the following functions are analytic: $w(z) = \sin(z)$, $w(z) = e^{-z}$, and $w(z) = \cosh(z)$. Is the function $w(z) = |z|$ analytic?

Conformal Mapping

Consider a collection of complex numbers whose points form a continuous contour in the z-plane. As was shown earlier, a function $w(z)$ maps these points into a set of points in the w-plane. Thus the function maps a contour in the z-plane into one in the w-plane. If the mapping function is analytic, the mapping will be *conformal*. A conformal mapping is one which preserves angles between intersecting contours. For example, suppose the contours C_1 and C_2 intersect at an angle ϕ_0 at some point z_0 in the z-plane. The angle of intersection of the contours at the corresponding point w_0 in the w-plane is also ϕ_0. We illustrate conformal mapping in Worksheet 7.6.

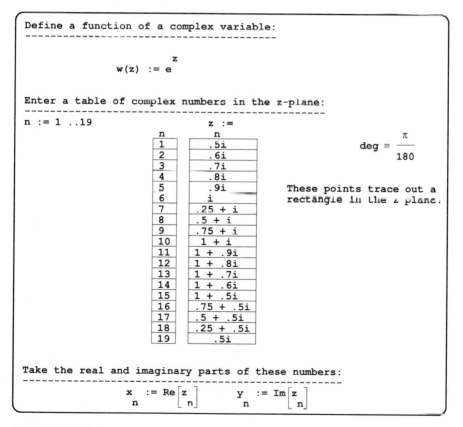

```
Define a function of a complex variable:
----------------------------------------------

                    z
        w(z) := e


Enter a table of complex numbers in the z-plane:
----------------------------------------------------
n := 1 ..19                      z :=
            n           n                        π
            1          .5i            deg ≡ ─────
            2          .6i                     180
            3          .7i
            4          .8i
            5          .9i          These points trace out a
            6           i           rectangle in the z plane.
            7        .25 + i
            8         .5 + i
            9        .75 + i
           10         1 + i
           11        1 + .9i
           12        1 + .8i
           13        1 + .7i
           14        1 + .6i
           15        1 + .5i
           16       .75 + .5i
           17        .5 + .5i
           18       .25 + .5i
           19          .5i


Take the real and imaginary parts of these numbers:
----------------------------------------------------
        x  := Re⎡z ⎤        y  := Im⎡z ⎤
         n       ⎣ n⎦         n       ⎣ n⎦
```

WORKSHEET 7.6
Conformal mapping with an analytic function (*cont. below*).

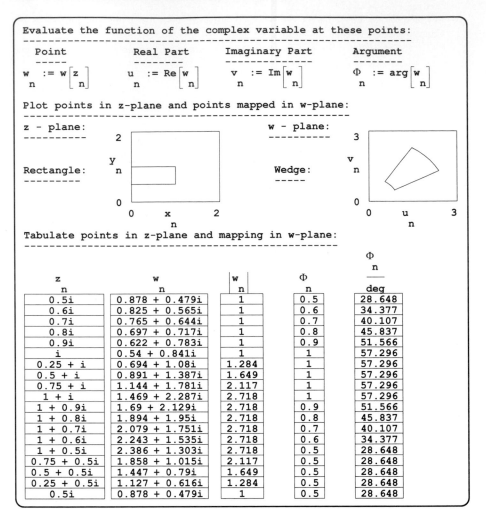

```
Evaluate the function of the complex variable at these points:
-----------------------------------------------------------------
   Point              Real Part        Imaginary Part         Argument
   -----              ---------        --------------         --------
 w   := w⎡z ⎤       u   := Re⎡w ⎤     v   := Im⎡w ⎤      Φ   := arg⎡w ⎤
  n        ⎣ n⎦       n        ⎣ n⎦      n       ⎣ n⎦      n         ⎣ n⎦

Plot points in z-plane and points mapped in w-plane:
-----------------------------------------------------------------
z - plane:                              w - plane:
----------           2                  ----------      3

              y                                     v
Rectangle:    n                         Wedge:      n
---------                               -----

                     0                                  0
                     0     x      2                     0    u     3
                           n                                 n
```

Tabulate points in z-plane and mapping in w-plane:
----

z$_n$	w$_n$	∣w$_n$∣	Φ$_n$	Φ$_n$ / deg
0.5i	0.878 + 0.479i	1	0.5	28.648
0.6i	0.825 + 0.565i	1	0.6	34.377
0.7i	0.765 + 0.644i	1	0.7	40.107
0.8i	0.697 + 0.717i	1	0.8	45.837
0.9i	0.622 + 0.783i	1	0.9	51.566
i	0.54 + 0.841i	1	1	57.296
0.25 + i	0.694 + 1.08i	1.284	1	57.296
0.5 + i	0.891 + 1.387i	1.649	1	57.296
0.75 + i	1.144 + 1.781i	2.117	1	57.296
1 + i	1.469 + 2.287i	2.718	1	57.296
1 + 0.9i	1.69 + 2.129i	2.718	0.9	51.566
1 + 0.8i	1.894 + 1.95i	2.718	0.8	45.837
1 + 0.7i	2.079 + 1.751i	2.718	0.7	40.107
1 + 0.6i	2.243 + 1.535i	2.718	0.6	34.377
1 + 0.5i	2.386 + 1.303i	2.718	0.5	28.648
0.75 + 0.5i	1.858 + 1.015i	2.117	0.5	28.648
0.5 + 0.5i	1.447 + 0.79i	1.649	0.5	28.648
0.25 + 0.5i	1.127 + 0.616i	1.284	0.5	28.648
0.5i	0.878 + 0.479i	1	0.5	28.648

WORKSHEET 7.6
(*cont.*)

MathCAD solution: Worksheet 7.6. We define a function of a complex variable $w(z)$. Using a table, we assign a set of nineteen points in the z-plane z_n. These are entered directly as complex numbers. To assign the complex number table, type **z[n:.5i,.6i,.7i** and so on. Next the real and imaginary components of these points are computed. Using the function $w(z)$, we compute the corresponding points in the w-plane w_n and assign their real and imaginary parts u_n and v_n. The argument (or phase) of each point is also computed.

The points are plotted in the z-plane and in the w-plane. Note that the points in the z-plane form a rectangle. The complex function maps the rectangle into a wedge in the w-plane. In each plot, the scales have been set manually (by filling the placeholders appropriately) so that the horizontal and vertical scales match. Furthermore, the plot sizes have been chosen **size= 7,15** to make them appear approximately square. This is done to minimize distortion of the interior angles in the wedge. The moduli and arguments of the points w_n are displayed in tabular form. Recall that to display the modulus of w_n, use the absolute value operation, and type ¦w[n=.

Observe from the tables that the wedge is bounded by a pair of arcs—the inner one at r= 1 and the outer one at r= e= 2.718.... The wedge is also bounded by two rays—one at θ = 28.6° and the other at θ = 51.6°. The interiors angles of the rectangle in the z-plane are 90°. Note however, that the interior angles of the wedge in the w-plane are also 90°, confirming the conformal nature of the mapping and the analytical property of the mapping function e^z.

Use other analytic functions such as $w(z) = \sin(z)$ and $w(z) = \cos(z)$ to map the rectangle. In each case, manually set the horizontal and vertical scales equal and keep the plot size a square. Make sure the scale used captures the entire mapping. Also try the function $w(z) = |z|$. Is the function analytic? Is the mapping conformal?

Contour Integrals and Residues

A function of a complex variable $f(z)$ may be integrated along a contour in the z-plane. The contour integral is defined as,

$$I = \int_C f(z)dz$$

where C is a symbol representing the contour. The contour can be represented mathematically by expressing the complex variable in parametric form as,

$$z(t) = x(t) + i \cdot y(t)$$

where $x(t)$ and $y(t)$ define the points on the contour in the xy-plane. Using the parametric form, the contour integral can now be written as,

$$I = \int_{t_1}^{t_2} f(z(t))z'(t) \cdot dt$$

where the derivative is,

$$z'(t) = x'(t) + i \cdot y'(t)$$

and t_1 and t_2 are the parameter values corresponding to the end points of the contour. If the contour is closed, we write

$$I = \oint_C f(z)dz$$

or

$$I = \int_{t_1}^{t_2} f(z(t))z'(t) \cdot dt$$

where t_1 and t_2 are the parameter values which *close* the contour.

If a function is analytic everywhere in a domain, then the integral over any closed contour in that domain will be zero. Consider a function $f(z)$ that is analytic everywhere except at points z_1 and z_2. If we integrate this function along any closed contour which *excludes* z_1 and z_2, the result is zero. If the contour encloses either or both of these points, the integral will, in general, *not* be zero. If both are enclosed, then by the Theorem of Residues,[3] the value of the integral I is equal to $2 \cdot \pi \cdot i \cdot (b_1 + b_2)$ where b_1 and b_2 are the *residues* of the function at z_1 and z_2 respectively.

Consider the function:
$$f(z) = \frac{\sin(z)}{[(z - z_1) \cdot (z - z_2)]}$$
This function is analytic everywhere except at $z = z_1$ and $z = z_2$ where it is singular (undefined). In Worksheet 7.7, we evaluate contour integrals using this function and compute its residues at z_1 and z_2.

> **MathCAD solution: Worksheet 7.7.** We assign values to the singular points ($z_1 = 0.7 + 0.7 \cdot i$, and $z_2 = 1.5 + 1.5 \cdot i$) and define the function to be integrated. Next we define a circle in parametric form; the circle has a radius $R = 3$ and is centered at $x0 = 0$, $y0 = 0$. The limits of the parameter t defining the circle are assigned ($t_1 = 0$ and $t_2 = 2 \cdot \pi$). The derivative is defined, the contour integral computed, and the result displayed ($I = 7.726 + 4.352 \cdot i$). Note that the contour encloses *both* singularities.
>
> The contour is plotted in parametric form with $Re(z(t))$ on the x-axis and $Im(z(t))$ on the y-axis. The points z_1 and z_2 are also plotted. We have used TYPE=1xo. The scale is manually set on each axis to range from $-S$ to $+S$ where $S = 3 \cdot R$. The scale factor 3 can be increased if necessary. The plot size parameters should be adjusted to make the contour appear approximately as a circle.
>
> Using the Theorem of Residues, the sum of the (two) residues is computed and displayed as:
> $$b_1 + b_2 = 0.693 - 1.23 \cdot i$$

Try the following:

a. Set R=0.2. You should get a residue of zero since both singularities reside outside the contour.

b. Set R=1.5. This circle encloses only the singularity at $z = z_1$. The residue there is found to be:
$$b_1 = -0.868 + 0.143 \cdot i$$

c. Set R=0.5, x0=1.5, and y0=1.5 and adjust the scale to S=5·R. This circle encloses only the singularity at z=z_2. The residue there is found to be:
$$b_2 = 1.561 - 1.372 \cdot i$$

Note that the sum of the residues in parts (b) and (c) do in fact give the original value.

Cauchy's Integral Formula

Consider the following function,
$$g(z, n) = \frac{f(z)}{[z - z_0]^{n+1}}$$
where $f(z)$ is analytic in some domain, z_0 is any point in that domain, and n is any non-negative integer. The function $g(z, n)$ is analytic everywhere in the domain

---

[3]If the contour encloses N singularities, then by the Theorem of Residues, we have $I = 2 \cdot \pi \cdot i \cdot \sum_{n=1}^{N} b_n$.

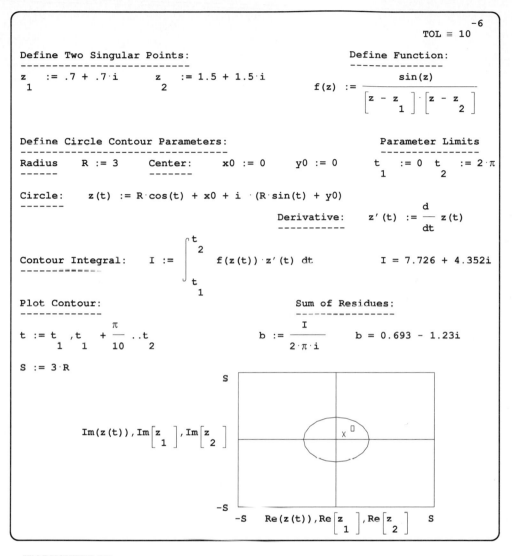

$$\text{TOL} \equiv 10^{-6}$$

Define Two Singular Points:

$z_1 := .7 + .7 \cdot i$ $z_2 := 1.5 + 1.5 \cdot i$

Define Function:

$$f(z) := \frac{\sin(z)}{\left[z - z_1\right] \cdot \left[z - z_2\right]}$$

Define Circle Contour Parameters:

Radius $R := 3$ Center: $x0 := 0$ $y0 := 0$

------   -------

Parameter Limits

$t_1 := 0$ $t_2 := 2 \cdot \pi$

Circle: $z(t) := R \cdot \cos(t) + x0 + i \cdot (R \cdot \sin(t) + y0)$

Derivative: $z'(t) := \dfrac{d}{dt} z(t)$

Contour Integral: $I := \displaystyle\int_{t_1}^{t_2} f(z(t)) \cdot z'(t)\, dt$

$I = 7.726 + 4.352i$

Plot Contour:

$t := t_1, t_1 + \dfrac{\pi}{10} \ .. t_2$

$S := 3 \cdot R$

Sum of Residues:

$b := \dfrac{I}{2 \cdot \pi \cdot i}$ $b = 0.693 - 1.23i$

$$\text{Im}(z(t)), \text{Im}\left[z_1\right], \text{Im}\left[z_2\right]$$

$$\text{Re}(z(t)), \text{Re}\left[z_1\right], \text{Re}\left[z_2\right]$$

WORKSHEET 7.7
Contour integration and residues.

except at the point $z = z_0$ where it is singular. As discussed earlier, the integral of $g(z, n)$ around any closed contour in the domain that encloses the singularity need not be zero. Specifically, Cauchy's formula states that:

$$\frac{n!}{2 \cdot \pi \cdot i} \cdot \oint_C \frac{f(z) \cdot dz}{[z - z_0]^{n+1}} = \frac{d^n f(z)}{dz^n}\bigg]_{z=z_0}$$

where C is any closed contour in the domain that encloses z_0. Cauchy's formula demonstrates the relationship between the closed contour integral of an analytic function and its derivative. For example, if $f(z) = \sin(z)$, Cauchy's formula gives:

$$(n = 0) \qquad \frac{1}{2 \cdot \pi \cdot i} \cdot \oint_C \frac{\sin(z) \cdot dz}{[z - z_0]} = \sin(z_0)$$

$$(n = 1) \qquad \frac{1}{2 \cdot \pi \cdot i} \cdot \oint_C \frac{\sin(z) \cdot dz}{[z - z_0]^2} = \cos(z_0)$$

$$(n = 2) \qquad \frac{2}{2 \cdot \pi \cdot i} \cdot \oint_C \frac{\sin(z) \cdot dz}{[z - z_0]^3} = -\sin(z_0)$$

In Worksheet 7.8, we demonstrate Cauchy's formula.

An arbitrary analytic Function: `f(z) := sin(z)`

An arbitrary point in the z plane: `z` `:= 1 + i`

Define integrand for Cauchy integral: $g(z,n) := \dfrac{f(z)}{\left[z - z_o\right]^{n+1}}$

Define contour which includes z :
----------------------------------●

  Circle Radius: `R := 3`   Parameter Range: `t` $:= 0$ `t` $:= 2 \cdot \pi$

  Contour is circle about origin: `z(t) := R·(cos(t) + i ·sin(t))`

  Derivative of contour function: $z'(t) := \dfrac{d}{dt} z(t)$

Cauchy's Integral Formula: $I(n) := \dfrac{n!}{2 \cdot \pi \cdot i} \cdot \displaystyle\int_{t_1}^{t_2} g(z(t),n) \cdot z'(t)\ dt$

Evaluate first few derivatives:

$f'(z) := \dfrac{d}{dz} f(z)$ $f''(z) := \dfrac{d}{dz} f'(z)$ $f'''(z) := \dfrac{d}{dz} f''(z)$

Compare Results:

$$f\left[z_o\right] = 1.298 + 0.635i$$

`n := 0 ..3`

n	I(n)
0	1.298 + 0.635i
1	0.834 - 0.989i
2	-1.298 - 0.635i
3	-0.834 + 0.989i

$$f'\left[z_o\right] = 0.834 - 0.989i$$

$$f''\left[z_o\right] = -1.298 - 0.635i$$

$$f'''\left[z_o\right] = -0.834 + 0.989i$$

WORKSHEET 7.8
Cauchy's integral formula.

MathCAD solution: Worksheet 7.8. We assign an analytic function ($f(z) = \sin(z)$) and choose an arbitrary point in the z-plane ($z_0 = 1 + i$). The function $g(x, n)$ for Cauchy's formula is constructed and a closed contour (a circle of radius = 3) is assigned in parametric form. It can be seen that the contour encloses z_0. The integral function $I(n)$ is computed using Cauchy's integral formula. The first three derivatives are assigned using MathCAD's derivative operation. Finally the Cauchy integral is displayed in tabular form. The function $f(z)$ and its first three derivatives are evaluated at z_0 and displayed. Note that the integrals and derivatives agree. The computation can be speeded up by using the analytical form for the contour derivative. For a circle centered at the origin, use $z'(t) = R \cdot [-\sin(t) + i \cdot \cos(t)]$.

   Verify Cauchy's formula using circles of different radii. Also try other analytic functions. What happens if the point z_0 in Cauchy's formula is on the contour?

PROBLEMS

1. Consider a coordinate system defined by a set of mutually perpendicular unit vectors $\{\mathbf{i}, \mathbf{j}, \mathbf{k}\}$. Consider also a point (x, y, z) in the system. Suppose that we rotate the coordinate system to one defined by $\{\mathbf{i}', \mathbf{j}', \mathbf{k}'\}$. The same point will now be represented by (x', y', z'). The coordinate values are related by,

$$\begin{bmatrix} x' \\ y' \\ z' \end{bmatrix} = \begin{bmatrix} R_{11} & R_{12} & R_{13} \\ R_{21} & R_{22} & R_{23} \\ R_{31} & R_{32} & R_{33} \end{bmatrix} \begin{bmatrix} x \\ y \\ z \end{bmatrix}$$

or

$$\mathbf{r}' = \mathbf{R} \cdot \mathbf{r}$$

where $\mathbf{R}$ is called the rotation matrix. We can construct this matrix by performing three successive rotations about the coordinate axes. The first is α radians about the original z-axis. The second is β radians about the current x-axis. The third rotation is Γ radians about the final z-axis. The angles α, β, and Γ are called the *Euler* angles. The three rotations are represented by the matrices,

$$\mathbf{R}_1(\alpha) = \begin{bmatrix} \cos(\alpha) & \sin(\alpha) & 0 \\ -\sin(\alpha) & \cos(\alpha) & 0 \\ 0 & 0 & 1 \end{bmatrix} \quad \mathbf{R}_2(\beta) = \begin{bmatrix} 1 & 0 & 0 \\ 0 & \cos(\beta) & \sin(\beta) \\ 0 & -\sin(\beta) & \cos(\beta) \end{bmatrix}$$

$$\mathbf{R}_3(\Gamma) = \begin{bmatrix} \cos(\Gamma) & \sin(\Gamma) & 0 \\ -\sin(\Gamma) & \cos(\Gamma) & 0 \\ 0 & 0 & 1 \end{bmatrix}$$

The overall rotation matrix is $\mathbf{R}(\alpha, \beta, \Gamma) = \mathbf{R}_3(\Gamma) \cdot \mathbf{R}_2(\beta) \cdot \mathbf{R}_1(\alpha)$.

(a) Assign each of the three matrix functions above and construct the overall matrix function $\mathbf{R}(\alpha, \beta, \Gamma)$.

(b) Set $\alpha = 30$ deg, $\beta = 45$ deg, and $\Gamma = 70$ deg and display $\mathbf{R}$ and $\mathbf{R}^{-1}$. Verify the properties $|\mathbf{R}| = 1$ and $\mathbf{R}^T = \mathbf{R}^{-1}$. Show that these properties of $\mathbf{R}$ are independent of the values of the rotation angles.

(c) Let a point have coordinates,

$$\mathbf{r} = \begin{bmatrix} 1 \\ 1 \\ 1 \end{bmatrix}$$

Find the new coordinates $\mathbf{r}'$ in the coordinate system generated by the rotation matrix $\mathbf{R}$ of part (b) and verify that $|\mathbf{r}| = |\mathbf{r}'|$.

2. Given the following system of equations:

$$1 \cdot w - 3 \cdot x + 2 \cdot y + 3 \cdot z = 1$$

$$3 \cdot w - 2 \cdot x - 1 \cdot y + 4 \cdot z = -3$$

$$-2 \cdot w + 1 \cdot x + 3 \cdot y - 3 \cdot z = 2$$

$$4 \cdot w + 5 \cdot x - 4 \cdot y + 1 \cdot z = -1$$

Using matrix methods, solve for w, x, y, and z.

3. Consider the rotation matrix obtained in Problem 1 part(b).
   (a) Find the eigenvalues of the matrix. In particular show that one eigenvalue is real and equal to one and that the other two form a complex conjugate pair of unit modulus. [This is Euler's theorem.]

   Hint: Follow Worksheet 7.3 and set the initial root guess to be $\lambda = -100 + 100i$. Set the complex tolerance ct=3 and use ORIGIN≡ 1 and TOL≡0.0001.
   (b) Find the eigenvector corresponding to the real eigenvalue. This vector represents the effective axis of rotation of the coordinate system.
   (c) Using MathCAD's **arg** function, find the argument ϕ of either of the complex eigenvalues. This angle represents the effective angle of rotation of the coordinate system.

4. A double pendulum is shown in Fig. 7.3. Each pendulum has the same mass $m_1 = m_2 = m$ and the same length $l_1 = l_2 = l$. The masses are displaced by the angles θ_{1_0} and θ_{2_0} and released from rest.

   For small displacements, the relevant differential equations are:

   $$\theta_1'' = -2 \cdot w_0^2 \cdot \theta_1 + w_0^2 \cdot \theta_2$$
   $$\theta_2'' = 2 \cdot w_0^2 \cdot \theta_1 - 2 \cdot w_0^2 \cdot \theta_2$$

where,

$$w_0 = \sqrt{\frac{g}{l}}$$

Note that the values of the masses play no role in the motions.
   (a) Taking $l = 1$ and $g = 9.8$, find the natural frequencies of vibration w_1 and w_2.
   (b) By filling the placeholders accordingly, show that,

   $$w_1 = w_o \cdot [2 + \sqrt{2}]^{1/2} \qquad w_2 = w_o \cdot [2 - \sqrt{2}]^{1/2}$$

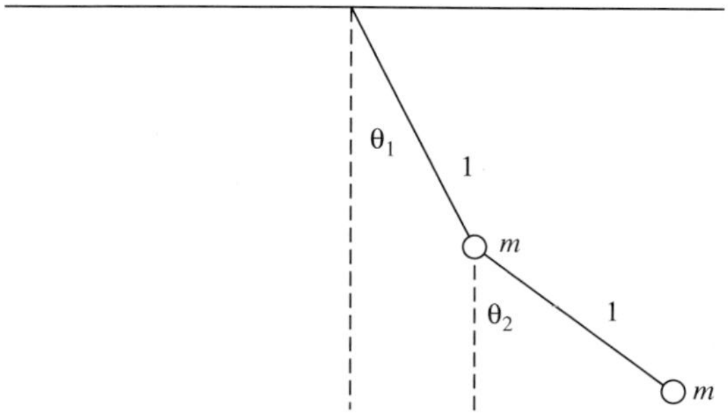

FIGURE 7.3

(c) If $\theta_{1_0} = 0.1$ and $\theta_{2_0} = 0.2$, plot the equations of motion for the masses $\theta_1(t)$ and $\theta_2(t)$.
Hint: Follow Worksheet 7.4.

5. Consider the following function of a complex variable,

$$w(z) = \sin(z).$$

Given the following points in the z-plane:

$$z_1 = 1 + 2i$$
$$z_2 = 2 + 3i$$
$$z_3 = 3 + 4i$$
$$z_4 = 4 + 5i$$
$$z_5 = 5 + 6i$$

(a) Find the corresponding points in the w-plane.
(b) Plot the points in both planes.

6. Show that the function $w = 1/z$ maps the points on a circle of radius 2 in the z-plane into a circle of radius $1/2$ in the w-plane.
Hint: Define the points in the z-plane using:

$$N = 20 \qquad n = 0..N - 1 \qquad \theta_n = 2 \cdot \pi \cdot \frac{n}{N} \qquad z_n = 2 \cdot e^{i \cdot \theta_n}$$

Define $w_n = w(z_n)$ and plot $Im(z_n)$ versus $Re(z_n)$ and $Im(w_n)$ versus $Re(w_n)$.

7. Evaluate the contour integral,

$$I = \oint_C f(z)dz$$

where $f(z) = \tan(z)$ and the contour is the circle $|z| = 2$.
Hint: The circle can be represented in parametric form as $z(t) = 2 \cdot \{\cos(t) + i \cdot \sin(t)\}$ where t goes from $t_1 = 0$ to $t_2 = 2 \cdot \pi$. The derivative is $z'(t) = 2 \cdot \{-\sin(t) + i \cdot \cos(t)\}$.

REFERENCES

Boas, M. L.: *Mathematical Methods in the Physical Sciences*, Wiley, New York, 1966.
Bradbury, T. C.: *Mathematical Methods*, Wiley, New York, 1984.
Chapra, S. C. and R. P. Canale: *Numerical Methods for Engineers*, McGraw-Hill, New York, 1985.
Churchill, R. V.: *Complex Variables and Applications*, McGraw-Hill, New York, 1960.
Kreyzig, E.: *Advanced Engineering Mathematics*, Wiley, New York, 1988.

CHAPTER 8

SPECIAL
TOPICS IN
ENGINEERING

STATISTICAL ANALYSIS AND HISTOGRAMS

Mean Value, Standard Deviation, and Variance of a Data Set

Given a set of N data elements Data_n, it is possible to define the *mean* (or average), the *standard deviation*, and the *variance* of the data set as:

$$\text{Mean} = \sum_{n=1}^{N} \frac{\text{Data}_n}{N}$$

$$\text{Variance} = \sum_{n=1}^{N} \frac{(\text{Data}_n^2 - \text{Mean}^2)}{N}$$

$$\text{Standard deviation} = [\text{Variance}]^{1/2}$$

MathCAD performs these computations with built-in functions. With the subscript ORIGIN set to one, consider the following objects:

n := 1 ..9   ORIGIN ≡ 1

Datan :=

1
3
4
1
2
3
7
2
2

$$\text{Data} = \begin{bmatrix} 1 \\ 3 \\ 4 \\ 1 \\ 2 \\ 3 \\ 7 \\ 2 \\ 2 \end{bmatrix}$$

mean(Data) = 2.778
stdev(Data) = 1.75
var(Data)   = 3.063

The nine data elements (n= 1 ..9) are entered into the table using:

Data[n:1,3,4,1,2,3,7,2,2

The data is displayed as a vector using **Data=**. The mean value of the data, the standard deviation, and the variance are obtained using MathCAD's **mean, stdev,** and **var** functions. To display the values, type:

mean(Data)= ,   **stdev(Data)=** ,   and   **var(Data)=**

These three statistical functions have vectors as arguments and use the data from the vectors to perform their computations. The nine data elements could be entered directly into a vector (without using subscripts). Type **Data:{‹Alt›M}** and set the vector dimensions by typing **9 1**. When the vector template appears, fill the placeholders with the data.

Histograms

Consider a data vector with the following nine elements:

$$\textbf{Data} = \begin{bmatrix} 1 \\ 3 \\ 4 \\ 1 \\ 2 \\ 3 \\ 7 \\ 2 \\ 2 \end{bmatrix}$$

We wish to construct another vector whose elements are to represent the frequencies of occurrence of the integers in the vector **Data** above. The elements of this new vector, which we arbitrarily call **Bin**, define the boundaries of the bins and will be used to classify and tally the number of times each integer appears in the vector **Data**. The elements of the vector **Bin** must be in *ascending* order. For example, to tally the integers in the vector **Data**, we define the vector **Bin** as,

$$\mathbf{Bin} = \begin{bmatrix} 1 \\ 2 \\ 3 \\ 4 \\ 5 \\ 6 \\ 7 \\ 8 \end{bmatrix}$$

The vector **Bin** will tally the data in integer intervals. In this case, the first bin will tally the integers $1 \le n < 2$ (i.e., all the ones) while the second bin will count the integers $2 \le n < 3$ (i.e., all the twos), etc. Notice that the **Bin** vector has *eight* elements but represents only *seven* bins. The last element does not define a new bin, but specifies the upper boundary for the last bin.

To produce the actual frequency vector, we use MathCAD's **hist** function. To apply this function to the above vectors, type **Freq:hist(Bin,Data)** and see,

    Freq := hist(Bin,Data) .

The **hist** function produces a new vector which we arbitrarily call **Freq**. We illustrate the process with the following objects:

$$\text{Data} := \begin{bmatrix} 1 \\ 3 \\ 4 \\ 1 \\ 2 \\ 3 \\ 7 \\ 2 \\ 2 \end{bmatrix} \qquad \text{Bin} := \begin{bmatrix} 1 \\ 2 \\ 3 \\ 4 \\ 5 \\ 6 \\ 7 \\ 8 \end{bmatrix} \qquad \text{Freq} := \text{hist(Bin,Data)} \qquad \text{Freq} = \begin{bmatrix} 2 \\ 3 \\ 2 \\ 1 \\ 0 \\ 0 \\ 1 \end{bmatrix}$$

In essence, the **hist** function produces a *histogram* vector **Freq** derived from the vector **Data** using the classification scheme defined by the vector **Bin**. The vector **Freq** tell us that there are 2 ones, 3 two's, 2 three's, etc. in the vector **Data**.

Note: The elements of the vector used as the first argument of the **hist** function (here called Bin) must be in *ascending* order. Otherwise MathCAD gives a must be increasing error.

To illustrate the statistical features of MathCAD, consider the following problem. A person throws a pair of dice 36 times. Statistically, what is the frequency table for achieving the different allowable totals, that is, totals of two through twelve?

Note that there are thirty-six (6^2) different ways in which two dice (with six faces) can be permuted. The total of the dice on each throw can range from two to twelve. A given total may be obtained with more than one combination of the dice. For a dice total of two, only one combination is possible—one-one. On the other hand, a dice total of three can be obtained with two different dice combinations—one-two and two-one. The probability of occurrence for any given total is given by,

$$\text{Probability(Total)} = \frac{\text{Combinations(Total)}}{36}$$

Thus for every thirty-six throws of the dice, the probability of getting a total of two is $1/36$ and a total of three is $2/36$. More generally, it can be shown that the frequency of occurrence (per 36 throws) is given by the table:

$$\text{Dice Total} = [2\ 3\ 4\ 5\ 6\ 7\ 8\ 9\ 10\ 11\ 12]$$
$$\text{Freq} = [1\ 2\ 3\ 4\ 5\ 6\ 5\ 4\ 3\ 2\ 1]$$

The frequency increases linearly from Freq=1 (for Dice Total=2) to a maximum of Freq=6 (for Dice Total=7). It then decreases linearly back to Freq=1 (for Dice Total=12). Thus the maximum probability is $6/36 = 1/6$ which occurs for a dice total of seven. We present a demonstration of dice statistics in Worksheet 8.1.

MathCAD solution: Worksheet 8.1. This worksheet uses a subscript ORIGIN=1.

We assign the number of dice to be thrown ($M = 2$) and a throw multiplier $T = 1$. For two dice, T determines the number of throws in a session in multiples of thirty-six. Next we use MathCAD's **ceil** and **rnd** functions to simulate the throws of each die. The object ceil(rnd(6)) generates random integers between one and six. We sum the resulting dice totals and assign each total to an element of the vector Data. The number of elements of the vector Data is therefore equal to the number of throws in the session, in this case thirty-six.

Next we use MathCAD's **mean, stdev**, and **var** functions to compute the mean value, standard deviation, and variance of the throw data contained in the vector Data. Note that the average value of the dice totals in this session is 7.139 and the standard deviation is 2.374. This will change somewhat for each session. We graph the vector Data using the plot format type=b. This format uses vertical "bars" to plot the data points. The lower-scale placeholder on the vertical axis has been manually set to zero. The upper-scale placeholder contains max(Data) which is the value of the largest element of the vector Data. Note that the maximum possible dice total in any session is twelve. Note also from the graph, that a twelve is relatively rare and occurs only once in our session (on the eleventh throw).

To establish the frequency histogram, we construct the vector Bin for M dice (M=2). The first bin has a value of BinMin= M (in this case two) and the last a value of BinMax= 6·M (in this case twelve). The number of bins is NumBins= 5·M + 1 (in this case eleven, i.e., two through twelve). The number of elements of the vector Bin must be one larger, namely twelve. The value of the last element is 6·M + 1=13; this establishes the upper boundary of the last bin. Thus the vector Bin has twelve integer elements ranging in value from two to thirteen.

We construct the frequency vector Freq using MathCAD's **hist** function as,

```
Freq := hist(Bin,Data)
```

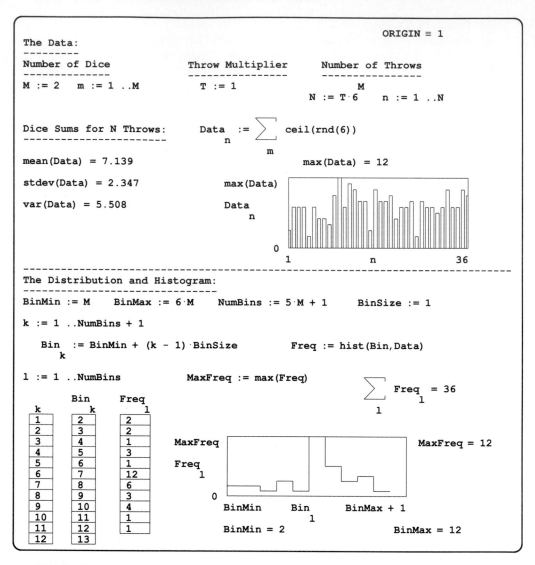

WORKSHEET 8.1
Dice statistics and the histogram.

As a check, we sum the elements of the Freq vector; we get thirty-six as expected. Finally we display the Bin and Freq vectors. The Freq vector shows that for thirty-six throws, a dice total of two occurred twice and a dice total of seven occurred twelve times. The vector Freq is plotted versus the vector Bin in a *histogram* using the format parameter type=s. This format uses "steps" to plot the data points. A horizontal line is drawn from each data point to the one on its immediate right. Note that since there is no point to the right of the last point, no line is drawn.

The above results do not agree with the predictions of the statistical theory. For a session of thirty-six throws, the predicted frequencies for dice totals of two and seven are one and six respectively. Statistical projections are only valid for sessions with very large numbers of throws.

Throw the dice another thirty-six times by typing **{F10}** (menu) **C** (compute) **P** (process). You will see the vector `Freq` change with each session The agreement with theory may or may not improve. Next try changing the throw multiplier to T=10 (360 throws). (This will take longer to compute.) The frequencies predicted by the theory for thirty-six throws should be multiplied by ten for a session of 360 throws. Note that the results in the worksheet are now in closer agreement with the statistical theory.

Reset the throw multiplier to T=1 and change the number of dice to M=3. There are now 216 different dice combinations and sixteen different possible dice totals ranging from three to eighteen. Repeat the trials using **{F10}** (menu) **C** (compute) **P** (process) and see if you can detect a pattern. The statistical theory for a session of 216 throws of three dice is:

Dice Total = [3 4 5 6 7 8 9 10 11 12 13 14 15 16 17 18]
     Freq = [1 3 6 10 15 21 25 27 27 25 21 15 10 6 3 1]

By changing the throw multiplier to T=10, you will be increasing the number of throws in a session to 2160. Using repeated trials, you should be able to detect a definite pattern. Be patient since each trial can take many minutes to compute.

CURVE FITTING AND SPLINES

In experimental science and engineering, laboratory data often consists of two sets of numbers. One set, which we call the **Y** (or dependent) observations, is plotted against the other, the **X** (or independent) observations. For example, X might represent a *cause* and Y an *effect*.

To do curve fitting with MathCAD, we assign the data to the pair of vectors **X** and **Y** each having N (k= 0 ..N-1) elements, where N is the number of data points. For N= 8, the assignment might look like:

$$\mathbf{X} = \begin{bmatrix} 1 \\ 2 \\ 3 \\ 4 \\ 5 \\ 6 \\ 7 \\ 8 \end{bmatrix} \qquad \mathbf{Y} = \begin{bmatrix} 4 \\ 7 \\ 8 \\ 16 \\ 19 \\ 22 \\ 28 \\ 25 \end{bmatrix}$$

We have arbitrarily chosen the 8 data points. Both vectors must have the same number of data elements. Otherwise, when we attempt to use the curve-fitting functions, MathCAD gives an `array size mismatch` error. In all curve fitting work, we use subscript ORIGIN=0. Therefore the subscripts of the eight elements of the **X** and **Y** vectors range from 0 to 7. Note also that except for linear regression analysis, the elements of the *independent* data vector (**X**) *must* be in *ascending* order.

Linear Regression

As shown in Chapter 2, a pair of data vectors can be analyzed using *linear regression*. The objective is to fit the data to a straight line. The line is chosen so that the sum of the squares of the vertical distances from each point to the line is a minimum. This type of curve fit is sometimes called a *least squares fit* or more commonly a linear regression. This is *not* an interpolation method since the resulting straight line does not contain the data points. It is actually used for *extrapolation* purposes to determine the values of Y_i for values of X_i outside the domain of the **X** vector.

MathCAD computes the linear regression curve using the **slope** and **intercept** functions to determine the slope (m) and intercept (b) of the line and the **corr** function to determine the correlation factor (σ, Pearson's r factor). This factor is a measure of how "good" the straight-line fit is. The closer the correlation factor is to ± 1, the better the fit. The syntax is as follows:

```
m := slope(X,Y)     b := intercept(X,Y)     σ := corr(X,Y),
```

where X and Y are the vectors containing the data points. Linear regression analysis will be applied to a data set in Worksheet 8.2.

Note: In all curve fitting work below you *must* use subscript ORIGIN=0.

Linear Interpolation

It is often necessary to interpolate data so that we can estimate y at values of x other than those in the data table. In curve-fitting, we attempt to construct a continuous function $y = y(x)$ which best fits the data points and which can be reliably used for interpolation. The particular form of the curve obtained depends on the assumptions made and the method used.

A simple but limited method is *linear interpolation*. The data points are connected with straight lines to produce a jagged curve. MathCAD performs a linear interpolation with its **linterp** function. The syntax is,

```
y(x) := linterp(X,Y,x)
```

The first argument is the vector that contains the X observations while the second contains the Y observations. The third argument becomes the independent variable of the linear-interpolation function. When plotted, the function y(x) consists of straight-line segments connecting the data points.

Note: The elements of the data vector used as the first argument of the **linterp** function (here called X) must be in *ascending* order. Otherwise MathCAD gives a must be increasing error.

Curve Fitting with Cubic Splines

It is often desirable to construct a smooth curve-fit. Equivalently, the derivative of the curve should exist everywhere. The linear interpolation uses straight-line segments to connect the data points. The derivative of the resulting curve is therefore undefined where the segments connect.

Consider instead connecting each pair of data points by a cubic (third degree) polynomial. A cubic polynomial has four arbitrary constants that determine its position and shape. Four equations are required to determine these constants. Two equations are obtained by requiring that the polynomial segment pass through the two bounding data points. The other two equations are obtained by requiring that the first and second derivatives be continuous at the data points.

To make the spline function unique, we must impose additional conditions at the end points to specify whether the spline function is to behave as a straight line, a parabola, or a cubic polynomial. Regardless of the end-point conditions, the resulting curve is called a *cubic spline*.

MathCAD performs cubic-spline, curve fitting using the following two steps.

Step I. Construct a spline vector using *one* of the following MathCAD functions: **lspline**, **pspline**, or **cspline**. The syntax is:

        Vs := lspline(X,Y)   (for linear end-point conditions)
        Vs := pspline(X,Y)   (for parabolic end-point conditions)
        Vs := cspline(X,Y)   (for cubic end-point conditions)

where X and Y are the vectors containing the data points x_n and y_n respectively. The spline vector, which we arbitrarily call Vs, actually contains the second derivatives of the spline function at the data points.

Note: The elements of the vector used as the first argument of the **lspline**, **pspline**, and **cspline** functions (here called X) must be in *ascending* order. Otherwise MathCAD gives a `domain error` message.

Step II. Compute the spline function using MathCAD's **interp** function. We type **y(x):interp(Vs,X,Y,x)** and see,

        y(x) := interp(Vs,X,Y,x),

where Vs is the spline vector obtained in Step I, X and Y are the data vectors, and x is the independent variable of the spline function (assigned here to y(x)).

We demonstrate curve fitting using both linear interpolation and the method of cubic splines in Worksheet 8.2.

MathCAD solution: Worksheet 8.2. This worksheet uses a subscript ORIGIN=0.

Two data vectors X and Y are assigned. Using MathCAD's **length** function, the number of data elements are extracted. A linear regression is performed using the **slope**, **intercept**, and **corr** functions and the results are used to assign a straight-line function w(x).

A linear interpolation is performed using the **linterp** function and the resulting curve is assigned to the function y(x).

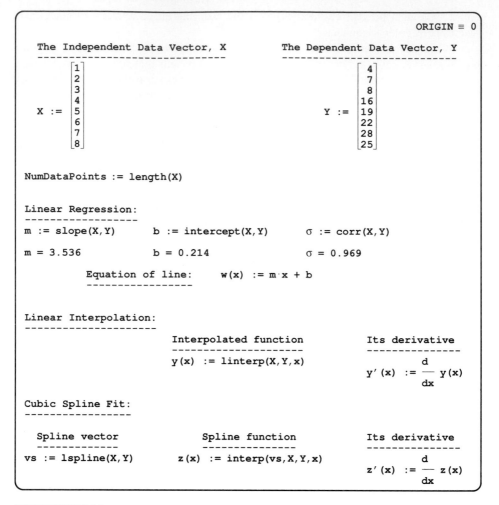

ORIGIN ≡ 0

The Independent Data Vector, X

$$X := \begin{bmatrix} 1 \\ 2 \\ 3 \\ 4 \\ 5 \\ 6 \\ 7 \\ 8 \end{bmatrix}$$

The Dependent Data Vector, Y

$$Y := \begin{bmatrix} 4 \\ 7 \\ 8 \\ 16 \\ 19 \\ 22 \\ 28 \\ 25 \end{bmatrix}$$

NumDataPoints := length(X)

Linear Regression:
----
m := slope(X,Y)   b := intercept(X,Y)   σ := corr(X,Y)

m = 3.536   b = 0.214   σ = 0.969

          Equation of line: w(x) := m·x + b

Linear Interpolation:

                         Interpolated function   Its derivative
                         ---------------------   ---------------
                         y(x) := linterp(X,Y,x)

                                                        y'(x) := $\dfrac{d}{dx}$ y(x)

Cubic Spline Fit:

   Spline vector   Spline function   Its derivative
   -------------   ---------------   ---------------
vs := lspline(X,Y)   z(x) := interp(vs,X,Y,x)

                                                        z'(x) := $\dfrac{d}{dx}$ z(x)

WORKSHEET 8.2
Curve fitting (*cont. below*).

Next the spline vector Vs is computed using the **lspline** function (assuming linear boundary conditions). This vector is then used in the **interp** function to compute the spline function z(x). The derivatives of both the y(x) (linear interpolation) and z(x) (cubic spline) functions are computed.

Finally, the data points and the curve-fits are plotted in three graphs and the derivatives of the curve-fits are plotted in a fourth. The derivative of the spline function generates a smooth curve whereas the derivative of the linear interpolation function leads to a series of discontinuous steps.

Note that the spline curve appears to approach a line at the endpoints. See how the curve changes when you use the **pspline** and the **cspline** functions.

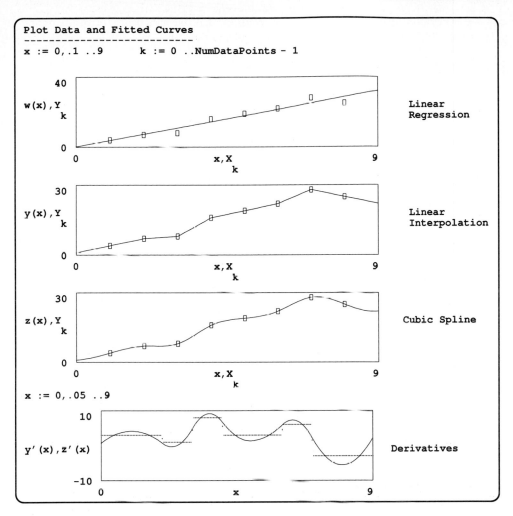

```
Plot Data and Fitted Curves
-----------------------------
x := 0,.1 ..9        k := 0 ..NumDataPoints - 1
```

WORKSHEET 8.2
(*cont.*)

Curve Fitting with the `Minerr` Function

Sometimes a set of data points x_i and y_i is to be fitted to an analytical form $F(x)$. The form is constructed with a set of parameters $\alpha, \beta, \ldots$, and written as $F(x, \alpha, \beta, \ldots)$. The objective is to determine the values of the parameters that will give an optimum fit to the data. To accomplish this, we construct the following function,

$$\text{SSE}(\alpha, \beta, \ldots) = \sum_i [y_i - F(x, \alpha, \beta, \ldots)]^2$$

This *sum of squares error* function represents the sum of the squares of the vertical distances from each point to the function.

The optimum fit is determined by requiring that the parameters $\alpha, \beta, \ldots$, minimize the SSE function. Using the principles of multivariable calculus, we set,

$$SSE_\alpha = \frac{\partial SSE}{\partial \alpha} = 0; \qquad SSE_\beta = \frac{\partial SSE}{\partial \beta} = 0, \ldots$$

This leads to a set of N coupled algebraic equations to be solved for the N unknowns $\alpha, \beta, \ldots$. Of the solutions sets (some represent minima, others maxima, and other saddle-like points), we choose the solution for which the SSE is a minimum.

MathCAD finds this minimum numerically using the **Minerr** function. Like the **Find** function, the **Minerr** function is used with a **Given**. Instead of finding the solution to a block of relational constraints, the **Minerr** function determines the values which minimize the error in the constraints. Consider the following objects:

```
α := .8      β := 1
Given
               SSE (α, β) ≈  0    1 ≈ 1
                                         ⎡α⎤
                                         ⎢ ⎥  := Minerr (α, β)
                                         ⎣β⎦
```

The first two objects make a reasonable guess for the unknowns α and β. After the **Given**, two relational constraints are assigned. The second relational constraint is always satisfied but is still required because there are two unknowns. Finally, the **Minerr** function is used to find those values of α and β for which SSE is closest to zero. Had we used the **Find** function instead, we would have received a `solution not found` error message since SSE is never zero unless the fit is perfect. MathCAD's **ERR** function gives the difference between the minimum value of SSE and zero. We illustrate the application of **Minerr** to curve fitting in Worksheet 8.3.

MathCAD solution: Worksheet 8.3[1]. The data elements (N=20) for x_i and y_i are entered into a pair of MathCAD vectors labeled x and y. The data will be fit to the following analytical form,

$$F(x, \alpha, \beta) = \alpha \cdot \beta \cdot x^{\beta-1} \cdot \exp(-\alpha \cdot x^\beta)$$

The SSE function is constructed and guesses are made for α and β. The **Given** is followed by a solve block containing relational constraints. The solve block is terminated with a **Minerr** function. The values of α and β which minimize SSE (α, β) are displayed along with the value of **ERR**. The minimum value of SSE (α, β) is shown to agree with **ERR**. The *mean* square error, SSE (α, β) / (N-2), is computed and shown to be small (0.001). The data points and the curve are plotted, demonstrating a rather good curve fit.

The optimum values of α and β are also computed using multivariable calculus and the result shown to agree with the values generated by the **Minerr** function. Because of the large number of calculations involved, this worksheet is very slow in computing.

---

[1]This worksheet is adapted from the *MathSoft User's Journal*, Winter 1990, p. 5 (with permission).

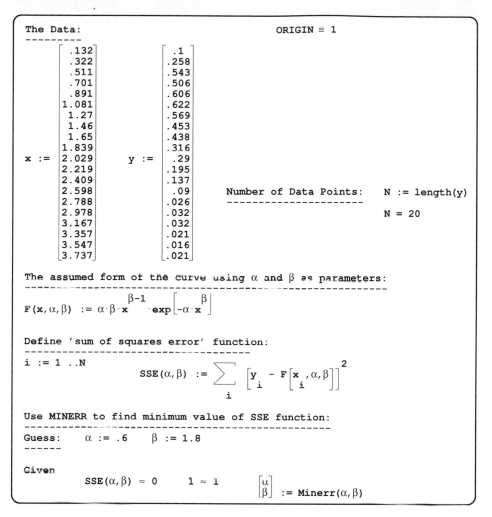

WORKSHEET 8.3
Using **MINERR** to find a least squares fit (*cont. below*).

FAST FOURIER TRANSFORMS, CONVOLUTIONS, AND LOGIC FUNCTIONS

The Fast Fourier Transform (FFT)

As shown in Chapter 6, it is possible to represent any piecewise continuous periodic function (period=T) by an infinite series of sines and cosines. Each sine (or cosine) has a frequency which is an integer multiple of the frequency of the original function. The series is called a Fourier series and is written:

$$f(t) = a_0 + \sum_{n=1}^{\infty} a_n \cdot \cos\left(n \cdot 2 \cdot \pi \cdot \frac{t}{T}\right) + \sum_{n=1}^{\infty} b_n \cdot \sin\left(n \cdot 2 \cdot \pi \cdot \frac{t}{T}\right)$$

```
      Solution:               Error:
      ---------               ------
  α = 0.502   β = 2.003       ERR = 0.02


  Mean square error:     SSE(α,β) = 0.02          SSE(α,β)
  ------------------                              --------  = 0.001
                                                   N - 2

  Plot of Data and Fitted Curve:
  ------------------------------
  z := 0,.1 ..4              0.7
```

$$F(z,\alpha,\beta),\underset{i}{y}$$

```
                            0
                             0              z,x              5
                                             i
```

```
  -----------------------------------------------------------------

  Check using multi-variable calculus:
  ------------------------------------
             d                                      d
  SSE (α,β) := ── SSE(α,β)        SSE (α,β) := ── SSE(α,β)
    α         dα                    β          dβ

  Guess:   α := .4     β := 1.9
  ------

  Given

    SSE (α,β) ≈ 0        SSE (α,β) ≈ 0         ⎡α⎤
      α                    β                   ⎢β⎥ := Find(α,β)

  Display Results
  ---------------
  α = 0.503    β = 2.002
```

WORKSHEET 8.3
(*cont.*)

where the coefficients are given by,

$$a_0 = \left[\frac{1}{T}\right] \cdot \int_0^T f(t) \cdot dt, \qquad a_n = \left[\frac{2}{T}\right] \cdot \int_0^T f(t) \cdot \cos\left(n \cdot 2 \cdot \pi \cdot \frac{t}{T}\right) \cdot dt$$

and

$$b_n = \left[\frac{2}{T}\right] \cdot \int_0^T f(t) \cdot \sin\left(n \cdot 2 \cdot \pi \cdot \frac{t}{T}\right) \cdot dt$$

To reproduce a general waveform with perfect accuracy, we must sum an infinite number of terms. We must therefore compute an infinite number of coefficients. If however we wish to reproduce the waveform *precisely* but only at a *finite* number of equally spaced points, the number of harmonics required and the number of coefficients to be computed are finite. To represent a waveform in this manner, we use the *discrete* or *fast* Fourier transform (FFT). As we increase the number of points used to represent or "sample" the function, we get a more complete description of the function but the calculation takes longer.

Let us assume that the waveform $y(x)$ is real and that it will be sampled at N points. Let the wave have the value y_n at the nth point ($n=0$ ..N-1). The fast Fourier transform of the waveform leads to a set of *harmonic amplitudes* a_k, given by the set of N equations,

$$a_k = \left[\frac{1}{\sqrt{N}}\right] \cdot \sum_{n=0}^{N-1} y_n \cdot \exp\left[\left(2 \cdot \pi \cdot i \cdot \frac{n}{N}\right) \cdot k\right] \qquad (k = 0..N-1)$$

These equations represent set of linear algebraic equations relating the N wave values y_n to the N harmonic amplitudes a_k. Note that while the wave points are real, the harmonic amplitudes are in general *complex*, each having a real and an imaginary part. The modulus and argument of a_k represent the amplitude and phase of the kth harmonic respectively.

The *inverse* fast Fourier transform relates the wave values to the harmonic amplitudes using the set of N equations,

$$y_n = \left[\frac{1}{\sqrt{N}}\right] \cdot \sum_{k=0}^{N-1} a_k \cdot \exp\left[\left(-2 \cdot \pi \cdot i \cdot \frac{k}{N}\right) \cdot n\right] \qquad (n = 0..N-1)$$

MathCAD computes the FFT with two functions **fft** and **cfft**. It computes the corresponding inverse FFT with **ifft** and **icfft**. The **cfft** and **icfft** functions are used when the original waveform is complex. We consider the **fft** and **ifft** functions that apply to real waveforms only. The transforms a_k remain, in general, complex.

MathCAD allows sampling of a waveform at N points where $N = 2^m$ (m= 3,4,5,...). Hence the sampling intervals must be in powers of two, e.g., N=8, N=16, N=32, etc. Furthermore, it can be shown that only the first $N/2+1$ of the a_k values are independent; the remaining values can be derived from them. MathCAD uses this fact and computes only the first $N/2+1$ values of a_k in the FFT.

We offer the following note of caution regarding FFTs. Since the FFT samples the original waveform only at a finite number of points, it may not give a true representation of the harmonic spectrum of wave. For example, suppose we have the following waveform:

$$y(t) = \sin(2 \cdot \pi \cdot t) + \sin(2 \cdot \pi \cdot 20 \cdot t)$$

In a continuous Fourier analysis, this waveform has a period of $T = 1$ and clearly has two spectral components, one with $k_1 = 1$ and the other with $k_2 = 20$. If we sample this waveform at $N = 32$ points, we obtain a harmonic range of $k = 0.. N/2$. The maximum value of k is equal to $K_{max} = N/2 = 16$. The FFT spectrum shows nonvanishing amplitudes at $k_1 = 1$ and $k_2 = 12$. This is somewhat surprising since the second harmonic is actually at $k_2 = 20$. The fact that we have sampled the wave at only 32 points means that the FFT cannot *resolve* harmonics higher than 16 and therefore assigns a value of $k = 12$. If we examine the waveforms $|\sin(2 \cdot \pi \cdot 20 \cdot t)|$ and

$|\sin(2 \cdot \pi \cdot 12 \cdot t)|$ carefully, we observe that they are actually indistinguishable when sampled at only 32 equally spaced points. Therefore, to produce an accurate spectral representation with a discrete Fourier transform, a sufficient number of sampling points (N) should be used. If a waveform is represented by a series of harmonics where the highest harmonic has $k = K_{max}$, then the number of sampling points should satisfy $N/2 > K_{max}$.

Note: In all fast Fourier transform work, use subscript `ORIGIN=0`.

To perform FFT analysis with MathCAD, we use the following steps:

Step I. Define the function to be analyzed.

```
Example:
y(x)  := 3·sin(x) + 5·sin(2·x)
```

Step II. Choose a sampling parameter which determines the number of points to be sampled. Define the coordinates of these points on the waveform.

```
Example:
m := 5    N := 2^m      N = 32

n := 0 ..N-1    Xn := [n/N]·2·π      Yn := y[Xn]
```

This choice of X_n covers an interval from zero to $2 \cdot \pi$ in subintervals of $2 \cdot \pi/N$. Note that X and Y are vectors, each of which contains N elements.

Step III. Take the FFT.

```
Example:
A := fft(Y)
```

The $N/2 + 1$ elements of the Fourier transform vector **A** represent the complex harmonic amplitudes A_k `(k= 0 ..N/2)`. This set of amplitudes is called the spectrum or spectral distribution of Y. Examine the spectral distribution.

Step IV. Modify the spectral distribution by processing the harmonic amplitudes. You may change any of these amplitudes. In practice, this is called "filtering." The new transform vector will be called **A'**.

Step V. Take the inverse FFT and plot the new resulting waveform.

```
Example:
Y'  :=  ifft(A')
```

If the spectral distribution is not changed in Step IV, we should find that Y' = Y or equivalently,

$$Y = ifft(fft(Y))$$

We apply the FFT to the demodulation (detection) of an amplitude modulated (AM) wave. Such a wave is represented by,

$$y(t) = \text{Signal}(t) \cdot \text{Carrier}(t)$$

where

$$\text{Carrier}(t) = \sin(2 \cdot \pi \cdot c \cdot t) \qquad (c = \text{carrier frequency})$$

The signal is represented by a finite Fourier series of the form:

$$\text{Signal}(t) = \sum_{n=1}^{N} A_n \cdot \cos(2 \cdot \pi \cdot n \cdot f \cdot t) + \sum_{n=1}^{N} B_n \cdot \sin(2 \cdot \pi \cdot n \cdot f \cdot t)$$

where f is the fundamental frequency and N is the maximum harmonic of the signal. The frequency of the highest harmonic is therefore $f_{max} = N \cdot f$. (The dc term $n = 0$ is omitted with no loss in generality.) In radio transmission, we require:

$$f_{max} \ll c$$

that is, the maximum harmonic frequency of the signal must be much lower than the carrier frequency. The objective is to separate the signal from the carrier. This is called *demodulation* or *detection*.

One method of detection is to multiply the modulated wave by the same waveform as the carrier (synchronous modulation). To illustrate the mathematics of synchronous modulation, we simplify the signal and assume that it contains only the lowest cosine harmonic. By multiplying the received waveform with a local waveform of the form $2 \cdot \sin(2 \cdot \pi \cdot c \cdot t)$, we obtain:

$$g(t) = A_1 \cdot \cos(2 \cdot \pi \cdot f \cdot t) \cdot \sin(2 \cdot \pi \cdot c \cdot t) \cdot [2 \cdot \sin(2 \cdot \pi \cdot c \cdot t)]$$
$$g(t) = 2 \cdot A_1 \cdot \cos(2 \cdot \pi \cdot f \cdot t) \cdot \sin(2 \cdot \pi \cdot c \cdot t)^2$$

or, using the trigonometric identity $\sin^2(\theta) = [1 + \cos(2 \cdot \theta)]/2$,

$$g(t) = A_1 \cdot \cos(2 \cdot \pi \cdot f \cdot t) \cdot [1 + \cos(2 \cdot \pi \cdot 2 \cdot c \cdot t)]$$
$$g(t) = [A_1 \cdot \cos(2 \cdot \pi \cdot f \cdot t)] + [A_1 \cdot \cos(2 \cdot \pi \cdot f \cdot t) \cdot \cos(2 \cdot \pi \cdot 2 \cdot c \cdot t)]$$

Using the identity,

$$\cos(a) \cdot \cos(b) = \frac{[\cos(a + b) + \cos(a - b)]}{2}$$

the synchronously modulated waveform can be written,

$$g(t) = [A_1 \cdot \cos(2 \cdot \pi \cdot f \cdot t)] \dots$$
$$+ A_1 \cdot \frac{[\cos\{2 \cdot \pi \cdot (2 \cdot c + f) \cdot t\} + \cos\{2 \cdot \pi \cdot (2 \cdot c - f) \cdot t\}]}{2}$$

This waveform consists of a low-frequency component (the signal at frequency f) and a pair of high-frequency components at frequencies of $2 \cdot c + f$ and $2 \cdot c - f$. If we include *all* the harmonics of the original signal, we obtain a *set* of low frequency components which make up the original signal and a *set* of high-frequency *sidebands* located symmetrically about twice the carrier frequency.

By taking the FFT of this waveform, filtering out the high frequencies, and then taking the *inverse* FFT of the result, we recover the original waveform. We demonstrate this in Worksheet 8.4.

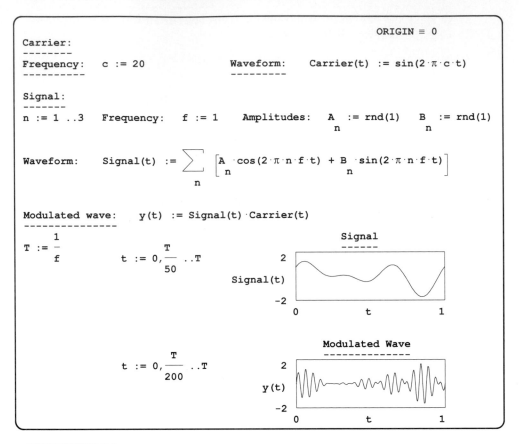

WORKSHEET 8.4

Demodulation of an amplitude modulated signal (*cont. below*).

MathCAD solution: Worksheet 8.4. Note: This worksheet exceeds the two page limit of the student edition. After it is loaded, delete the expository text and "repack" the material so that it fits into two pages.

The carrier and signal waveforms are assigned. The carrier frequency is c= 20. The signal consists of a finite Fourier series of three harmonics where the three frequencies are $f_1=1$, $f_2=2$, and $f_3=3$. The harmonic amplitudes of the signal are assigned using the **rnd** function. The modulated wave y(t) is constructed. Both the signal and the modulated wave are plotted. The wave is remodulated by multiplying it with a local carrier waveform and the result g(t) is plotted.

The function g(t) is sampled using a factor of m=7 corresponding to L= 2^m= 128 points. The elements g_j make up the waveform vector **g**.

We take the FFT of the vector **g** and assign the result to a vector **G**. This transform vector has L/2 + 1 (in our case 65) elements representing the amplitudes of the Fourier harmonics. The highest harmonic is L'= L/2 (L=64). The sampling factor was chosen to be m= 7 in order to have L'=64. This covers all the harmonics of the waveform, the highest of which is $k_{max} = 2 \cdot c + 3 \cdot f = 43$. An integer range variable k=0 ..L' references the L'+1 harmonics.

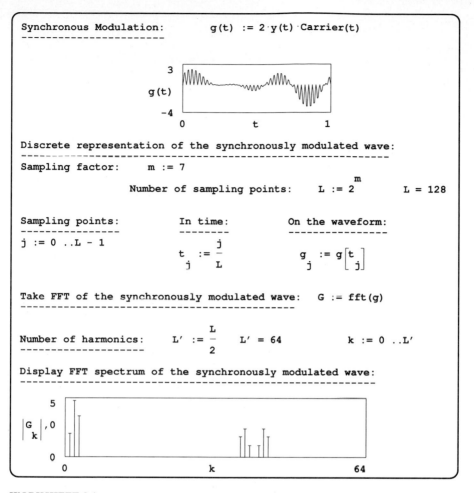

WORKSHEET 8.4
(*cont. below*)

The spectral distribution is plotted using the modulus (absolute value) of the complex harmonic amplitudes $|G_k|$. The plot format is type=e. The e produces error bars and generates vertical lines which run from the x-axis to the data point. Note that there are two groups of harmonics. The low frequency set contains the three components of the signal (f, $2 \cdot f$, and $3 \cdot f$). The high frequency set is centered at $2 \cdot c$ (i.e., $2 \cdot c \pm f$, $2 \cdot c \pm 2 \cdot f$, and $2 \cdot c \pm 3 \cdot f$).

We filter the spectral components using a function of the form (Butterworth filter),

$$H(\alpha, \beta, x) = \frac{1}{\left[1 + \left[\frac{x}{\alpha} \right]^{2 \cdot \beta} \right]^{1/2}}$$

The variable x represents the frequency. The parameters α and β set the cutoff frequency and the number of stages in the filter (cutoff sharpness). The filter allows low frequencies below the cutoff to pass through while blocking the high frequencies above the cutoff. We

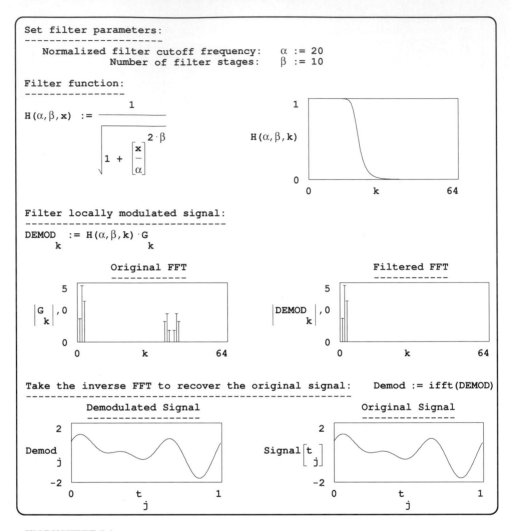

WORKSHEET 8.4
(*cont.*)

set $\alpha = 20$. This cutoff is well above the highest component harmonic of the signal and yet well below the lowest of the high frequency components. The sharpness parameter is set to $\beta = 10$. The filter function for these values of α and β is plotted.

The vector **G** is multiplied by the filter function to form the vector DEMOD. The inverse FFT of DEMOD is taken using MathCAD's **ifft** function and the result assigned to the vector Demod. The L elements of this vector represent the discrete points of the demodulated signal. The elements $Demod_j$ are plotted versus t_j and compared with the original signal.

Try different filter function values of α and β. In particular, reduce the number of stages by setting $\beta = 1$. What does the demodulated signal look like? Why does it look this way?

Discrete Convolutions

The continuous convolution of two functions $f(x)$ and $g(x)$ is defined by:

$$h(x) = f(x) * g(x) \equiv \int_{-\infty}^{\infty} f(t) \cdot g(x-t) \cdot dt$$

The symbol $*$ is used to represent the convolution. If the functions are zero outside the interval $[a, b]$, then the upper and lower limits on the integral are replaced by b and a respectively.

Like the discrete FFT, it is possible to approximate the continuous convolution by a *discrete convolution* where the functions are sampled at N equally-spaced points on the interval. The discrete convolution is defined as:

$$h_n = \sum_{k=0}^{N-1} f_k \cdot g_{n-k} \qquad (n = 0, 1..N - 1)$$

where h_n, f_k, and g_{n-k} are discrete representations of the functions $h(x)$, $f(x)$, and $g(x)$. They are evaluated by sampling the functions at the points x_k on the interval $[a, b]$ Note that the subscript $n - k$ in the convolution equations becomes negative when $n < k$.

There are a number of ways to handle the negative subscript problem with MathCAD:

METHOD 1. This method uses ORIGIN shifting. When ORIGIN is altered in a worksheet, all previously defined subscripted variables shift accordingly. Consider the following objects:

```
ORIGIN := 0        a0  := 1     a1  := 2
ORIGIN := -5       a_5 = 1      a_4 = 2
```

Note that with the subscript origin initially at zero, we assign the values of $a_0 = 1$ and $a_1 = 2$. After the origin shift, these numerical values are now stored in a_{-5} and a_{-4}.

We "down shift" the subscript origin to ORIGIN $\equiv$ -N. This allows MathCAD to handle the required negative subscripts without giving a index out of bounds error. The convolution is then computed. The origin is reset to ORIGIN $\equiv$ 0 and the results reassigned. This is an awkward method and is presented in Worksheet 8.5 only to demonstrate ORIGIN shifting.

METHOD 2. A second approach is to redefine the subscript using a subscript "function." Consider the following objects:

```
n := 0 ..N-1              k := 0 ..N/2 - 1

m(n,k)  := if((n - k) ≥ 0,n - k,N - 1)     hn := ∑ fk gm(n,k)
                                               k
```

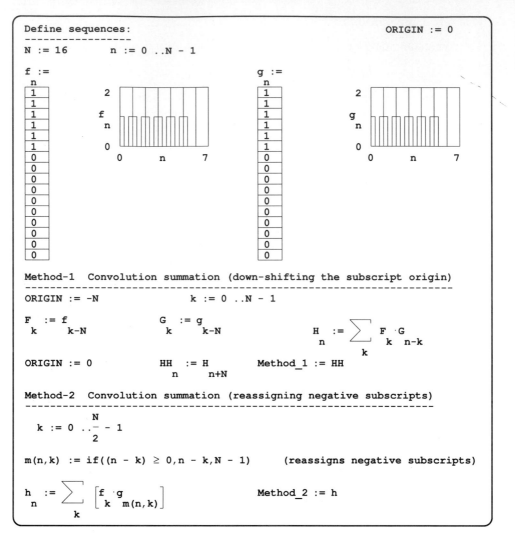

WORKSHEET 8.5
Convolution of sequences of samples(*cont. below*).

Note that the **if** function is used to take each negative subscript and shift it to some positive value ($N - 1 = 15$) where the value of g_m is zero. Hence, terms with negative $n-k$ subscripts will not contribute to the sum. This method is awkward and is presented in Worksheet 8.5 only to demonstrate the use of functions as subscripts.

METHOD 3. The best way of handling the negative subscripts in the convolution equations is to exclude them in the summation. We do so using the following,

$$n := 0 \ ..N-1 \qquad h_n := \sum_n (n \geq k) \cdot f_k \cdot g_{n-k}$$

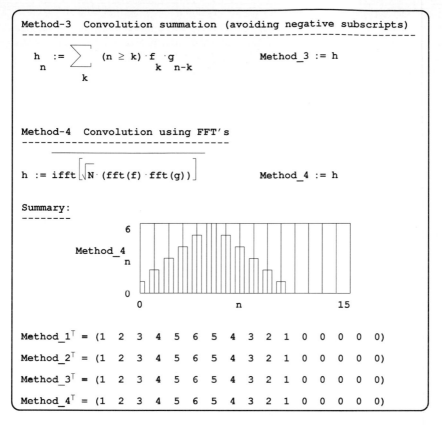

WORKSHEET 8.5
(*cont.*)

The Boolean expression is zero when $n < k$ and effectively excludes terms with negative subscripts from the summation. Since MathCAD does not evaluate these terms, the `index out of bounds` error is avoided.

METHOD 4. Convolutions can also be computed using FFTs. It can be shown that the convolution of two functions is proportional to the inverse FFT of the product of the FFTs of the functions. Using MathCAD vectors f, g, and h, we write the convolution as,

$$h := \overrightarrow{\text{ifft}[\sqrt{N} \cdot (\text{fft}(f) \cdot \text{fft}(g))]}$$

A limitation of this method is that MathCAD's **fft** function requires the number of sampling points be a power of two. We illustrate all four methods in Worksheet 8.5.

   MathCAD solution: Worksheet 8.5. Sampled values of f and g are assigned for N (N=16) points. Note that although only the first six entries are nonzero, we have created a table with sixteen entries (or equivalently a MathCAD vector of length sixteen) and have "padded" the last ten values with zeros. We do this because the convolution vector will contain eleven nonzero elements. To allow for this size, we must extend the input sample tables to at least eleven. We have extended the length of the data vectors f and g to sixteen because Method 4 uses FFTs. With MathCAD, FFTs require vectors whose lengths are in powers of two. Hence the choice sixteen.

Using Method 1, the subscript origin is down-shifted to $-N$ and the range set for k. Next the sampled data is reassigned to new variables F_k and G_k whose subscripts begin with zero. The convolution sums are computed. The ORIGIN is then reset to zero and the subscripted results H_n reassigned to HH_n to conform to ORIGIN$\equiv$0. The final vector HH is assigned to the variable Method_1.

The remaining methods use ORIGIN$\equiv$0. Method 2 reassigns the negative subscripts using the **mod** function. The subscript m(n,k) becomes m=15 when n−k is negative (i.e., when $n < k$). Since g_{15}=0, the terms with negative subscripts do not contribute to the sum.

Method 3 uses the relational condition to exclude negative subscripts in the summation. Method 4 uses MathCAD's **fft** and **ifft** functions to compute the convolution.

The results are displayed in graphical form. The four Method vectors are displayed in transposed form. This saves space in the worksheet.

Note the particular choice of data elements for the MathCAD vectors f and g. Each vector has ones for the first six elements and zeros for the rest. This data represents the frequency of getting a number from one through six when throwing a single die. The statistical frequency of getting any number from one through six on a session of six throws is obviously one (i.e., all faces are equally probable). The frequency for higher numbers is clearly zero. It can be shown that the statistical frequencies for obtaining a particular dice total when throwing *two* dice is the *convolution* of the statistical frequencies associated with throwing a *single* die. Note that the convolution result in Worksheet 8.5 gives the same frequencies as those for the two-dice throwing session (of 36 throws) shown earlier in this chapter.

Boolean Logic

A Boolean variable can take on one of two values—*true* or *false*. MathCAD represents true with one and false with zero. The following shows how MathCAD's *relational* operators generate Boolean variables:

```
a := 5      b := 4

c := a ≈ b    c = 0      c := a ≠ b    c = 1      c := a ≤ b    c = 0

c := a ≥ b    c = 1      c := a > b    c = 1      c := a < b    c = 0
```

We have arbitrarily set a= 5 and b= 4. If we assign to c the condition that a is equal to b (**a{<Alt>=}b**), we obtain a value of c=0 (false) because a=b is false. Similarly, if we assign to c the condition that a is not equal to b (**a{<Alt>#}b**), we find c=1 (true) because a≠b is true. A less than or equal to condition (**a{<Alt(}b**) gives a false result, while a greater than or equal to condition (**a{<Alt>)}b**) gives a true result. Thus c is a Boolean variable and can only be true (1) or false (0). Try changing the values of a and b and see the effect on c.

Boolean variables are often the arguments of *logical* operators such as *AND*, *OR*, *NOT*, *NAND*, *NOR*, and *XOR*. Although MathCAD does not have these operators built in, they can easily be constructed. Assume that we have only two Boolean variables a and b. We first construct the shifted Heaviside function:

$$f(x) \equiv \Phi(x - 0.5)$$

The function $f(x) \equiv \Phi(x - x_0)$ is one for $x \geq x_0$ and zero for $x < x_0$. [The value $x_0 = 0.5$ is somewhat arbitrary. Any value of x_0 greater than zero and smaller than one can be used.] Using $f(x)$, the following logical functions can be constructed:

Logical function	Conditions for being true (else false)
$AND(a, b) \equiv f(a \cdot b)$	If both a and b are true.
$OR(a, b) \equiv f(a + b)$	If either a or b (or both) is true.
$NOT(a) \equiv f(1 - a)$	If a is false.
$NOR(a, b) \equiv NOT(OR(a, b))$	If neither a nor b is true.
$NAND(a, b) \equiv NOT(AND(a, b))$	If either a or b (or both) is false.
$XOR(a, b) \equiv NAND(a, b) \cdot OR(a, b)$	If either a or b is true but *not* both.

These logical functions can be generalized for more than two variables. For example, ANDing and ORing three variables can be expressed as $AND3(a, b, c) \equiv f(a \cdot b \cdot c)$ and $OR3(a, b, c) \equiv f(a + b + c)$.

Logical functions can be applied to digital gate circuits. A typical gate circuit in shown in Fig. 8.1. The output state of the circuit is determined by the logical states of the three inputs. In Worksheet 8.6, we analyze the gate circuit shown in Fig. 8.1.

MathCAD solution: Worksheet 8.6. In the circuit, the three logical inputs (Boolean variables) A, B, and C are processed by three inverters (NOTs designated by triangles

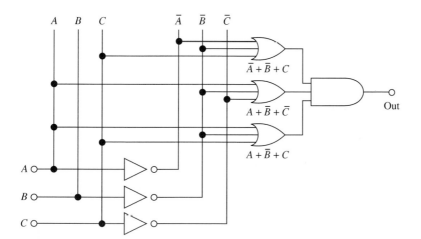

FIGURE 8.1

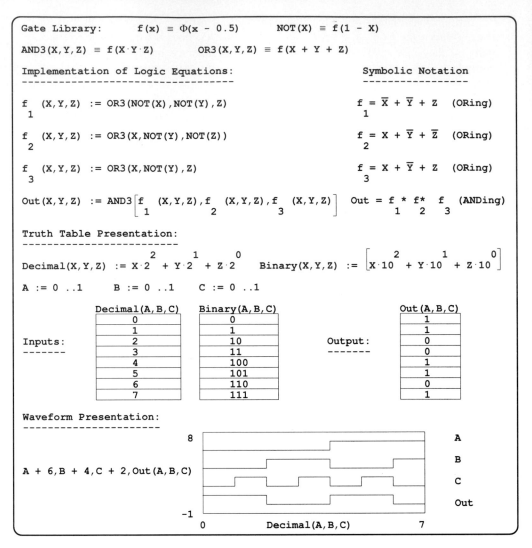

WORKSHEET 8.6
Analysis of a combinational logic circuit.

with small circles) in conjunction with three triple OR gates. The outputs of the OR gates are then processed by a triple AND gate.

In Boolean algebra, a NOT is symbolized with a bar on top of a variable. OR and AND operations are represented symbolically by addition and multiplication signs respectively. We construct OR and AND functions of three variables and assign the function using the names AND3 (x, y, z) and OR3 (x, y, z).

The three ORing functions are processed to give logical states f_1, f_2, and f_3. These are then ANDed to produce the final output called Out.

Since there are three binary inputs, there are $2^3 = 8$ possible logical input states of the circuit. The input can be displayed either as a three bit binary number or as a decimal number from zero to seven. MathCAD allows the format `rd` `(radix)` to be either decimal (base 10), hexadecimal (base 16) or octal (base 8) but *not* binary (base 2). To display a number in binary form, we use the function,

$$\texttt{Binary(X,Y,Z)} = \texttt{X} \cdot 10^2 + \texttt{Y} \cdot 10^1 + \texttt{Z} \cdot 10^0$$

For example, if `X=1`, `Y=0`, and `Z=1`, the Binary function gives the number 101. This is *not* a true binary representation of the number for mathematical purposes; it is only a trick to make the number *appear* in binary format.

To represent the input state by a decimal number 0 ..7, we define the following function,

$$\texttt{Decimal(X,Y,Z)} = \texttt{X} \cdot 2^2 + \texttt{Y} \cdot 2^1 + \texttt{Z} \cdot 2^0$$

For example, the number zero means that all three inputs are false (zero). On the other hand, if `X` is true `(X=1)`, `Y` is false `(Y=0)`, and `Z` is true `(Z=1)`, then `Decimal(X,Y,Z)= 5`. The Decimal function gives a true decimal representation of the eight input configurations.

The eight different logical states of the three inputs are listed both in decimal and binary form using a truth table. The output is shown for these eight states. The results are also shown in a graphical representation. The waveforms are shifted using offsets on the vertical axis.

In Chapter 9, we present special topics in MathCAD. We consider the enhancements of version 2.5 including surface plots, sketches and sorting. We also look at special editing and file handling functions.

PROBLEMS

1. Suppose we sample a set of M random numbers ranging from zero to one and take their sum. If we repeat this process N times, we obtain a set of numbers $\texttt{Sum}_n$ `(n=1, ..N)`. While the sums can range between zero and M, the two extremes are very unlikely. Sums in the vicinity of $M/2$ are more probable.

   (a) Setting `M=10` and `N=50`, find both the mean value and the standard deviation of $\texttt{Sum}_n$.

   (b) Plot a histogram of the statistical distribution of $\texttt{Sum}_n$. Find the maximum frequency using `MaxFreq=max(Freq)`.

   (c) Compare the above histogram with the Gaussian distribution,

   $$y(x) = \texttt{MaxFreq} \cdot e^{-\frac{1}{2} \cdot \left[\frac{x - Mean}{\sigma}\right]^2}$$

   where the theoretical mean and standard deviation are given by `Mean= M/2` and σ = $\sqrt{\texttt{(M/12)}}$. [Use {**Esc**} **PROcess** to process the worksheet and generate different distributions.]

2. An experiment is set up to measure the decay constant of a nuclear material. The following data is recorded:

T	Y
0	0.549
1	0.301
2	0.165
3	0.091
4	0.050
5	0.027
6	0.015
7	0.008

where Y is the amount of material present at the time T. The theoretical formula is,

$$y(t) = e^{-\alpha \cdot t}$$

where $y(t)$ is the fraction of the radioactive material present at a time t. The decay constant is α.

(a) Using MathCAD's **slope**, **intercept**, and **corr** functions, find the straight line that best fits the data vectors T and Y. Display the correlation factor.

(b) Using MathCAD's **lspline** function, construct a cubic spline from the data.

(c) On a single plot, graph the data points along with the functions obtained in parts (a) and (b).

From the above results we see that the straight line is a poor fit to the data. Recall that for a good fit, the correlation factor should be close to ± 1. If we take the natural logarithm of both sides of the theoretical formula, we obtain,

$$z(t) = \ln[y(t)] = -\alpha \cdot t$$

Note that z is a linear function of t with a slope$= -\alpha$.

(d) Using vectorization, assign a data vector LOGY with the following keystrokes: **LOGY:{<Alt>-}(ln(Y))**. Compute the slope that best fits the data vectors T and LOGY and determine the decay constant of the material. Verify the accuracy of your answer by displaying the correlation factor.

3. Consider the function:

$$f(x) = x \cdot \sin(x) \qquad \text{for} \qquad 0 \le x \le \frac{\pi}{2}$$

(a) Using a spline with 50 points, construct the inverse function $g(x)$ over the interval $0 \le x \le \pi/2$. Hint: Assign subscripted variables $Y_j = (j/50) \cdot (\pi/2)$ and $X_j = f(Y_j)$ for j=0 ..50. Using the vectors X and Y, construct the function g(x) from Vs=cspline(X,Y) and g(x)=interp(Vs,X,Y,x).

(b) Plot $f(x)$, $g(x)$, and $f(g(x))$ over the interval specified in part (a) and compare the results with those in Worksheet 4.10 of Chapter 4.

4. A noisy signal is represented by,

$$y(t) = A \cdot \sin(\omega \cdot t) + B \cdot [rnd(1) - 0.5],$$

where $\omega = 2 \cdot \pi$, $A = 10$, and $B = 10$.

(a) Using L=2^7 sampling points, construct y_j (j=0, ..L-1) and compute Y=fft(y).

(b) Plot the spectral distribution of Y_k (k=0, ..L/2).

(*c*) Using a Butterworth filter as in Worksheet 8.4, set $\alpha=3$ and $\beta=10$ and filter the FFT function.

(*d*) Reconstruct the filtered function using an IFFT.

5. When throwing *three* dice 216 times, the statistical frequency of getting dice totals of 3 through 18 is:

$$\text{Dice Total} = [3\ 4\ 5\ \ 6\ \ 7\ \ 8\ \ 9\ 10\ 11\ 12\ 13\ 14\ 15\ 16\ 17\ 18]$$
$$\text{Freq} = [1\ 3\ 6\ 10\ 15\ 21\ 25\ 27\ 27\ 25\ 21\ 15\ 10\ \ 6\ \ 3\ \ 1]$$

Derive this distribution by convolving the following vectors:

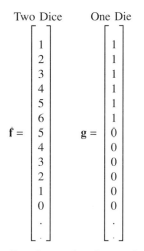

Pad the vectors with zeros until each contains sixteen elements.

6. Consider a three-stage up counter using toggle flip-flops. Suppose the circuit is to count rectangular input clock pulses using negative edge triggering. The counter's output ranges from zero to seven after which it resets to zero.

In negative edge triggering, a toggle flip-flop changes its logical output state when the input state changes from positive (true) to zero (false). Hence the counter is triggered on the falling edge of each clock pulse.

(*a*) Using a logical *NOT* function, simulate the action of the counter using MathCAD.

(*b*) Graph both the clock pulses and the toggle states of the flip-flops versus time.

(*c*) Display the output state of the counter versus time using a table. Hint: to toggle a single flip-flop, use the following:

```
NOT(a)  ≡  Φ(0.5-a)
C₀ := 0       Q1₀ :=0              Initialize clock and flip-flop

t := 0 ..17                        Set time points

Cₜ₊₁ := if(Cₜ ≈ 0,1,0)            Generate alternating clock

Q1ₜ₊₁ := if[Cₜ₊₁   Cₜ < 0,not[Q1ₜ],Q1ₜ]    Toggle flip flip
                                              on clock going
                                              from 1 to 0
```

REFERENCES

Cheung, J. Y. and J. G. Bredeson: *Modern Digital System Design*, West, St. Paul, Minn., 1980.

Defatta, D. J., J. G. Lucas, and W. S. Hodgkiss: *Digital Signal Processing*: *A Systems Approach*, Wiley, New York, 1988.

Kreyzig, E.: *Advanced Engineering Mathematics*, Wiley, New York, 1988.

Mano, M. M.: *Computer Engineering—Hardware Design*, Prentice-Hall, Englewood Cliffs, N.J., 1988.

Strum, R. D. and D. E. Kirk: *Discrete Systems and Digital Signal Processing*, Addison Wesley, Reading, Mass., 1988.

CHAPTER
9

ADVANCED TOPICS IN MATHCAD

ENHANCEMENTS IN VERSION 2.5

Moving a Block of Objects

With MathCAD version 2.0, it is possible to delete, move, or copy objects *one at a time* within a worksheet—or, with a split window, between two worksheets (see below)—by using a combination of the **{F2}** (copy), **{F3}** (cut), and **{F4}** (paste) keys. With version 2.5, the same operations can be performed on a *block* of objects. The **{<Ctrl>Y}** key is used to mark the beginning and end of the region containing the objects to be processed. Place the cursor inside the *first* object of the block and type **{<Ctrl>Y}**. A box will appear around the object. Next, move the cursor inside the *last* object of the block and type **{<Ctrl>Y}** again. Boxes will appear around *all* the objects defined by the block. The **{F3}** (cut) key, for example, now acts on the entire block by erasing all the objects of the block and placing the contents in a buffer or "clipboard." The **{F4}** (paste) key copies the entire block of objects to the current position of the cursor. The **{F2}** (copy) key copies the block into the buffer without erasing it. The **{F2}** (copy) and **{F4}** (paste) keys can be used to duplicate a block of objects in the worksheet.

Sorting Vectors and Matrices

Sorting of vectors and matrices is accomplished with the following four MathCAD functions: **sort**, **csort**, **rsort**, **reverse**. To sort a vector **V** we use sort (V). Consider the following vector objects:

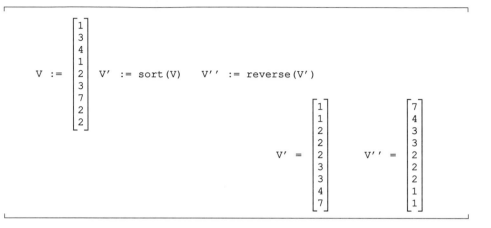

The **sort** function produces a vector whose elements are sorted in ascending order. The **reverse** function reverses the order of the elements (rows) of the vector. While **sort** operates only on a vector (i.e., a column matrix), **reverse** operates on any matrix.

The following objects illustrate the sorting of matrices:

$$M := \begin{bmatrix} 1 & 5 & 7 & 5 \\ 4 & 4 & 8 & 5 \\ 3 & 3 & 7 & 1 \\ 2 & 2 & 6 & 9 \end{bmatrix} \qquad ORIGIN \equiv 0$$

M' := reverse (M)   M'' := csort (M, 3)   M''' := rsort (M, 2)

$$M' = \begin{bmatrix} 2 & 2 & 6 & 9 \\ 3 & 3 & 7 & 1 \\ 4 & 4 & 8 & 5 \\ 1 & 5 & 7 & 5 \end{bmatrix} \qquad M'' = \begin{bmatrix} 3 & 3 & 7 & 1 \\ 1 & 5 & 7 & 5 \\ 4 & 4 & 8 & 5 \\ 2 & 2 & 6 & 9 \end{bmatrix} \qquad M''' = \begin{bmatrix} 5 & 1 & 5 & 7 \\ 5 & 4 & 4 & 8 \\ 1 & 3 & 3 & 7 \\ 9 & 2 & 2 & 6 \end{bmatrix}$$

MathCAD's reverse (M) function reverses the order of the *rows* of a matrix M. The csort (M, n) (column sort) function sorts the matrix M on the *column* n in ascending order. The rsort (M, n) (row sort) function sorts the matrix M on the *row* n in ascending order. Since ORIGIN=0 (the default) is used, the first row and first column are referenced by n=0.

The sort functions are useful in analyzing unsorted data. Suppose we have two data vectors, **X** (independent), and **Y** (dependent), and wish to produce a histogram, construct a spline function, or perform a linear interpolation. Each of these MathCAD operations requires that the independent data vector **X** be in ascending order. If the

x-data is not in ascending order, we perform the required sorting using **csort** or **rsort**. This is illustrated with the objects below.

$$\text{ORIGIN} \equiv 0$$

$$\text{Data} := \begin{bmatrix} 1 & 5 \\ 4 & 15 \\ 3 & 17 \\ 2 & 12 \end{bmatrix} \qquad \text{Data}' := \text{csort (Data, 0)}$$

$$\text{Data}' = \begin{bmatrix} 1 & 5 \\ 2 & 12 \\ 3 & 17 \\ 4 & 15 \end{bmatrix}$$

$$\text{X} := \text{Data}'^{<0>} \qquad \text{Y} := \text{Data}'^{<1>}$$

$$\text{X} = \begin{bmatrix} 1 \\ 2 \\ 3 \\ 4 \end{bmatrix} \qquad \text{Y} = \begin{bmatrix} 5 \\ 12 \\ 17 \\ 15 \end{bmatrix}$$

The matrix **Data** contains the data. Note that the first column (column 0 with ORIGIN$\equiv$0) of the matrix **(X)** is not in ascending order. Using the **csort** function, we sort the matrix on column 0. We then construct the data vectors **X** and **Y** using column extraction. To assign **X**, for example, we type: **X:Data'{<Ctrl>^}0**. The data vectors **X** and **Y** can now be used for linear interpolation, splines, and histograms.

Surface Plots

Version 2.5 of MathCAD can perform three-dimensional surface plots. The space is defined with three mutually perpendicular axes labeled x, y, and z. The x and y axes are set in a horizontal plane and the z-axis is oriented vertically. A function of two variables $z = f(x, y)$ can now be plotted as a surface in this three-dimensional space.

We first assign a "grid" of points in the xy-plane for which the function $f(x, y)$ will be plotted. Suppose, for example, that we wish to plot the function $f(x, y) = \sin(x) \cdot \cos(y)$. Let the x-coordinates of the grid x_n range from $x = -2$ to $x = 2$ in steps of 0.2 and the y-coordinates y_m range from $y = -3$ to $y = 3$ in steps of 0.6. We construct the matrix z, whose elements z_{nm} represent the values of the function at the grid points x_n, y_m. The steps are illustrated with the following objects:

$$f(x, y) := \sin(x) \cdot \cos(y) \qquad \text{ORIGIN} \equiv 1$$

$$n := 1 \ .. 20 \qquad x_1 := -2 \qquad x_{n+1} := x_n + .2$$

$$m := 1 \ .. 10 \qquad y_1 := -3 \qquad y_{m+1} := x_m + .6$$

$$n := 1 \ .. 21 \qquad m := 1 \ .. 11 \qquad z_{n,m} := f[x_n, y_m]$$

The singly subscripted variables x_n and y_m form vectors while the doubly subscripted variable z_{nm} represents the element of a matrix. Since we have used ORIGIN$\equiv$1, the matrices display as:

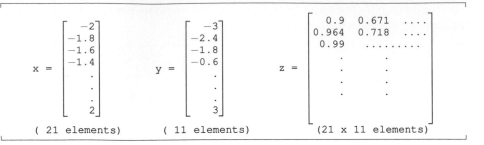

$$x = \begin{bmatrix} -2 \\ -1.8 \\ -1.6 \\ -1.4 \\ . \\ . \\ . \\ 2 \end{bmatrix} \qquad y = \begin{bmatrix} -3 \\ -2.4 \\ -1.8 \\ -0.6 \\ . \\ . \\ . \\ 3 \end{bmatrix} \qquad z = \begin{bmatrix} 0.9 & 0.671 & .... \\ 0.964 & 0.718 & .... \\ 0.99 & .... \\ . & . \\ . & . \\ . & . \\ . & . \end{bmatrix}$$

$\quad\quad\quad$ (21 elements) $\quad\quad\quad$ (11 elements) $\quad\quad\quad$ (21 x 11 elements)

The vectors x and y define the grid points at which the function $z(x, y)$ is to be plotted. These points must be equally spaced along the x-axis and along the y-axis.

$\quad$ To plot the function, type **{<Alt>@}** and a surface plot template with a single placeholder will appear as follows:

Fill the placeholder with the matrix variable to be plotted (in this case z) and the surface plot will be performed. Note that MathCAD actually makes the surface plot entirely from the elements of the z-matrix. The plot template makes no reference to the vectors x and y. The plot consists of a mesh of two sets of grid lines intersecting at the points x_n and y_m. The height of each intersection point above the xy-plane is determined by the value of the corresponding element in the z-matrix. In the default mode, the orientation of the surface is determined approximately by,

$$z = \begin{bmatrix} 0.9 & 0.671 & .... \\ 0.964 & 0.718 & ... \\ 0.99 & .... \\ . & . \\ . & . \\ . & . \end{bmatrix} \quad - - \text{ (toward right)}$$

$\quad\quad\quad\quad\quad\quad\quad$ |
$\quad\quad\quad\quad\quad\quad\quad$ |
$\quad\quad\quad\quad\quad\quad\quad$ |

$\quad\quad$ (toward observer)

In our example, each column of the z-matrix represents the variation of z with x for a fixed y, while each row represents the variation of z with y for a fixed x. Hence the x-axis will be oriented toward the observer while the y-axis will be oriented toward the right.

$\quad$ The complete worksheet is shown in Fig. 9.1. The positive x-axis, defined by the columns of the z-matrix, is oriented toward the observer. The positive y-axis, defined by the rows of the z-matrix, is oriented to the right. The positive z-axis is upward.

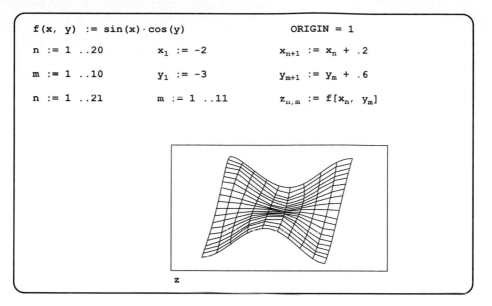

```
f(x, y)  := sin(x)·cos(y)                    ORIGIN = 1

n := 1 ..20           x₁ := -2            xₙ₊₁ := xₙ + .2

m := 1 ..10           y₁ := -3            yₘ₊₁ := yₘ + .6

n := 1 ..21           m := 1 ..11         zₙ,ₘ := f[xₙ, yₘ]
```

z

FIGURE 9.1

To illustrate the above, we use MathCAD to produce a surface plot of a function of a complex variable. Consider the function $w(z) = \ln(z)$ where z is the complex variable $z = x + i \cdot y = re^{i\theta}$. This function can be written as,

$$w(x, y) = u(x, y) + i \cdot v(x, y)$$

where the real and imaginary parts are,

$$u(x, y) = \ln(r) \qquad \text{and} \qquad v(x, y) = i \cdot \theta$$

The modulus and argument of z are defined as,

$$r = |z| = (x^2 + y^2)^{1/2} \qquad \text{and} \qquad \theta = \tan^{-1}\left(\frac{y}{x}\right)$$

Note that at $r = 0$ ($x = 0$, $y = 0$), the function $f(z)$ is undefined. This is because $u(x, y) = \ln(r)$ approaches $-\infty$ as r approaches zero. Note also that the function $\ln(z)$ is multi-valued. Consider, for example, the angles $\theta = 0, 2 \cdot \pi, 4 \cdot \pi, 6 \cdot \pi$, etc. While they all represent the same line (i.e., the positive x-axis), each of the angles generates a different value for the function $v(x, y) = \theta$. To make $\ln(z)$ single valued, we restrict the angle to the domain $-\pi < \theta \leq \pi$. This restriction is built into MathCAD's complex `ln(z)` function. Although the function is now single valued, its value changes abruptly by $2 \cdot \pi$ as we cross the negative x-axis. As we approach the negative x-axis from above, the function's imaginary part has a value $v = \theta = +\pi$. As we approach from below, it has the value $v = \theta = -\pi$. The negative x-axis is called a *branch line* or *branch cut* and the origin is called a *branch point*.

In Worksheet 9.1, we use MathCAD's surface plot to illustrate the properties of the complex `ln(z)` function.

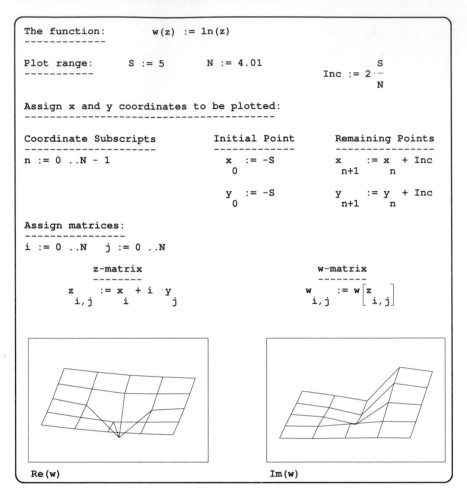

The function: w(z) := ln(z)

Plot range: S := 5   N := 4.01
-----------   Inc := 2·$\frac{S}{N}$

Assign x and y coordinates to be plotted:

Coordinate Subscripts   Initial Point   Remaining Points
--------------------   -------------   ----------------
n := 0 ..N - 1   x := -S   x   := x + Inc
                                 0   n+1   n

                                y := -S   y   := y + Inc
                                 0   n+1   n

Assign matrices:
----
i := 0 ..N   j := 0 ..N

            z-matrix   w-matrix
            --------   --------

      z   := x + i ·y   w   := w$\left[z_{i,j} \right]$
       i,j   i   j   i,j

      Re(w)   Im(w)

WORKSHEET 9.1
A surface plot of a complex function.

MathCAD solution: Worksheet 9.1. We define the function to be plotted and assign the plot domain in the xy-plane. The plot will cover the range $-S \leq x \leq S$ and $-S \leq y \leq S$ in increments of N. We have set S= 5 and N= 4.01.[1] The odd choice for N is made to avoid the origin as a plot point. The plot points x_n and y_n are assigned and then reassigned in complex form as the z-matrix $z_{i,j}$. The elements of the w-matrix are defined using the function $w = \ln(z)$. Finally the real and imaginary parts of the w-matrix are plotted.

---

[1]Note: Since the student edition of MathCAD limits matrices to 5 × n or n × 5, we must limit the value of N in the worksheet to 4.01. The graph resolution is not very good but the features are still discernible. If you are using the professional edition, you may increase N to 10.01 for improved resolution.

The real part $u=Re(w)=ln(r)$ shows the singularity at the origin. The imaginary part $v=Im(w)=\theta$ shows the discontinuity along the branch line.

Formatting Surface Plots

To locally format a surface plot, place the cursor within the plot area and type **f**. The following `Local Surface Format` pull-down menu will appear:

```
Size = 15,30
Rotation = 10
Tilt = 35
Hidden Lines = y
Vertical Scale = 20
Global Default
Revert
Done
```

Move to the desired option, type **{Enter}** and make the changes. When finished, move to `Done` and type **{Enter}**. The plot will be formatted according to the parameters in the menu.

The `Local Surface Format` options are:

`Size=n,m:`	Adjusts the size of plot. The parameters n and m refer to the vertical and horizontal dimensions respectively.
`Rotation=n:`	Rotates the plot n degrees about the vertical axis. The rotation is clockwise looking down from above. The range of the angle rotation must be from zero to ninety degrees. For `Tilt=0°` and `Rotation=0°`, the viewer is looking along the columns of the z-matrix (usually defined as the x-axis). For `Tilt=0°` and `Rotation=90°`, the viewer is looking along the rows of the z-matrix (usually defined as the y-axis).
`Tilt=n:`	Tilts the vertical axis n degrees. The range of the tilt angle must be from zero to ninety degrees. If Tilt is 0°, you are looking along the xy-plane. If `Tilt = 90°`, the view is down the z-axis.
`Hidden Lines=:`	An n shows all lines including hidden lines giving a fish-net-like appearance. A **y** hides hidden lines making the surface appear opaque. A **y** requires a longer plot time.
`Vertical Scale=n:`	Expands or compresses the vertical scale plot.
`Global Default:`	Sets the parameters in the menu back to their global default values.
`Revert:`	Resets the parameters to the current local format settings.
`Done:`	Leaves the menu and formats the plot.

To leave the menu without having any changes take effect, type the **{Esc}** key.

Note: To change the global surface plot, type **{Esc} SURFACEFORMAT** (or its abbreviation **{Esc} SUR**). A "Global Surface Format" menu similar to the one above will appear. Instead of a "Global Default" option you will see an "Overall Default" option. This sets the global default to the MathCAD's "startup" default value. (The startup default value is determined by the configuration file `MCAD.MCC`. For a discussion of this file, see the section "Changing the Configuration File" below.) Changes in this menu are made the same way as in the local surface format menu.

Sketches

Although MathCAD version 2.5 cannot draw sketches, it can import graphics files produced by other CAD packages provided these files have been translated into the MathCAD format. MathCAD sketch files have the DOS extension `.MCS`. They are generated by the translating program called `MCSTRANS.EXE` provided by MathCAD on the distribution diskette. At this writing the only standard format that can be translated into a `.MCS` format is an *HPGL* (Hewlett-Packard Plotter Language) file.

To import a sketch into a worksheet, the following steps are required:

Step I. Invoke your CAD or graphics software and create your sketch.

Step II. Save the sketch as a graphics file using the option which will result in an HPGL format. Assume that this sketch file is named `SKETCH.PGL`

Step III. Use the MathCAD program `MCSTRANS.EXE` to translate this `.PGL` file into an `.MCS` file. At the DOS prompt, type

      MCSTRANS SKETCH.PGL {Enter}

A file called `SKETCH.MCS` will be generated.

Step IV. Begin a worksheet. Place the cursor where you wish to position the sketch. Type **{<Alt>%}** and the following sketch template will appear:

Step V. Fill the placeholder with the filename `SKETCH` and the sketch will appear in the worksheet.

Formatting Sketches

To locally format a sketch, place the cursor within the sketch area and type **f**. The following `Local Sketch Format` pull-down menu will appear:

```
Size = 15,30
Magnification = 1,1
Center = 0.5,0.5
Box = y
Global Default
Revert
Done
```

Move to the desired option, type **{Enter}** and make the changes. When finished, move to `Done` and type **{Enter}**. The sketch will be formatted accordingly.

The `Local Sketch Format` options are:

`Size=n,m:`	Adjusts the size of the sketch region (sketch box). The numbers n and m set the vertical and horizontal dimensions of the box defining the sketch region.
`Magnification=n,m:`	Changes the vertical n and horizontal m magnification within the box area. Values of $(1,1)$ fit the sketch exactly into the box area. Values of $(2,2)$ double the size of the sketch within the box. The sketch box size does not change.
`Center=n,m:`	Positions the sketch in relation to the center of the box. The values $(0.5,0.5)$ position the center of the sketch at the center of the box. By changing the coordinates, you can shift the sketch within the box. Using $(0.25,0.75)$, for example, positions the center of the box to a point that is 25% from the top of the sketch and 75% of the way from the left edge of the sketch.
`Box=:`	The setting y displays the border box; the setting n hides it.
`Global Default:`	Sets the parameters in the menu back to the global default values.
`Revert:`	Resets the parameters to the current local format settings.
`Done:`	Leaves menu and formats the sketch.

To leave the menu without having any changes take effect, type the **{Esc}** key.

Note: To change the global surface plot, type **{Esc} SKETCHFORMAT** (or its abbreviation **{Esc} SKE**). A "Global Sketch Format" menu similar to the one above will appear. Changes are made the same way as for the local format.

MISCELLANEOUS TOPICS

Importing and Exporting Files

While MathCAD provides a quick and convenient way to perform computations and display results, it often does not have the power to handle complex problems. In such cases we rely on programming languages which have powerful mathematical libraries. We can, however, use MathCAD to perform preliminary computations and use the results as input to a more sophisticated program. We can also use the data derived from such a program as input for further MathCAD analysis and display. To accomplish these tasks, we must see how MathCAD "exports" its own data to disk and also how it "imports" data from data files generated by other programs.

MathCAD imports and exports data tables using matrices assigned for that purpose. MathCAD exports data to a disk file in a format known as a standard PRN file. For data to be imported into a worksheet, the disk file must also conform to a PRN format.

Importing Data

To illustrate the importing procedure, we create a PRN file using an elementary BASIC program. The file will contain a trigonometry table of sines and cosines. The data elements of each row are numbers separated by spaces. Each row of data is terminated with a carriage return character. Consider the following QuickBASIC program:

```
'*************************** TRIG.BAS ****************************
Pi = 4 * ATN(1)        'Define Pi
Format$ = "###       ##.##       ##.#####       ##.#####"
FileName$ = "C:\MCAD\MCFILES\TRIG.PRN"

OPEN FileName$ FOR OUTPUT AS #1      'Open file for sequential output

CLS       'Clear screen

FOR Deg% = 0 TO 360 STEP 10
   Rad = Pi * Deg% / 180         'Convert to radians
   PRINT USING Format$; Deg%; Rad; SIN(Rad); COS(Rad)   'Screen Display
   PRINT #1, USING Format$; Deg%; Rad; SIN(Rad); COS(Rad) 'File output
NEXT Deg%

CLOSE #1

END
'****************************************************************
```

The program begins by defining pi as $4 \cdot \tan^{-1}(1)$. Next a string variable For-mat$ is assigned specifying the format of the data to be sent to the output. The file generated will contain data in rows or records. The format string specifies that each row contain four numbers (degrees, radians, sine, cosine) with spaces in between. The number of decimal places printed is determined by the number of #'s after the decimal place in the format string.

The output file is named (TRIG.PRN) and opened for sequential output using buffer #1. The screen is cleared and a computation loop is performed for angles ranging from 0° to 360° in steps of 10°. The angle is converted into radians and the sine and cosine computed. The data is printed to the screen and to a disk file using the specified format. BASIC automatically adds a carriage return character at the end of each PRINT statement. When the FOR/NEXT loop terminates, the file is closed and the program ends. The output file contains the following data:

```
Angle1(Deg)    Angle1(Rad)    Sine(Angle1)    Cosine(Angle1)    <CR>
Angle2(Deg)    Angle2(Rad)    Sine(Angle2)    Cosine(Angle2)    <CR>
Angle3(Deg)    Angle3(Rad)    Sine(Angle3)    Cosine(Angle3)    <CR>
    .
    .
    .

etc
```

In order to import (or export) data from a disk file such as the one created above, we assign a variable name to the file. That variable name will be used in the worksheet to reference the file. This procedure is called *association*; it is made with the following keystrokes: **{F10}** (menu) **F** (file) **F** (filename). A prompt will appear on the message line asking for a file variable name. Enter a variable name to be

```
                                                    ORIGIN ≡ 0

Use [F10] F(ile) F(ilename) to associate
   File variable: Trig   with   Disk filename: TRIG  .
-----------------------------------------------------
Read Data table (Trig) into matrix Data:   Data := READPRN(Trig)
---------------------------------------

Display Data Matrix:                        Extract Data Vectors:
-------------------                         ---------------------
                                                    <0>              <1>
           │  0    0        0       1│      degs := Data      rads := Data
           │ 10  0.17   0.17365  0.98481│
           │ 20  0.35   0.34202  0.93969│           <2>              <3>
           │ 30  0.52      0.5   0.86603│     sine := Data      cosine := Data
           │ 40   0.7   0.64279  0.76604│
  Data =   │ 50  0.87   0.76604  0.64279│
           │ 60  1.05   0.86603     0.5│      Plot Data
           │ 70  1.22   0.93969  0.34202│      ---------
           │ 80   1.4   0.98481  0.17365│       i := 0 ..36
           │ 90  1.57      1        0│
           │100  1.75   0.98481  -0.17365│              1
           │110  1.92   0.93969  -0.34202│
           │120  2.09   0.86603    -0.5│    sine , cosine
           │130  2.27   0.76604  -0.64279│      i       i
           │140  2.44   0.64279  -0.76604│
           │150  2.62      0.5   -0.86603│            -1
           │160  2.79   0.34202  -0.93969│               0   degs   360
           │170  2.97   0.17365  -0.98481│                     i
           │180  3.14      0       -1│
           │190  3.32  -0.17365  -0.98481│
           │200  3.49  -0.34202  -0.93969│
           │210  3.67     -0.5   -0.86603│
           │220  3.84  -0.64279  -0.76604│
           │230  4.01  -0.76604  -0.64279│
           │240  4.19  -0.86603    -0.5│
           │250  4.36  -0.93969  -0.34202│
           │260  4.54  -0.98481  -0.17365│
           │270  4.71     -1        0│
           │280  4.89  -0.98481   0.17365│
           │290  5.06  -0.93969   0.34202│
           │300  5.24  -0.86603      0.5│
           │310  5.41  -0.76604   0.64279│
           │320  5.59  -0.64279   0.76604│
           │330  5.76     -0.5    0.86603│
           │340  5.93  -0.34202   0.93969│
           │350  6.11  -0.17365   0.98481│
           │360  6.28      0        1│
```

WORKSHEET 9.2
Reading a data file with **READPRN**.

associated with the file and type {Enter}. In Worksheet 9.2 we use the variable name Trig. Note that a variable name *is* case sensitive.

Next the message line will display a prompt with a default DOS filename which is identical to your variable name. If this is in fact the file you wish to use, just type {Enter}. Otherwise use the {BkSpc} key to erase the default and enter the DOS filename which contains the data to be imported (in our example, TRIG.PRN). The DOS filename is *not* case sensitive. Once the association is made, MathCAD will reference the DOS file TRIG.PRN by the variable name Trig.

The default extension used by MathCAD is PRN. If the file has this extension you need not add it to the filename. Thus, if you use TRIG for the filename, MathCAD will assume a DOS filename of TRIG.PRN. If your DOS filename has another extension, you must specify it explicitly.

In Worksheet 9.2, we import the data file TRIG.PRN into a MathCAD worksheet using MathCAD's **READPRN** function. We make sure that this data file is in the current file subdirectory (e.g., C:\MCAD\MCFILES) along with the other MathCAD worksheet files.

> **MathCAD solution: Worksheet 9.2.** We type **{F10}** (menu) **F** (file) **F** (filename) and assign the variable name Trig to the DOS file TRIG. Once the association is made, MathCAD will reference the DOS file TRIG.PRN by the variable name Trig. To read the data file into a matrix, we use MathCAD's **READPRN** function. We type **Data:READPRN(Trig)** and see,
>
> Data := READPRN(Trig)
>
> The trigonometry data is read from the disk file and retrieved in a 37×4 matrix, arbitrarily named Data. To display the matrix, we type **Data=** and we see the data retrieved from the disk file. Note that we are using the default subscript ORIGIN (zero).
>
> To separate the data, we extract the columns (labeled 0–3) one-by-one from the matrix. [Recall that to extract a column use **{<Ctrl>^}**.] These four vectors contain the data for the angle in degrees, the angle in radians, the sine, and the cosine respectively.
>
> Finally, the data is plotted. Since there are a total of 37 data points (0–36), we set the subscript range accordingly and complete the plots of the sine and cosine. We have manually set the scale on the horizontal axis by filling the right placeholder with 360.

You can also import data generated by programs such as Lotus or Quattro. The file should contain only numeric data and no labels. Simply use the spreadsheet software to generate a PRN file. (Consult your documentation for details.) You should then be able to import the PRN file directly into a MathCAD worksheet.

Exporting Data

Suppose you wish to produce an elaborate plot of the first few Bessel functions using Lotus or Quattro. MathCAD can compute these functions directly and export the data to a PRN file. We will call this file BESSEL.PRN. The exporting procedure is accomplished by *reversing* the importing procedure. We first compute the Bessel functions and store the data in a matrix arbitrarily called Data. We then assign a variable name (e.g., Bessel) to be associated with the file. (Recall—use **{F10}** (menu) **F** (file) **F** (filename) to make the association.) Next we use MathCAD's **WRITEPRN** function to write the data to a disk file. We type: **WRITEPRN(file variable):Data** where Data is the variable name of the data matrix and file variable is the variable name associated with the DOS file to which the data will be exported. The disk file is *not* generally updated when you make changes. To invoke the writing process to the disk and update the file, use the command: **{F10}** (menu) **C** (compute) **P** (process). You may also use **{Esc} PRO {Enter}**.

The format in which data is written to a disk file is determined by two MathCAD format controls—PRNCOLWIDTH (default=8) and PRNPRECISION (default=4). The first sets the column width and aligns the data neatly into columns by inserting the required spaces between the data elements. The second control determines the number of significant digits to be used in representing the data. If the value is either too small or too large to fit the format, the data is written to the file in exponential notation. PRNCOLWIDTH and PRNPRECISION may be changed using the {Esc} **SET** command or they can be entered directly into the worksheet.

The process of exporting data is illustrated in Worksheet 9.3.

ORIGIN $\equiv$ 0

Use [F10] F(ile) F(ilename) to associate
 File variable: Bessel with filename: BESSEL .   PRNCOLWIDTH $\equiv$ 12

Define i and x: i := 0 ..30 $x_i := \dfrac{i}{2}$ PRNPRECISION $\equiv$ 4

Construct Data Vectors: $B0_i$:= $Jn\left[0, x_i\right]$ $B1_i$:= $Jn\left[1, x_i\right]$ $B2_i$:= $Jn\left[2, x_i\right]$

Construct Data Matrix:

Data := augment(x, B0)   Data := augment(Data, B1)   Data := augment(Data, B2)

Write Matrix table (Data) into file (BESSEL):   WRITEPRN(Bessel) := Data
----

Data =

0	1	0	0
0.5	0.9385	0.2423	0.0306
1	0.7652	0.4401	0.1149
1.5	0.5118	0.5579	0.2321
2	0.2239	0.5767	0.3528
2.5	-0.0484	0.4971	0.4461
3	-0.2601	0.3391	0.4861
3.5	-0.3801	0.1374	0.4586
4	-0.3971	-0.066	0.3641
4.5	-0.3205	-0.2311	0.2178
5	-0.1776	-0.3276	0.0466
5.5	-0.0068	-0.3414	0.1173
6	0.1506	-0.2767	-0.2429
6.5	0.2601	-0.1538	-0.3074
7	0.3001	-0.0047	-0.3014
7.5	0.2663	0.1352	-0.2303
8	0.1717	0.2346	-0.113
8.5	0.0419	0.2731	0.0223
9	-0.0903	0.2453	0.1448
9.5	-0.1939	0.1613	0.2279
10	-0.2459	0.0435	0.2546
10.5	-0.2366	-0.0789	0.2216
11	-0.1712	-0.1768	0.139
11.5	-0.0677	-0.2284	0.0279
12	0.0477	-0.2234	-0.0849
12.5	0.1469	-0.1655	-0.1734
13	0.2069	-0.0703	-0.2177
13.5	0.215	0.038	-0.2094
14	0.1711	0.1334	-0.152
14.5	0.0875	0.1934	-0.0609
15	-0.0142	0.2051	0.0416

$B0_i$, $B1_i$, $B2_i$

WORKSHEET 9.3
Writing a data file with **WRITEPRN**.

MathCAD solution: Worksheet 9.3. We enter PRNCOLWIDTH≡12 and PRNPRECIS-
ION≡4 directly into the worksheet. This insures proper spacing between the data elements. We next associate a DOS filename which we call BESSEL.PRN with the file
variable Bessel. The association is made using the following keystrokes: {**F10**} (menu)
F (file) **F** (filename). The PRN extension in the filename is optional. If omitted, Math-
CAD will automatically add it. If you wish to use another extension, you must add it
explicitly.

We next assign a range subscript i and define the subscripted variable x_i. [We
are using a subscript ORIGIN of zero.] The vector **x** contains the points at which the
Bessel functions are to be tabulated. The first three Bessel functions are computed at the
points x_i and assigned to the vectors **B0**, **B1**, and **B2**. The four vectors **x**, **B0**, **B1**, and
B2 are augmented to form the 31×4 data matrix Data. The data is written to the disk
file BESSEL.PRN using the **WRITEPRN** function.

The data matrix is displayed and plotted.

The PRN file created by MathCAD can now be imported into Lotus or Quattro
for plotting. See the documentation provided with your spreadsheet software. A graph
produced by Quattro Pro from data imported from Worksheet 9.3 is shown in Fig. 9.2.

Note: In a standard PRN file, spaces are used to separate data elements within
a row. You can see if spaces are properly embedded between the elements by using
the DOS TYPE command. At the DOS prompt, enter **TYPE BESSEL.PRN**. The data
will appear on the screen. If any two data elements in any row are not separated by at
least one space, increase the parameter in the PRNCOLWIDTH function and reprocess
the MathCAD worksheet to produce an updated PRN file.

Following is a simple QuickBASIC program to read and print the data in the
file BESSEL.PRN created in Worksheet 9.3.

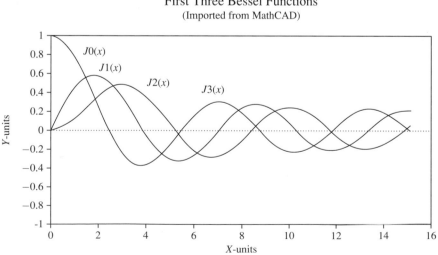

First Three Bessel Functions
(Imported from MathCAD)

FIGURE 9.2

```
'*********************** BESSEL.BAS *****************************
Format$ = "###.##      ##.#####      ##.#####      ##.#####"
FileName$ = "Bessel.Prn"

OPEN FileName$ FOR INPUT AS #1      'Open file for sequential input

CLS        'Clear screen

DO WHILE NOT EOF(1)
   INPUT #1, x, Bessel0, Bessel1, Bessel2              'Input Data
   PRINT USING Format$; x; Bessel0; Bessel1; Bessel2   'Display Data
   LPRINT USING Format$; x; Bessel0; Bessel1; Bessel2  'Print Data

LOOP

CLOSE #1
END
'****************************************************************
```

In this program, the file is named and opened for sequential input using buffer #1. The screen is cleared and the data is accessed in a `DO WHILE/LOOP` using BASIC's `INPUT#` statement. The data is read and displayed on the screen and sent to the printer. The process exits the loop when the `end-of-file` marker is reached

If you use **WRITEPRN** to write data to an existing data file, that file will be destroyed and replaced with one containing the new data. If you wish to *add* data to an existing file, use MathCAD's **APPENDPRN** function. For example, to add data to the existing file `BESSEL.PRN`, type **APPENDPRN(Bessel):DataAdd** where `DataAdd` is the matrix containing the data to be appended and `Bessel` is the file variable name associated with the existing file `BESSEL.PRN`.

You can also read and write data sequentially from an *unstructured* file using **READ**, **WRITE**, and **APPEND**. The syntax can be seen from the following objects:

$$i := 1 .. 10 \qquad N_i := READ(filevar1)$$
$$WRITE(filevar2) := N_i \qquad APPEND(filevar3) := N_i$$

Each time one of the above objects is executed, a single data element (starting from the first) is read, written, or appended. In the above example, ten data elements are read from `filevar1`, written to `filevar2`, and appended to `filevar3`.

Split Windows

MathCad allows you to work with two *separate* worksheets at the same time. This is done by loading one worksheet in the standard manner. Type either **{F10}** (menu) **F** (file) **L** (load) or **{F5}** (load). Supply the filename to be loaded and type **{Enter}**. If you type **{Enter}** without supplying a filename, a list of all the worksheets stored in the current subdirectory will be displayed. Move the cursor to the desired filename and type **{Enter}**. After the first worksheet is loaded, move the cursor midway down the screen to the line where you want the windows to split. Type **{F10}** (menu) **W** (window) **S** (split) or simply type the **{F7}** (split) key. You will see the screen split into two windows with the upper one containing the worksheet already loaded and the lower one blank. Type the **{F5}** (load) key and the lower window will display a message line requesting the name of a second file to be loaded. Supply the filename in the usual way and the second worksheet will appear in the lower window. You may switch from one window to the other using **{F10}** (menu) **W** (window) **J** (jump) or by typing the **{F8}** (jump) key. You can move and copy objects from one window to the other using the **{F2}** (Copy) or **{F3}** (Cut) and **{F4}** (Paste) keys. You can also edit in the usual way. To save the worksheet, type **{F10}** (menu) **F** (file) **S** (save) or simply type the **{F6}** (save) key. To change the sizes of the windows, move the cursor to the desired line and type **{F10}** (menu) **W** (window) **S** (split) or type the **{F7}** (split) key again.

To unsplit the window, type **{<Ctrl>F7}** (unsplit). The lower window will disappear and you will be returned to the upper window. If you have edited the lower worksheet, a message prompt will appear asking if you wish to save it.

Cursor Motion

The cursor can be moved in single steps with the arrow keys. In blank regions, it can moved to the right in steps of ten spaces with the **{Tab}** key (or the **{<Ctrl>→ }** key) and to the left with the **{<Shift>Tab}** (or the **{<Ctrl> ←}** key) key. Within mathematical object regions, the **{Tab}** moves the cursor between placeholders; within text regions, it moves the cursor between words. The cursor can be moved down in steps of five lines with the **{PgUp}** key and up with the **{PgDn}** key. Using **{<Ctrl>PgUp}** and **{<Ctrl>PgDn}** moves up or down by 80% of the screen. To move to the first object use **{<Ctrl>Home}** and to the last object use **{<Ctrl>End}**.

To move the cursor directly to a specified position in the worksheet, use the "Goto" command **{F10}** (menu) **E** (edit) **G** (goto) **l c**, where **l** and **c** represent the destination line and column of the worksheet. The cursor will generally be moved to the upper left of the screen and the worksheet manipulated so that the cursor ends up on line **l** and column **c**. You may move a certain number of lines and columns *relative* to your current position by using the "Move" command **{F10}** (menu) **E** (edit) **M** (move) **l c**. Negative values of **l** and **c** locate the cursor **l** lines above and **c** columns to the left of your current position.

Text Editing

A *textband*[1] is a predefined region for text extending across the worksheet from margin to margin. You create a text band using the command **{F10}** (menu) **T** (text) **T** (textband) or simply **{<Ctrl>T}**. As you write within the text band, words automatically wrap to the next line so that the band may actually contain many lines. No other

---

[1]The textband feature is not available in the student edition of MathCAD.

objects can reside on the lines of a text band. As a text band region grows downward, it extends into other object regions. When you finish editing the text band, type **{<Ctrl>N}** (see the text justify command below) and the other objects will be relocated.

A regular text region is one whose width is not fixed at a screen width but extends as you type. You can preset the width of a text region for word wrap using the command **{F10}** (menu) **T** (text) **W** (width). When the message line appears, set the value of the column width. Note that you must first create a text region (using the double-quote key **"**) and be in that region in order to set the width for text rewrapping. Since a regular text region need not be a full screen width, it can be placed alongside other objects.

To start a new paragraph in any text region, type the carriage return key **{Enter}**. You will see a paragraph termination character (a solid arrow) embedded in the text. *Never use the* **{Enter}** *key to leave a text region.* Use any of the arrow (or **<Ctrl>** arrow) keys.

To center text on a line, use **{F10}** (menu) **T** (text) **C** (center). Sometimes after editing a text region (i.e., removing certain words), a paragraph will have a relatively ragged edge at the margin. To justify the paragraph and improve its appearance, use the command **{F10}** (menu) **T** (text) **J** (justify) or simply type **{<Ctrl>N}**.

Within a text region, it is possible to move the cursor with any of the following:

To skip by:	use	delimiter
words	**{<Ctrl>W}**	spaces
lines	**{<Ctrl>L}**	margins
sentences	**{<Ctrl>S}**	periods
paragraphs.	**{<Ctrl>P}**	indents or blank lines

For the above commands to execute forward in the text, set the text motion parameter to forward using **{F10}** (menu) **T** (text) **F** (forward) or **{<Ctrl>F}**. For reverse motion, use **{F10}** (menu) **T** (text) **B** (backward) or **{<Ctrl>B}**.

To search for specific text, place the cursor at the beginning of the worksheet and use the command **{F10}** (menu) **E** (edit) **F** (find) or **{<Ctrl>F5}**. On the message line, enter the text to be searched for and type the **{Enter}** key. When the first occurrence is found, type **(+)** to continue the search forward for successive occurrences or type **(-)** for a backward search for previous occurrences.

To perform a search and replace with specific text, start at the beginning of the worksheet and type the command **{F10}** (menu) **E** (edit) **R** (replace) or **{<Ctrl>F6}**. Enter the text to be searched for and then the text to replace it with. As the cursor moves through the found text, you may approve the change **(y)**, bypass the change **(n)**, quit **(q)**, or make the change at all further occurrences **(a)**.

You can cut, copy, or paste text using the following procedure. First mark the desired text using **{F10}** (menu) **T** (text) **M** (mark) or **{<Ctrl>X}**. Do so at both the beginning and end of the text. You will see a color change in the marked text. Use the In-region Copy command **{F10}** (menu) **I** (in-Region) **C** (copy) or **{<Ctrl>F2}** (incopy) to leave the marked text as is but copy it into the text buffer. Use the In-

`Region Cut` command **{F10}** (menu) **I** (in-Region) **C** (cut) or **{<Ctrl>F3}** (incut) to delete the marked text but copy it into the text buffer. Finally, move the cursor to the new position and use the `In-region Paste` command **{F10}** (menu) **I** (in-Region) **P** (paste) or **{<Ctrl>F4}** (inpaste) to copy the text buffer contents into the worksheet at the current cursor position. When you leave a text region, any marked text becomes unmarked but the buffer contents remain intact.

Printing Reports

Before printing a report, make sure that MathCAD is configured for your printer by typing **{F10}** (menu) **S** (system) **S** (select printer). From the menu choose your printer. Use **{F10}** (menu) **S** (system) **C** (configuration save) to store this information in MathCAD's configuration file `MCAD.MCC`.

You can customize the printing format using the command **{F10}** (menu) **W** (window/page). You can set the page length with the **P** (pagelength) subcommand (use `pagelength=0` for no page breaks). The left margin is fixed with the **M** (margin) subcommand. You may insert a "hard" pagebreak using the subcommand **I** (insert pagebreak). You may delete such a break with the **{F3}** (cut) key. If any objects inadvertently fall on a pagebreak, they may be moved using the **B** (break pages) subcommand. The text band line width can be set using the **L** (linelength) subcommand.[2]

To print the worksheet, type **{F10}** (menu) **S** (system) **P** (print) or **{<Ctrl>O}**. The message line indicates the coordinates of the upper left and lower right corners of the worksheet to be printed. The default is the entire worksheet. These values can be changed to print only a portion of the worksheet. After entering the coordinates, indicate the port to which the printer is attached (default is PRN which is the first parallel printer port, LPT1). The worksheet will be printed as a report on the printer.

Appending a Worksheet File from Disk

To append a worksheet from a disk file to the one currently being edited in the workspace, type **{F10}** (menu) **F** (file) **A** (append). Supply the filename and the worksheet on disk will be appended at the end of the current worksheet.

Changing the Configuration File

When MathCAD is invoked, the default parameters for formatting numbers and plots as well as the parameters for setting the subscript origin (`ORIGIN`) and computation tolerance (`TOL`) are read from a special configuration file called `MCAD.MCC`. This file contains a list of MathCAD commands which are executed in sequence and determine the default values of MathCAD's configuration parameters. You may change this

---

[2]Since the student edition of MathCAD limits a worksheet to two pages with 80 characters across, most of the print formatting features are not available with this version.

file using an ASCII file editor such as DOS's `EDLIN.COM` program. A typical `MCAD.MCC` file may have the following commands:

```
SURFACEFORMAT rot=10 tilt=35 hidden=n size=15,30
SKETCHFORMAT mag=1.00,1.00 center=0.50,0.50 size=15,30 box=y
PLOTFORMAT logs=0,0 subdivs=1,1 size=5,15 type=1
FORMAT   rd=d ct=10 im=i et=3 zt=15 pr=3 mass length time charge
SET ORIGIN 0
SET TOL 0.001
MARGIN 0
LINELENGTH 78
SET PRNCOLWIDTH 8
SET PRNPRECISION 4
SELECTPRINTER 7
PAGELENGTH 0
DIMENSIONS M=mass L=length T=time Q=charge
```

For example, if you will be working primarily with vectors and matrices, you might want to edit the configuration file `MCAD.MCC` by changing `SET ORIGIN 0` to `SET ORIGIN 1` in the appropriate line.

You may configure MathCAD for your default printer by typing **{F10}** (menu) **S** (system) **S** (select printer). The current parameters can be preserved in the configuration file using **{F10}** (menu) **S** (system) **C** (config save). The message line will prompt for confirmation. To save the configuration in the `MCAD.MCC` file, type **{Enter}**.

You may also leave the file `MCAD.MCC` as is, but create a similar file (using `EDLIN.COM`) called, for example, `MCAD1.MCC` in which the appropriate parameters have been altered. To invoke MathCAD with this configuration, type (at the DOS prompt) `MCAD/RMCAD1`. The invocation "`MCAD/R` *filename*" allows you to use the configuration file of your choice. If you invoke MathCAD and `MCAD.MCC` is not found or another configuration file is not specified, MathCAD loads using its *internal* default values. If you load a modified configuration at invocation time, you can return to the internal default values by typing **{F10}** (menu) **F** (file) **R** (reset). This clears the work space and resets the default parameters. To simply clear a work space and keep the MCAD.MCC configuration, type: **{F10}** (menu) **F** (file) **C** (clear).

MathCAD Command Files and the Execute Command

A file with the extension `.MCC` (such as `MCAD.MCC`) is called a MathCAD "command" file and can be invoked from within MathCAD. Suppose you find that you are frequently issuing a set of MathCAD commands. For example, at the start of a new worksheet you wish to switch into the manual mode, set the subscript origin equal to one and set the tolerance equal to .00001. Using the **{Esc} SET** command, you could execute these three commands manually, one after the other. However, it is faster and more convenient to store them in a command file with the extension `.MCC`. By executing this command file, the three commands take effect automatically.

You create such a file using an ASCII word processor such as DOS's `EDLIN.COM`. You can also use **{F10}** (menu) **S** (system) **C** (config save) and choose a custom name to store the current configurations in the worksheet. For our specific case, the file, which we arbitrarily name `FASTSET.MCC`, should contain the following commands:

```
MAN
SET ORIGIN 1
SET TOL .00001
```

This file should be placed in the current (\MCAD\MCFILES) subdirectory. After beginning the worksheet, we invoke the command **{F10}** (menu) **S** (system) **E** (execute) or in abbreviated form **{Esc} EX**. A list of MathCAD command files in the current subdirectory (those having the extension `.MCC`) will appear. If we choose the command file `FASTSET`, the compute manual mode will be set, the subscript origin will be changed to one, and the tolerance will be increased to .00001 *automatically*. (To invoke this command file, you can also use: **{Esc} EX FASTSET**.) You may create as many different command files as you require. Data file format functions such as **WRITEPRN** and **READPRN** cannot be executed from a command file.

Optional Invocation Switches

By invoking MathCAD with software "switches," you can load it in different ways. For example if you invoke it as `MCAD/M`, it will run in the manual calculate mode by default [unless you change it during the session with **{F10}** (menu) **C** (compute) **A** (automatic)]. If you wish to invoke MathCAD and load a worksheet in one step, type **MCAD** *filename*.

If you are using a color monitor, you can adjust the colors of the foreground and background by using the invocation `MCAD/F##/B##` where `##` represents the following numbers: `Red=32 Green=16, Blue=08, Intense Red=04, Intense Green=02, Intense Blue=01`. To produce yellow, for example, use `yellow= red + green = 32 + 16 = 48`. Use 63 for white and 00 for black. A list of invocation options is given in Appendix A.

While MathCAD senses your video adapter card and configures itself automatically, there are a number of switches that can be used to override the default values if problems arise. Consult Appendix A and your display/adaptor card documentation for information.

Setting Paths for a Hard Disk

Copy all MathCAD files into a subdirectory called `C:\MCAD`. Place all worksheet files into a lower subdirectory `C:\MCAD\MCFILES`. You can invoke MathCAD from any drive or subdirectory if you add the path information to your `AUTOEXEC.BAT` file as follows:

```
REM AUTOEXEC.BAT
PATH=C:\MCAD
SET MCADDIR=C:\MCAD
```

The `PATH` statement tells DOS where to find the MathCAD program. The `SET` command tells MathCAD where to find the auxiliary information it needs. If you already have a `PATH` statement in your `AUTOEXEC.BAT` file, then add the path `C:\MCAD` to it.

If you place the following batch file called `MC.BAT` in the subdirectory `C:\MCAD`,

```
REM MC.BAT
CD \MCAD\MCFILES
MCAD
```

you will be able to invoke MathCAD at any time by typing `MC`. Your worksheets will be readily available from the current subdirectory.

The DOS Shell, Available Memory, and Help

It is possible to execute DOS commands while developing a worksheet by "shelling" to DOS. Use the command **{F10}** (menu) **S** (system) **D** (dos). The message line will display the prompt `DOS>`. You may execute any single DOS command after which you will automatically be returned to the worksheet. To return temporarily to DOS for a session of commands, type **{Enter}** at the message prompt `DOS>`. (If this does not work, invoke the DOS command processor `COMMAND.COM` by typing `\COMMAND`, assuming that `COMMAND.COM` is in the root directory of your current drive). You will see the DOS prompt (e.g., `C>`). You can now execute any number of DOS commands. When you finish, type `EXIT` and you will be returned to the worksheet.

To see how much memory is available to MathCAD and how much is actually being used by your worksheet, type the command **{F10}** (menu) **S** (system) **M** (memory). The message line will display the available memory.

Note: On occasion, MathCAD will run out of memory. When this happens you will be forced to exit MathCAD. However, MathCAD will let you save your work on disk before exiting.

To display MathCAD's on-line help menu, use the command, **{F10}** (menu) **S** (system) **H** (help). Use **{Esc}** to return to MathCAD.

Issuing Commands in Command Lines

Throughout this book, we have been using the commands from the "pull-down" menus. When you become proficient in MathCAD, you will likely want to invoke commands using the "command line." Any command can be initiated using the **{Esc}** key. A message line will appear with the prompt `Command:`. Type the first few letters of the command to invoke it. Commands are *not* case sensitive. Some examples are:

{Esc} + Abbreviated Command	Effect
HEL	on-line help
QUI	exit MathCAD
MAN	manual compute
AUT	automatic compute
PRO	process
FORM	format (global)
PRI	print report
SET	invoke SET submenu
SET ORIGIN	set origin
SET ORIGIN 1	set origin equal to one
PLO	plotformat (global)
SUR	surfaceformat (global)
SKE	sketchformat (global)

For example, to change to the manual calculation mode, you can type **{Esc} MAN**. Certain commands such as **SET** and **PLOTFORMAT** (**SKETCHFORMAT** and **SUR-FACEFORMAT** in version 2.5) can only be invoked using the **{Esc}**+Command. They do not appear as **{F10}** (menu) options.

We list a summary of the commands in Appendix A.

PROBLEMS

1. Show how to sort a 3×3 matrix **M** on a *column* using only **rsort** (i.e., without using **csort**. [Requires MathCAD version 2.5.]

2. Obtain surface plots of the real and imaginary parts of the function $f(z) = e^z$, where $z = x + iy$. [Requires MathCAD version 2.5.]

3. Using surface plots, examine the properties of the real and imaginary parts of the function $f(z) = z^{1/2}$. [Requires MathCAD version 2.5.]

4. Create a complex data vector of the form:

$$\text{Data} = \begin{bmatrix} -2 + 3i \\ 3 - 2i \\ -1 - 2i \\ 4 + 1i \\ 2 + 5i \\ 4 - 3i \\ -3 - 2i \\ 2 + 5i \end{bmatrix}$$

   (a) Export this vector to a disk file named COMPLEX.PRN using the **WRITEPRN** function. Hint: Use **{F10}** (menu) **F** (file) **F** (filename) to associate the variable name Complex with the DOS file name COMPLEX and make the assignment WRITEPRN(Complex) := Data.

   (b) Using the DOS command **TYPE**, examine the structure of COMPLEX.PRN.

5. Use either your spreadsheet software or a suitable programming language program to retrieve and display the real and imaginary parts of the data from the data file COMPLEX.PRN generated in Problem 4.

APPENDIX
A

SUMMARY OF COMMANDS AND FUNCTIONS

[Adapted from the MathCAD Version 2.5 Reference Manual with permission from MathSoft, Inc.]

FUNCTION KEYS

[F1]	help	**[F2]**	copy
		<Ctrl>[F2]	incopy
[F3]	cut	**[F4]**	paste
<Ctrl>[F3]	incut	**<Ctrl>[F4]**	inpaste
[F5]	load	**[F6]**	save
<Ctrl>[F5]	search	**<Ctrl>[F6]**	replace
[F7]	split	**[F8]**	switch
<Ctrl>[F7]	unsplit		(jump)
[F9]	calculate	**[F10]**	command menus
<Ctrl>[F9]	insertline	**<Ctrl>[F10]**	deleteline

TEMPLATE CREATION AND FORMATTING KEYS

Keystroke	Effect
@	Create plot template.
\<Alt>@	Create surface plot template.*
\<Alt>%	Create sketch template.*
"	Create text region.
\<Ctrl>T	Create text band.†
\<Alt>M	Create matrix template.‡
f	(With cursor in region to be formatted, invokes local format menu.)
d	(With cursor in region to be formatted, returns to global default.)

*Not available in version 2.0.

†Not available in student edition.

‡Number of columns limited in student edition.

KEYS FOR MATHEMATICAL OPERATIONS

		Simple keys:	
Keystroke	Symbol	Meaning	Example
+ (plus)	+	Addition	$a+b$
- (minus)	—	Subtraction	$a-b$
- (minus)	—	Negation	$-a$
* (asterisk)	·	Multiplication	$a \cdot b$
/ (slash)	—	Division	$\frac{a}{b}$
^ (caret)		Raise to power	a^n
' (apostrophe)	( )	Pair of parentheses	(a)
[(left bracket)		Subscript	a_n
! (exclamation pt.)	!	Factorial	$a!$
" (double quote)	—	Complex conjugate	$\bar{a}$
\ (back slash)	$\sqrt{\ }$	Square root	$\sqrt{a}$

¦ (pipe symbol)	| |	Absolute value (modulus)	|a|
> (greater-than)	$>$	Greater-than relational operator	a>b
< (less-than)	$<$	Less-than relational operator	a<b
, (comma)	,	Range variable delimiter	x := 1,1.1 ..5
; (semi-colon)	..	Range variable delimiter	n := 0 ..10
$ (dollar sign)	$\sum$	Series summation	$\sum_n a_n$
# (pound sign)	$\prod$	Series product	$\prod_n a_n$
? (question mark)	$\frac{d}{dx}$	Derivative	$\frac{d}{dx} y(x)$
& (ampersand)	$\int$	Integral	$\int_a^b f(x)\ dx$

Compound keys:

Keystroke	Symbol	Meaning	Example
<Alt>* (asterisk)	x	Vector cross product.	a x b
<Alt>M		Create or edit matrix.	
<Alt>! (exclamation)	T	Transpose of a matrix.	M^T
<Alt>^ (caret)	$<\ >$	Column extract of a matrix.	$M^{<1>}$
<Alt>@ ("at" symbol)		Create surface plot template.*	
<Alt>% (percent)		Create sketch region template.*	
<Alt>= (equals)	$\approx$	Relation equals.	if(a$\approx$0,b,c)
<Alt># (pound)	$\neq$	Relational not equals.	if(a$\neq$0,b,c)
<Alt>((left parenthesis)	$\leq$	Less-than or equal-to relational operator.	if(a$\leq$0,b,c)
<Alt>) (right parenthesis)	$\geq$	Greater-than or equal-to relational operator.	if(a$\geq$0,b,c)
<Alt>- (hyphen)	$\rightharpoondown$	Vectorize equation operator.	a:=$\overrightarrow{(b+c)}$
<Alt>$ (dollar sign)	$\sum$	Sum the elements of a vector.	Sum := $\sum_n v_n$
<Ctrl> {Enter}		Addition with line break.	x1 ... + x2

*Not available in version 2.0.

FUNCTIONS

Trigonometry

z may be complex, x and y are real.

sin(z)	Sine.	Argument in radians.
cos(z)	Cosine.	Argument in radians.
tan(z)	Tangent.	Argument in radians.
asin(z)	Inverse sine.	Result in radians.
acos(z)	Inverse cosine.	Result in radians.
atan(z)	Inverse tangent.	Result in radians.
angle(x,y)	Angle from x-axis to point (x, y).	Result in radians.

Log and Exponential

z may be complex.

exp(z)	e raised to power z.
ln(z)	Natural logarithm.
log(z)	Common (base 10) logarithm.

Hyperbolic

z may be complex.

sinh(z)	Hyperbolic sine.
cosh(z)	Hyperbolic cosine.
tanh(z)	Hyperbolic tangent.
asinh(z)	Inverse hyperbolic sine.
acosh(z)	Inverse hyperbolic cosine.
atanh(z)	Inverse hyperbolic tangent.

Bessel

x must be real, n must be non-negative integer.

J0(x)	Bessel function $J_0(x)$.
J1(x)	Bessel function $J_1(x)$.
Jn(n,x)	Bessel function $J_n(x)$.
Y0(x)	Neumann function $Y_0(x)$ $(x > 0)$.
Y1(x)	Neumann function $Y_1(x)$ $(x > 0)$.
Yn(n,x)	Neumann function $Y_n(x)$ $(x > 0)$.

Complex number functions

z is complex.

Re(z)	Real part of z.	
Im(z)	Imaginary part of z.	
arg(z)	Argument of z	$(-\pi < \arg(z) \leq \pi)$.

Statistical

x must be real, z may be complex.

mean(v)	Mean value of data contained in vector **v**.
stdev(v)	Standard deviation of data contained in vector **v**.
var(v)	Variance of data contained in vector **v**.
Γ(z)	Euler's gamma function.
erf(x)	Error function.
cnorm(x)	Cumulative normal distribution.
hist(intervals,data)	Histogram of vector **data** using components of vector **intervals** to mark intervals.

Linear Regression

`slope(vx,vy)`	Slope of regression line for data vectors vx and vy.
`intercept(vx,vy)`	Intercept of regression line for data vectors vx and vy.
`corr(vx,vy)`	Correlation (Pearson's r) of data vectors vx and vy.

Interpolation

`linterp(vx,vy,x)`	Linearly interpolated value at **x** based on **vx** and **vy**.
`cspline(vx,vy)`	Coefficients of cubic spline with cubic ends derived from **vx** and **vy**.
`lspline(vx,vy)`	Coefficients of cubic spline with linear ends derived from **vx** and **vy**.
`pspline(vx,vy)`	Coefficients of cubic spline with parabolic ends derived from **vx** and **vy**.
`interp(vs,vx,vy,x)`	Interpolated value at **x** derived from **vx** and **vy**, based on coefficients of **vs**.

Fast Fourier Transforms

`fft(v)`	Fast Fourier transform of real data vector **v**.
`ifft(v)`	Inverse fast Fourier transform of real data vector **v**.
`cfft(v)`	Fast Fourier transform of complex data vector **v**.
`icfft(v)`	Inverse fast Fourier transform of complex data vector **v**.

Vectors

length(v)	Number of elements in vector **v**.
last(v)	Index of last element in vector **v**.
max(v)	Maximum element in vector **v**.
min(v)	Minimum element in vector **v**.

Matrices

rows(M)	Number of rows in matrix **M**.
cols(M)	Number of columns in matrix **M**.
identity(n)	Identity (or unit) matrix of size **n**.
tr(M)	Trace of matrix **M**.
augment(M1,M2)	Matrix made by putting M1 and M2 side by side.

Miscellaneous

x must be real.

floor(x)	Greatest integer smaller than or equal to x.
ceil(x)	Smallest integer greater than or equal to x.
rnd(x)	Random number between zero and x.
if(cond,f1,f2)	If cond=0 (false condition) then f2 else f1.
Φ(x)	Heaviside (step) function. Returns 1 if $x \geq 0$; 0 otherwise.
δ(n1,n2)	Kronecker delta. Returns 1 if $n1 = n2$; 0 otherwise.
ϵ(n1,n2,n3)	Levi-Civita density. (Completely antisymmetric tensor of rank 3.)
mod(x1,x2)	Remainder on dividing x1 by x2. (Modular division.)
until(x1,x2)	Returns x2 until x1<0, then halts iteration.

Sorting[1]

sort (v)	Sort vector **v** in ascending order.
csort (M, n)	Sort rows of matrix **M** according to nth column.
rsort (M, n)	Sort columns of matrix **M** according to nth row.
reverse (M)	Reverse order of rows of matrix **M**.

Equation Solving

root (expr, var)	Value of var where expr is zero. (Root function.)
Given .. Find(var1, var2, ..)	Values that solve constraints in solve block.
Given .. Minerr(var1, var2, ..)	Values that minimize errors for constraints in solve block.

File Access

READ (file)	Single value read from unstructured data file.
WRITE (file)	Single value written to unstructured data file.
APPEND (file)	Single value appended to unstructured data file.
READPRN (file)	Matrix read from structured data file.
WRITEPRN (file)	Matrix written to structured data file.
APPENDPRN (file)	Matrix appended to structured data file.

---

[1]Not available in version 2.0.

SUFFIXES FOR NUMBERS

Suffix	Meaning	Example
i (or j)	Imaginary	4i, 3 + 2j
H (or h)	Hexadecimal	0ff2H, 6ah
O (or o)	Octal	530, 772o
M (or m)	Standard unit of mass	6.2M, 2.097m
L (or l)	Standard unit of length	1L, 100l
T (or t)	Standard unit of time	1T, 60t
Q (or q)	Standard unit of charge	1Q, .00001q

PREDEFINED VARIABLES

Value	Meaning	Default
π	Pi	3.14159..
e	Base of natural logarithm	2.71828..
∞	Infinity (MathCAD's largest number)	10^{307}
%	Percent	0.01
TOL	Tolerance for numerical approximations	10^{-3}
ORIGIN	Origin for arrays (matrices)	0
PRNCOLWIDTH	Column width used for WRITEPRN	8
PRNPRECISION	Number of decimal places used for WRITEPRN	4

FORMAT MENUS

Display Numeric Results

To set local result display format, move cursor onto numeric result and type **f**. To set the global format, type **{Esc}Form** and then **{Enter}**. In version 2.0, the menu appears on the message line. In version 2.5 it appears as a pull-down menu.

Menu Item	Meaning/Options
Radix=d/h/o	Radix for display: d for decimal h for hexadecimal o for octal
Precision Displayed=n	Number of decimal places shown.
Exponential Threshold=n	Results shown in exponential format when $x \geq 10^n$ or $x \leq 10^{-n}$.
Imaginary Symbol=i/j	Use indicated symbol to display imaginary unit.
Zero Tolerance=n	Result shown as zero when $x \leq 10^{-n}$.
Complex Tolerance=n	Result shown as: pure real when $Im(x)/Re(x) \leq 10^{-n}$, pure imaginary when $Re(x)/Im(x) \leq 10^{-n}$.
Global Default* (or type **d** on result)	Use global display format.
Revert† (or **{Esc}**)	Undo changes just made.
Done‡	Apply changes to displayed result.

*In Version 2.0 type **d** on result.

†In Version 2.0 use **{Esc}**.

‡In Version 2.0 use **{Enter}**.

Plots

To set local plot format, move cursor into region and type **f**. To set the global format, type **{Esc}PLOT** and then **{Enter}**. In version 2.0, the menu appears on the message line. In version 2.5 it appears as a pull-down menu.

Menu Item	Meaning/Options
Size=y, x	Height and width of plot region.
Trace Types=letters	One letter per trace, as follows: **l** for lines **d** for dots **s** for step **e** for error bar **b** for bar chart **x** for X's **X** for connected X's **p** for pluses **P** for connected pluses **o** for rectangles **O** for connected rectangles **v** for diamonds **V** for connected diamonds
Log Cycles=y, x	Number of log cycles on each axis, as follows: **0** for linear (non-logarithmic) axis **1** for a logarithmic axis of one cycle **n** for logarithmic axis with n evenly-spaced cycles ($n > 1$)
Subdivisions=y, x	Number of subdivisions on each axis. For linear axis, subdivisions are evenly spaced grid lines. For log axis, subdivisions are logarithmically spaced within each cycle. (Log axis subdivisions must be 1, 2, or 9.)
Global Default* (or type **d** on result)	Use global plot format.
Revert[†] (or {Esc})	Undo changes just made.
Done[‡]	Apply changes to plot.

*In Version 2.0 type **d** on result.

[†]In Version 2.0 use **{Esc}**.

[‡]In Version 2.0 use **{Enter}**.

Surface Plots

To set local surface plot format, move cursor into plot region and type **f**. To set the global format, type **{Esc}SURF** and then **{Enter}**. (Not available in version 2.0.)

Menu Item	Meaning/Options
`Size=y,x`	Height and width of plot region.
`Rotation=n`	Number of degrees to rotate plot counterclockwise (between 0 and 90).
`Tilt=n`	Number of degrees to elevate viewer above plot (between 0 and 90).
`Vertical Scale=n`	Amount that vertical scale is magnified (between 0 and 100).
`Global Default` (or type **d** on result)	Use global surface format.
`Revert (or {Esc})`	Undo changes just made.
`Done`	Apply changes to surface plot.

Sketches

To set local sketch plot format, move cursor into sketch region and type **f**. To set the global format, type **{Esc}SKETCH** and then **{Enter}**. (Not available in version 2.0.)

Menu Item	Meaning/Options
`Size=y,x`	Height and width of sketch region.
`Magnification=y,x`	Degree to which sketch is magnified in each direction. Any positive or negative real number is allowed. A value of `1.0` makes the sketch stretch exactly from edge to edge in box.
`Center=y,x`	Point to show in center of sketch box. Measured from upper left corner in units equal to height and width of sketch. To show sketch centered in box, use `0.5,0.5`.
`Box=y/n`	Use `y` to show border box. Use `n` not to show border box.
`Global Default`	Use global sketch format.
`Revert (or {Esc})`	Undo changes just made.
`Done`	Apply changes to sketch.

ALT KEYS FOR GREEK LETTERS

Keystroke	Symbol	Meaning	
<Alt>A	α	alpha	
<Alt>B	β	beta	
<Alt>D	δ	delta	(also Kronecker delta)
<Alt>E	ϵ	epsilon	(also Levi-Civita density)
<Alt>F	ϕ	phi	
<Alt>G	Γ	gamma	(also Gamma function)
<Alt>H	Φ	phi	(also Heaviside function)
<Alt>L	λ	lambda	
<Alt>N	η	eta	
<Alt>O	Ω	omega	
<Alt>P	π	pi	(also constant = $3.14159\ldots$)
<Alt>Q	θ	theta	
<Alt>R	ρ	rho	
<Alt>S	σ	sigma	
<Alt>T	τ	tau	
<Alt>U	μ	mu	
<Alt>W	ω	omega	

Other symbols

e	e	(Constant= $2.71828\ldots$)	
<Alt>I	∞	Infinity	(MathCAD's largest number, 10^{307})

CTRL KEYS

Keystroke	Meaning
<Ctrl>{Break}	Abort current action.
<Ctrl>A	Abort printing or calculation.
<Ctrl>B	Set text motion commands to *backward*.
<Ctrl>D	Change display colors (EGA/VGA only).
<Ctrl>E	Move left 80 columns.
<Ctrl>F	Set text motion commands to *forward*.
<Ctrl>G	Move right 80 columns.
<Ctrl>L	Move to next/previous line in text.
<Ctrl>N	Justify text ("nudge").
<Ctrl>O	Print worksheet ("output").
<Ctrl>P	Move to next/previous paragraph in text.
<Ctrl>Q	Quit to DOS.
<CTRL>R	Redraw or retrace screen.
<Ctrl>S	Move to next/previous sentence in text.
<Ctrl>T	Create text band.*
<Ctrl>V	Toggle draw box mode around objects on/off.
<Ctrl>W	Move to next/previous word in text.
<Ctrl>X	Set mark in text.
<Ctrl>Y	Mark first or last region of a block of objects.[†]
{Esc}	Command by name.

*Not available in student edition.

[†]Not available in version 2.0.

CURSOR MOTION AND DISPLAY SCROLLING KEYS

Keystroke	Effect
{Tab}	In text, move forward one word. In equation or plot, move to next placeholder. Between object regions, move right to next 10-character tab stop.
<Shift>{Tab}	In text, move backward one word. In equation or plot, move to previous placeholder. Between object regions, move left to next 10-character tab stop.
{PgUp}	Move up five lines at a time.
{PgDn}	Move down five lines at a time.
<Ctrl>{PgUp}	Move up 80% of page.
<Ctrl>{PgDn}	Move down 80% of page.
<Ctrl>{left arrow}	Move left to next tab stop.
<Ctrl>{right arrow}	Move right to next tab stop.
<Ctrl>E	Move left 80 columns.
<Ctrl>G	Move right 80 columns.
{Home}	Move to beginning of current object region. If already at beginning, move to previous object.
{End}	Move to end of current object region. If already at end, move to next object.
<Ctrl>{Home}	Scroll to beginning of document and move cursor to first object.
<Ctrl>{End}	Scroll to end of document and move cursor to last object.
{Enter}	In text, start new line. In equation or plot, move below object. Between regions, move cursor to column 0 on next line.

COMMANDS FROM MENUS
System Commands

Menu Item	Keystroke	Purpose
help	[F1]	Call help screens.
quit	<Ctrl>Q	Quit MathCAD and return to DOS.
dos *command*		Execute DOS command.
memory		Show available memory.
redraw	<Ctrl>R	Redraw screen.
print	<Ctrl>0	Print current worksheet.
selectprinter *n*		Select printer type.
configsave *filename*		Save current configuration.
execute *filename*		Execute command file.

File Commands

Menu Item	Keystroke	Purpose
load *filename*	[F5]	Load worksheet from disk.
save *filename*	[F6]	Save worksheet on disk.
append *filename*		Append disk file to current worksheet.
filename *var filename*		Associate a variable with a file.
clear		Clear document and reload configuration.
reset		Reset MathCAD and use system defaults.

Compute Commands

Menu Item	Keystroke	Purpose
calculate	**[F9]**	Process and calculate visible equations.
process		Process and calculate whole worksheet.
automatic		Enter automatic calculation mode.
manual		Enter manual calculation mode.
format		Set global display result format.
randomize *seed*		Reset random number generator.
dimensions		Change basic dimension names.
equation (on/off)		Disable or re-enable equation calculation.
matrix *rows cols*	**<Alt>M**	Generate or change size of matrix.

Edit and Move Commands

Menu Item	Keystroke	Purpose
copy	**[F2]**	Copy region into clipboard buffer.
cut	**[F3]**	Delete region and store in clipboard buffer.
paste	**[F4]**	Paste contents of clipboard buffer onto worksheet.
mark*	**<Ctrl>Y**	Mark first and last region of block.
separate		Separate overlapping regions.
insertline	**<Ctrl>[F9]**	Insert a blank line.
deleteline	**<Ctrl>[F10]**	Delete a blank line.
goto *line column*		Go to indicated position.
move *lines columns*		Scroll indicated number of positions.
find *text*	**<Ctrl>[F5]**	Find specified text.
replace *text text*	**<Ctrl>[F6]**	Find and replace specified text with new text.

*Not available in version 2.0.

In Region Commands

Menu Item	Keystroke	Purpose
incopy	<Ctrl>[F2]	Copy marked text or part of an equation and store in clipboard buffer.
incut	<Ctrl>[F3]	Delete marked text or part of an equation and store in clipboard buffer.
inpaste	<Ctrl>[F4]	Paste contents of clipboard buffer onto worksheet.

Text Commands

Menu Item	Keystroke	Purpose
width *chars*		Specify width for text region; rewrap.
textmark	<Ctrl>X	Set beginning or end of marked text.
textband[†]	<Ctro>T	Start textband.
center		Center line of text.
backward	<Ctrl>B	Interpret text motion commands as backward.
forward	<Ctrl>F	Interpret text motion commands as forward.
justify	<Ctrl>N	Rewrap text and realign regions with textbands.

Window and Page Commands

Menu Item	Keystroke	Purpose
split	[F7]	Split screen into two windows.
unsplit	<Ctrl>[F7]	Unsplit screen.
switch*	[F8]	Switch cursor to other window.
pagelength *lines*		Set pagelength. Use 0 for no page breaks.
linelength *cols*[†]		Set global line length for text wrap.
breakpages[†]		Shift regions off page breaks.
margin *cols*[†]		Set left margin for printing.
pagebreak[†]		Insert hard page break.

*Appears as "jump" on menu.

[†] Not available in student edition.

Commands Not on Menus

The following commands must be invoked by typing **{Esc} CCCC** and then **{Enter}** where **{CCCC}** stands for the first four letters of the command.

Menu Item	Keystroke	Purpose
PLOTformat		Invoke global plot format menu.
SURFaceformat*		Invoke global surface plot format menu.
SKETchformat*		Invoke global sketch format menu.
SET		Set value of system variable.
SKIPword	<Ctrl>W	Skip to next/previous word in text.
SKIPline	<Ctrl>L	Skip to next/previous line in text.
SKIPsentence	<Ctrl>S	Skip to next/previous sentence in text.
SKIPparagraph	<Ctrl>P	Skip to next/previous paragraph in text.

*Not available in version 2.0.

INVOCATION LINE OPTIONS

To invoke MathCAD at the DOS prompt with special options, type **MCAD** followed by one or more of the following commands:

filename	**Start with a worksheet stored as "filename."**
/A	Force AT&T 6300 display (640 × 400).
/B*nn*	Use background color *nn* (EGA/VGA only).
/C	Force CGA display.
/E	Force EGA display.
/EC	Force EGA display (640 × 200).
/EH	Force EGA display (640 × 350).
/EM	Force EGA display for monochrome monitor.
/F*nn*	Use foreground color *nn* (EGA/VGA only).
/H	Force Hercules Monochrome Graphics display.
/L*nnnn**	Use *nnnn*K bytes of LIM expanded memory.
/M	Start in manual calculation mode.
/R *filename*	Run alternate configuration (filename.mcc) at startup. Default is MCAD.MCC.
/T	Force Toshiba T3100 display (640 × 400).
/V*	Force VGA display (640 × 480 color).
/VM*	Force VGA display (640 × 480 monochrome).

Note: MathCAD automatically senses the display adaptor being used. Forcing displays should be used only in special circumstances or when problems are encountered.

*Not available in student edition.

ERROR
MESSAGES

[Adapted from the MathCAD Version 2.5 Reference Manual with permission from MathSoft, Inc.]

ARRAY SIZE MISMATCH. You tried to perform a vector or matrix operation on arrays whose sizes don't match. Many operations require vectors that are the same size, for example, the dot product and the `linterp` and `corr` functions. Vector addition and subtraction requires vectors or matrices that are the same size. Matrix multiplication requires that the number of columns in the first matrix match the number of rows in the second matrix.

CANNOT BE DEFINED. You put something other than a legally definable expression on the left side of the definition symbol (`:=`). MathCAD accepts any of the following on the left side of a definition:

- A variable name: x.
- A variable name with a subscript: x_i.
- A variable name with a superscript: $x^{<i>}$.
- An explicit vector or matrix generated by typing **{<Alt>M}**. The vector or matrix can hold variable names or subscripted variable names only.
- A function name with arguments: $f(x,y)$.

Any other expression is illegal. If you want to compute a result instead of defining a variable, use an equals sign (`=`) instead of a colon.

CANNOT TAKE SUBSCRIPT. You used a subscript on something other than a vector or matrix.

CANNOT TAKE SUPERSCRIPT. You used a superscript on something other than a matrix.

DEFINITION STACK OVERFLOW. You used too many nested function definitions.

DID NOT FIND SOLUTION. In a solve block, MathCAD was unable to find a solution to the constraints. To see the results of the solve block anyway, use `Minerr` instead of `Find`.

DIMENSION TO NONREAL POWER. You raised an expression with units to a complex or imaginary power. If an expression is defined with units, you can raise it only to a real scalar power; otherwise, MathCAD cannot determine units for the result.

DOMAIN ERROR. You evaluated a function at an illegal argument value. For example, you see this error if you try to compute `ln(0)`.

DUPLICATE. You tried to define the same variable twice in the same definition. You see this error if you create a vector on the left side of a definition and use the same name twice in that vector.

EQUATION TOO LARGE. You entered an equation too complicated for MathCAD to evaluate. Break the equation down into two or more subequations.

ERROR IN CONSTANT. MathCAD has interpreted the indicated expression as an invalid constant. MathCAD tries to interpret anything beginning with a digit as a constant. If you enter a digit immediately followed by a few letters, MathCAD will interpret it as an invalid constant.

ERROR IN LIST. The indicated function definition contains an invalid list of arguments. A valid function definition begins like this:

```
functionname (argument list) := ...
```

The argument list must be a name or a list of names separated by commas. Any other expression is illegal.

You also see this error message if you create an invalid list in another context, for example, in the list of y-axis expressions for a plot.

ERROR IN SOLVE BLOCK. You see this error if you evaluate a user function that is defined in terms of a solve block, and there is an error in the solve block. To fix the error, fix the problem in the solve block. (If you evaluate the solve block directly, instead of defining a function with it, you will see a more specific error message.)

FILE ERROR. MathCAD encountered an error trying to read values from a data file using `READ` or `READPRN`.

FILE NOT FOUND. MathCAD was unable to find the data file for `READ` or `READPRN`.

ILLEGAL ARRAY OPERATION. You applied a function or an operation that requires a scalar to a vector or matrix. For example, you see this message if you try to take the sine or square root of a matrix.

ILLEGAL CONTEXT. You used an operater or a function in a context that MathCAD does not allow. For example, you see this error message if:

- You entered a semicolon somewhere other than in a legal range definition. (The semicolon appears as two dots called an *ellipsis*.) You can use a semicolon only in the definition of a range for a range variable.
- You used a `WRITE` or `APPEND` function anywhere other than on the left side of a definition. These functions cannot appear in expressions or on the right side of a definition.
- You used an existing function name as a variable name or an existing variable name as a function name.
- You used a constraint with $\neq$ in a solve block.

ILLEGAL FACTOR. You entered an illegal expression for the placeholder at the end of a calculation equation. The placeholder at the end of a calculation equation requires real, nonzero, scalar values.

ILLEGAL FUNCTION NAME. You used an expression that MathCAD interprets as a function, but the function name is invalid. You see this error, for example, if you use a number as a function name: `6(x)`. You may see this error if you omit an operator like +, causing MathCAD to interpret the parentheses in your equation as defining a function instead of as a way to group operations.

ILLEGAL ORIGIN. You defined `ORIGIN` with a noninteger value or a value of magnitude greater than 25000. This error marks the first use of a subscript after the illegal definition of `ORIGIN`.

ILLEGAL RANGE. You defined a range variable with a range MathCAD could not interpret. When you define a range, you must use one of the following forms:

```
Rvar := n1 ..n2 (type Rvar:n1,n2)
Rvar := n1,n2 .n3 (type Rvar:n1,n2;n3)
```

You can use at most one comma and one semicolon in the definition of a range for a range variable. If you use the second form, the value of `n2` must lie between the values of `n1` and `n3`, but not equal `n1`.

ILLEGAL TOLERANCE. This error marks an expression that uses TOL—an integral, derivative, or instance of `root`, `Find`, or `Minerr`—for which TOL>1 or TOL<0. To fix the error, define TOL with a value between 0 and 1 above the indicated expression.

INCOMPATIBLE UNITS. You entered an expression that adds, subtracts, or performs another operation that is illegal for two expressions with different dimensions. For example, you see this error if you try to add 1L (one length unit) and 1M (one mass unit).

INDETERMINATE DIMENSION. You raised an expression with units to a power involving a range variable or vector. MathCAD cannot determine the dimensions of the result; they would vary depending on the exponent. If an expression is defined with units, you can raise it only to a fixed real power.

INDEX OUT OF BOUNDS. This message marks a subscript or superscript that refers to a non-existent array value. You see this message if you use a subscript or superscript less than 0 (or less than ORIGIN, if ORIGIN≠0), or if you use a subscript or superscript to refer to an array value beyond those defined earlier in the document.

INDEX TOO LARGE. You tried to use a subscript or superscript that exceeds Math-CAD's limit of 8000.

INTERRUPTED. You interrupted MathCAD by pressing {**<Ctrl>A**} or {**<Ctrl>Break**} while it was calculating. To recalculate the marked equation, put the cursor in the equation and press {**F9**}.

LIST TOO LONG. You entered too many elements in a list separated by commas. This can occur if you try to plot more expressions than MathCAD's capacity.

MISPLACED COMMA. You used a comma in an illegal place. You can use a comma in any of the following ways:

- to separate function arguments
- to separate the first two elements of a range in the definition of a range variable
- to separate y-axis expressions in a plot
- to separate elements in an input table
- to separate subscripts for a matrix variable

Any other use of commas is illegal in MathCAD expressions.

MISSING OPERAND. An operand is missing from an expression. For example, you see this message if you enter a plus sign without entering two expressions to add. MathCAD shows a placeholder (a small rectangle) in place of the missing operand.

MISSING OPERATOR. An operator is missing from an equation or expression.

MUST BE 3-VECTOR. You used a cross product on expressions that are not three-element vectors. The cross product works only on three-element vectors.

MUST BE ARRAY. You performed an operation that requires an array on a scalar. For example, you see this error if you define a superscripted variable as a scalar. Since a superscripted variable represents a column of a matrix, you must define it as a vector.

MUST BE DIMENSIONLESS. The indicated expression uses units but appears in a place where units are not permitted. Units are not permitted in the arguments for certain functions (for example, `cos` and `ln`) or in exponents. For example, the expressions $\cos(1L)$ and 10^{1M} are invalid.

MUST BE INCREASING. You used a vector whose elements are not in increasing order as the argument to a function that requires a strictly increasing argument. The first argument of `lspline`, `pspline`, `cspline`, `interp`, `linterp`, and `hist` must be a vector whose elements are strictly increasing. (Note that MathCAD includes v_0 as a vector element. If you do not explicitly define it, MathCAD sets $v_0 = 0$.)

MUST BE INTEGER. You used a non-integer expression where an integer is required, for example, as an argument to the `identity` function or as a subscript or superscript. (Although you can define range variables with fractional values—for example, $x := 1, 1.1 \ldots 10$—you cannot use such ranges as subscripts.)

MUST BE NONZERO. You evaluated a built-in function at zero, and the function is undefined at zero. For example, `J0` and `ln` are undefined at zero.

MUST BE POSITIVE. This error message marks a plot in which the limits or values for a logarithmic axis are zero or negative. MathCAD can plot only positive values on a logarithmic axis.

MUST BE RANGE. You used something other than a range variable in a place that requires a range variable, for example, as the index for a summation. The index for a summation appears below the summation symbol. The index must be a variable that is defined earlier as a range variable.

MUST BE REAL. You used an imaginary- or complex-valued expression where Math-CAD requires a real-valued expression. For example, MathCAD requires a real-valued expression. For example, MathCAD requires real-valued subscripts and real-valued arguments for some built-in functions, including `J0`, `mod`, and Φ.

MUST BE SCALAR. You used a vector or matrix expression where a scalar is required, for example, as the argument to the `identity` function.

MUST BE SQUARE. This error marks a non-square matrix in an operation that requires a square matrix, such as determinants, inverse, or raising to a power.

MUST BE VECTOR. This error marks a matrix or scalar in an operation that requires a vector, for example, with the $\sum$ operator.

NESTED SOLVE BLOCK. You used two `Givens` in a row with no intervening `Find` or `Minerr`. MathCAD does not allow nested solve blocks, although you can define functions with solve blocks and use those functions in other solve blocks.

NO MATCHING GIVEN. This error marks a `Find` or `Minerr` function with no matching `Given`. Each solve block that ends with `Find` or `Minerr` must begin with a region containing only the name `Given`.

NON-SCALAR VALUE. You used a vector or ranged expression where a scalar is required. For example, you see this message if i is a range variable and you try to enter an equation like **x := i**. You cannot define one range variable in terms of another. To define x in terms of the range variable i, enter an equation like $x_i := i$.

NOT A NAME. You used a number or other combination of symbols where MathCAD requires a name, for example, as the second argument of the `root` function.

NOT CONVERGING. MathCAD was unable to compute an answer for an integral, derivative, `root`, `Find`, or `Minerr` function within the required tolerance. See the descriptions of these operators and functions for more information.

OVERFLOW. You evaluated an expression that exceeds the largest number that Math-CAD can represent (about 10^{308}).

SIGNIFICANCE LOST
SIGNIFICANCE REDUCED. These error messages indicate that you tried to evaluate a function for a value beyond the accurate range for the function. For example, you see this message if you try to evaluate $\sin(10^{100})$. Since the value of $\sin(10^{100})$ depends on the ones digit of 10^{100}, any value that MathCAD could return would have no significant digits. Instead of returning a value of dubious accuracy, MathCAD shows one of these error message.

SINGULARITY. You evaluated a function or performed an operation at an illegal value. For example, you see this error if you divide by zero or if you try to invert a singular (determinant = 0) matrix.

STACK OVERFLOW. You evaluated an expression that overflows MathCAD's internal stack. Simplify the expression or divide it into two subexpressions.

TOO FEW ARGUMENTS. The indicated expression contains a function with fewer than the required number of arguments. For built-in functions, the number of arguments is fixed. For user functions, the number of arguments depends on the definition in your document.

TOO FEW CONSTRAINTS. This error marks a `Find` or `Given` with fewer constraints than variables to be solved. Add dummy constraints or decrease the number of variables to be solved.

TOO FEW ELEMENTS. This error message marks a Fourier transform, cubic spline, or linear interpolation function applied to a vector with too few elements. Splines and linear interpolation require vectors with at least two elements. Fourier transform functions and their inverses require at least four elements.

TOO FEW SUBSCRIPTS. You used one subscript on a matrix. You must use two subscripts separated by a comma to specify a matrix element.

TOO LARGE TO DISPLAY. You tried to display a vector or matrix bigger than Math-CAD can display.

TOO MANY ARGUMENTS. The indicated expression contains a function with more than the required number of arguments. For built-in functions, the number of arguments is fixed. For user functions, the number of arguments depend on the definition in your document.

TOO MANY CONSTRAINTS. You included more than fifty constraints in a solve block.

TOO MANY SUBSCRIPTS. You used two or more subscripts on a vector.

TOO MANY POINTS. You tried to plot more points than MathCAD can handle in one plot.

UNDEFINED. The indicated variable or function is undefined. To define it, enter the variable name, followed by a colon (:) and an expression or number for its definition. This error often means you have typed an equals sign (=) instead of a colon to define a variable. To define a variable, you must use a colon. If you use an equals sign, MathCAD assumes you want to `calculate` the value of the variable.

   You also see this message if you use a variable incorrectly in a global definition. If you use a variable on the right side of a global definition, the variable must be globally defined `above` the definition in which it is used. If you use a locally defined variable or a variable whose global definition is `below` the place where it is used, MathCAD marks the variable as undefined.

   An `undefined` error is often an indication that another equation further up in the document is in error. If a definition is in error, then any other equations further down in the document that depend on that definition will be marked **undefined**.

UNDERFLOW. You evaluated an expression smaller in magnitude than the smallest positive number that MathCAD can represent (about 10^{-308}).

UNMATCHED PARENTHESIS. You entered or calculated an equation that contains a left parenthesis without the matching right parenthesis. Edit the equation by removing the left parenthesis or adding a matching right parenthesis.

WRONG SIZE VECTOR. This error marks a Fourier transform function whose argument has the wrong number of elements. `fft`, `cfft`, and `icfft` require as arguments vectors with 2^n elements, where n is a whole number greater than 1. `ifft` requires an argument vector with 2^n+1 elements, where n is a whole number greater than 0. MathCAD includes v_0 as an element of the argument vector (unless you change `ORIGIN`).

APPENDIX
C

INSTALLATION
PROCEDURES

PART A

If the version of the book you have purchased includes *MathCAD Version 2.5, Student Edition*, read the following; otherwise skip to Part B.

Installation and Limitations

The enclosed diskette(s) contains both the MathCAD programs (Student Edition version 2.5) as well as the worksheets and problems discussed in the text. To install them on your hard disk, do the following:

   I. Turn your computer on and allow it to boot from the hard disk.
   II. After the C> prompt appears, insert the diskette marked "Disk #1" into drive-A of your computer. (If you are using the 3.5″ floppy format version there is only one diskette. The 5.25″ floppy format requires two diskettes.) Type **A:** followed by the {Enter} key to make drive-A the default drive. You should see the A> prompt. Next, type **INSTALL** followed by the {Enter} key.
   III. The software will ask for the drive letter corresponding to the hard drive to which MathCAD will be copied (usually C). Type that letter (e.g., **C**) followed by the {Enter} key.
   IV. The software will ask for the subdirectory on the hard disk to which the MathCAD system software will be copied. The default is \MCAD. If this is acceptable, then type the {Enter} key; otherwise supply an alternate subdirectory and then type the {Enter} key.

V. The installation software will ask the user if the `AUTOEXEC.BAT` file is to be patched. The user should allow the patching. The effect is to add the MathCAD subdirectory (`\MCAD` by default) to the `DOS PATH` command and also to add the command `SET MCADDIR=\MCAD`.

VI. The MathCAD software will be copied to the specified subdirectory (`\MCAD` by default) and the worksheets and problem solutions will be copied to the subdirectory `\MCAD\MCFILES`. If you are using the 5.25″ floppy diskettes, you will be prompted, at the appropriate time, to insert the disk marked "Disk #2." The entire installation process may take a few minutes, so be patient.

After installation, it is recommended that you make a backup copy of the software and the worksheets from your hard disk.

The worksheets are named `WKSn_m.MCAD`, where n refers to the chapter and m to the number. For example, `WKS4_3.MCD` and `WKS5_B.MCD` refer to Worksheets 4.3 and 5.11 respectively. The problems are named `PROBn_m.MCD`, where n refers to the chapter and m to the number. Thus `PROB6_1.MCD` refers to Problem 1 of Chapter 6.

You may find it more convenient to separate the problems from the worksheets. After the installation, you may create a new subdirectory `\MCAD\PROBS`. Copy the problems from `\MCAD\MCFILES` into this subdirectory and then delete them from `\MCAD\MCFILES`.

To invoke MathCAD, first log into the `\MCAD\MCFILES` subdirectory by typing **CD `\MCAD\MCFILES`**. Then type **MCAD** and MathCAD will load. You will be able to easily load the worksheets from the file menu. If you have moved the problems to the subdirectory `\MCAD\PROBS`, and you wish to study the problems, first type **CD `\MCAD\PROBS`** and then type **MCAD**.

If you wish to automatically perform the above procedures, create the following batch file, called `MC.BAT`, in the `\MCAD` subdirectory:

```
CD C:\MCAD\MCFILES
C:\MCAD\MCAD
```

When you type **MC** and then **{Enter}** you will be logged into `C:\MCAD\MCFILES` and MathCAD will load automatically.

The limitations of the Student Edition are:

1. Workspace is limited to 120 lines by 80 columns. You can load documents larger than this but only the first 120 lines by 80 columns will be accessible.

2. All printouts have the text "The Student Edition of MathCAD 2.5. For Educational Use Only." printed on the first line.

3. No textbands are allowed.

4. No pagebreaks can be created.

5. No VGA support. VGA systems will run in EGA mode.

   Important Note: On IBM PS/2s equipped with MCGA monochrome monitors, better display results may be obtained if you start MathCAD by typing MCAD/C, thereby overriding the program's automatic display monitor selection.

6. Matrices are limited to $5 \times n$ or $n \times 5$.

7. Solve blocks are limited to 10 unknowns.

8. No technical support.

9. No support of expanded memory.

10. A reduced number of printer modes is supported.

PART B

If the version of the book you have purchased does *not* include the student edition of MathCAD, read the following:

1. The enclosed diskette contains the worksheets and the problems discussed in the text. The worksheets are in a subdirectory called \WKSHTS; the problems are in a subdirectory called \PROBS. The worksheets are named WKSn_m.MCD, where n refers to the chapter and m to the number. For example, WKS4_3.MCD and WKS5_B.MCD refer to Worksheets 4.3 and 5.11 respectively. The problems are named PROBn_m.MCD, where n refers to the chapter and m to the number. Thus PROB6_1.MCD refers to Problem 1 of Chapter 6.

2. It is suggested that you keep the MathCAD system programs (which you have purchased elsewhere) on your hard disk (drive-C) in a subdirectory called \MCAD. Create two new subdirectories \MCAD\WKSHTS and \MCAD\PROBS using the DOS command CD. Insert the floppy disk into drive-A. Copy the files from the diskette to these subdirectories. At the DOS prompt, type:

   COPY A:\WKSHTS*.* C:\MCAD\WKSHTS .

Then type:

   COPY A:\PROBS*.* C:\MCAD\PROBS .

3. Add the path C:\MCAD to the PATH statement in your AUTOEXEC.BAT file. Also add the following line to the AUTOEXEC.BAT file: SET MCADDIR= C:\MCAD.

4. To invoke MathCAD, first log into the worksheet subdirectory \MCAD\WKSHTS by typing **CD \MCAD\WKSHTS**. Then type **MCAD** and MathCAD will load. You will be able to easily load the worksheets from the file menu. If you have moved the problems to the subdirectory \MCAD\PROBS, and you wish to study the problems, first type **CD \MCAD\PROBS** and then type **MCAD**.

If you wish to automatically perform the above procedure for the worksheets, create the following batch file, called MC.BAT, in the \MCAD subdirectory:

```
CD C:\MCAD\WKSHTS
C:\MCAD\MCAD
```

When you type **MC** and then **{Enter}**, you will be logged into C:\MCAD\WKSHTS and MathCAD will load automatically. You will then be able to load the worksheets easily from the file menu.

It is recommended that you make a backup copy of the worksheets and problems.

Important Note: Except for Worksheet 9.1 and Problems 9.1–9.3, all MathCAD disk files should compute with version 2.0. However, some files were developed with verson 2.5. When one of these files is loaded with version 2.0, it will give an "unrecognized command" error on the message line. Ignore the error and hit the **{Enter}** key a few times. The file should appear in the workspace.

תושלב"ע.

INDEX

aborting printing, calculation, or current action, 9, 268

absolute value operation, 39

AC circuit, 128, 180

acos (inverse cosine) function, 38, 258

acosh (inverse hyperbolic cosine) function, 39, 258

addition with line break ($\langle$Ctrl$\rangle${Enter} key), 17, 257

ALT (Alternate) keys for Greek letters, 14

AM, 219

Ampersand (&) key (for integration), 16, 49, 257

analytic function, 192

ANDing, 227

angle function, 38, 258

apostrophe key for parentheses, 15, 256

append cursor, 3, 18

APPEND subcommand, 247, 250, 262, 270

APPENDPRN function, 247, 262

arc length, 81

area under a curve, 49

arg (argument) function, 130, 131, 181, 259

arrays
  and matrices, 171
  and vectors, 23, 30, 57

asin (inverse sine) function, 38, 258

asinh (inverse hyperbolic sine) function, 38, 258

assignment using colon (:), 3, 4, 7

association for file names, 242

atan (inverse tangent) function, 38, 258

atanh (inverse hyperbolic tangent) function, 39, 258

augment function, 175, 261

augmenting matrices, 172, 175

automatic recalculate mode, 9, 254, 271

average value, 204

Backquote key for prime symbol, 15, 65

Backslash (\\) key for square root operation, 7, 256

Backspace key for deleting, 3, 4, 8, 9

BACKWARD text motion subcommand ($\langle$Ctrl$\rangle$B key), 249, 268, 272

beats, 112

Bessel functions, 164, 244, 259

blank lines (inserting and deleting), 18, 249, 271

Boolean variable, 40, 225

break ($\langle$Ctrl$\rangle${Break} key), 9, 268

BREAKPAGES subcommand, 250, 272

Butterworth filter, 221

CALCULATE subcommand ({F9} key), 10, 255, 271

calorimetry, 117

carrier frequency, 219, 220

Cauchy's integral formula, 198

Cauchy-Riemann equations, 192, 193

ceil (ceiling) function, 39, 207, 261
cfft (complex fast Fourier transform) function, 217, 260
characteristic (secular) equation, 183
circumference, 81
CLEAR subcommand, 5, 7, 251, 270
cnorm function, 166, 259
collisions, 108
colon as assignment, 3, 4, 7
cols function (for matrices), 261
column extraction (using ⟨Alt⟩^ key), 177, 186, 235, 257
command summary, 255
complex numbers, 21, 22, 130, 148, 180, 187
complex tolerance, 13, 14, 264
    see also FORMAT menus
complex variables, 191–201, 237
COMPUTE command, *see* automatic recalculate and manual recalculate
concavity of a curve, 64
condition (relational), 40, 226, 261
CONFIG SAVE subcommand, 5, 251, 270
configuring MathCAD, 250, 270, 274
conformal mapping, 195, 197
conic sections, 77
conjugate (complex) operation, 130, 256
constraints in solve blocks, 22, 214, 262
contour integrals, 195, 197, 198
control (⟨Ctrl⟩) key, 255–257, 268–273
convolutions, 223
COPY subcommand ({F2} key), 17, 233, 248–250, 255, 271
corr (correlation) function, 31, 210, 260
cos (cosine) function, 38, 258
cosh (hyperbolic cosine) function, 39, 258
Coulomb's law, 123
coupled vibrations, 187
cross product (of vectors), 58, 59, 177, 179, 257
csort (matrix column sort) function, 234, 262
cspline (cubic spline) function, 211, 260
cumulative normal distribution function, 166, 259
cursor append and insert, 3, 18
cursor motion and scrolling, 248, 269, 272
curve-fitting, 31, 210
CUT subcommand ({F3} key), 6, 17, 18, 233, 248, 249, 255, 271
cycloid (arc length of), 81

damped vibrations, 149, 155
DC circuits, 127, 180
decimal, 13, 229, 263, 264
    see also radix
degenerate matrix, 184
Del key for deleting, 3, 9

delete (matrix) rows, cols, 174
DELETELINE subcommand (⟨Ctrl⟩{F10} key), 18, 255, 271
demodulation, 219
derivative (?) template, 15, 44, 89, 257
detection, 219
determinant of a matrix, 173, 176, 179
deviation (standard), 204, 207, 259
dice statistics, 206, 226
differential equations, 140–164
DIMENSION subcommand, 34, 99
dimensions (units), 32, 34, 98, 122, 251, 271
diode, 128
Dirac delta function, 155
discontinuity (integration over), 158
discriminant, 149
display-result, 12
document (worksheet), 1, 5
done, 13, 14, 264
    see also FORMAT menus
DOS subcommand, 253, 270
dot product (of vectors), 58, 59, 60
double integral, 53, 86
double-quote (complex conjugate), 130
double-quote (text), 17, 249, 256
draw box mode, 18, 268
driving term, 150
driving voltage, 128, 130

e (base of natural logarithm), 14, 43, 134, 142, 267
EDIT/MOVE command, 249, 271
Eigenfrequencies, 188
Eigenvalue, 182, 185, 186
Eigenvector, 184, 185, 186
ellipse, 77
ellipse (arc length of), 81, 82, 85, 86, 110, 111
ellipse (area of), 86
ellipsoid (volume of), 84
elliptic integral, 82
enhancements to MathCAD version 2.5, 229, 233
EQUATION (enable/disable) subcommand, 271
erasing with CUT ({F3} key), 6, 17, 18, 233, 248, 249, 255, 271
erf function, 166, 259
ERR function, 214
error message listing, 275
Esc key with abbreviated commands, 254, 273
Euler identity, 149
Euler's gamma function, 259
Euler-Heun method, 140, 142
EXECUTE subcommand, 251, 252, 270
exit from DOS shell, 253
exp (exponential) function, 15, 39, 43, 134, 142, 214, 258

expanded LIM memory, 274, 285
exponential threshold, 13, 14, 264
   see also FORMAT menus
exponentiation, 39
exporting data, 241, 244, 245
extensions to file names, 2, 5, 240, 244, 246, 251, 252
extrapolation, 32, 210
extrema, 48, 64, 65

factorial, 53, 56, 256
false (Boolean variable), 40, 226, 227, 229, 261
fft (fast Fourier transform) function, 215, 223, 260
file
   appending, 250, 270
   association, 242, 270
   loading, 5, 6, 247, 255, 270
   saving, 5, 248, 255, 270
FILE command, 5, 7, 242, 244, 246, 247, 248, 250, 251, 254
filename (association) subcommand, 242, 244, 246, 254
filtering a waveform, 218, 222
Find function, 22, 80, 83, 84, 122, 123, 128, 129, 153, 214, 262
FIND (search) text subcommand (⟨Ctrl⟩{F5} key), 249, 271
first-order differential equations, 140
floor function, 39, 261
forced vibrations, 152
FORMAT numeric results menu command, 12, 13, 14, 256, 264, 271
FORMAT plot menu command, 10, 14, 273
FORMAT sketch menu command, 240, 266, 273
FORMAT surface plot menu command, 239, 266, 273
FORWARD (text motion, ⟨Ctrl⟩F key) command, 249, 268, 272
Fourier series, 157, 158, 159, 161
Fourier transform, 215, 220, 260
   see also fft, cfft, ifft, and *icfft*
frequency of occurrence, 206, 207
function keys summary, 255
functions summary, 258–262

gamma (Euler's) function, 166, 167, 259, 267
gate circuit, 227
Gaussian curve, 166
Gauss' law, 125
GENERATE matrix subcommand (⟨Alt⟩M key), 28, 256
geometric series, 73
Given (*/Find, /Minerr*) function, 22, 24, 83, 84, 122, 123, 128, 153, 214, 262

global assignment (using tilde key), 22, 25, 32
global default, 13, 14, 264
   see also FORMAT menus
GLOBAL FORMAT (numeric results) command, 14, 256, 264, 271
GLOBAL FORMAT (plot) command, 14, 273
GLOBAL FORMAT (sketch) command, 241, 273
GLOBAL FORMAT (surface plot) command, 239, 273
GOTO subcommand, 248, 271
gradient operation, 89, 123
graphing a function, 7
greater-than condition, 40, 226, 257
Greek letter listing, 14, 267
Green's theorem, 91
grids for plotting, 20, 235, 265

half-lives of nuclei, 133
halting recursion with the until function, 75, 261
harmonic motion, 110, 188, 217
harmonics, 112, 157, 216
heat-transfer, 121
Heaviside (unit step) function, 42, 61, 155, 169, 227, 261, 267
HELP subcommand ({F1} key), 18, 253, 254, 255, 270
Hermitian (self-adjoint) matrix, 187
hexadecimal, 13, 229, 263, 264
   see also radix
hist (histogram) function, 206, 207, 259
histogram, 204, 229, 234, 259
homogeneous differential equation, 148
hook-to-left (append) cursor, 3, 18
hook-to-right (insert) cursor, 18
HPGL file, 240
hyperbolic functions, 39, 258

icfft (inverse complex fast Fourier transform) function, 217, 260
identity (unit) matrix, 176, 261
if function, 39, 40, 41, 261
ifft (inverse fast Fourier transform) function, 217, 222, 225, 226, 231, 260
imaginary numbers, 13, 21, 130, 149, 181, 191, 217, 259, 263, 264
imaginary unit symbol, 13, 14, 264
   see also GLOBAL FORMAT result menu
impedance, 128, 131, 180, 181
importing data, 241–244, 246
improper integrals, 51
impulse (Dirac delta) function, 155, 157
incline (mass on), 106, 107
INCOPY subcommand (⟨Ctrl⟩{F2} key), 18, 249, 255, 272

increment for range definition, 8, 26, 47, 238

INCUT subcommand ($\langle$Ctrl$\rangle${F3} key), 18, 250, 255, 272

index, *see* subscripts

inelastic collisions, 108, 109

infinite series, 73, 157, 162, 215, 216

infinity (∞, $\langle$Alt$\rangle$I key), 14, 181, 263, 267

inflection points, 64, 66

INPASTE subcommand ($\langle$Ctrl$\rangle${F4} key), 18, 250, 255, 272

insert matrix rows, cols, ($\langle$Ctrl$\rangle$M key), 174

INSERT PAGEBREAK subcommand, 250, 272

INSERTLINE subcommand ($\langle$Ctrl$\rangle${F9} key), 18, 255, 271

installation of software, 2, 283, 284

integral (&) template, 16, 49, 50, 53, 71, 86, 257

integrals (definite), 16, 49, 50

interference of waves, 114, 116

interp function (for splines), 211, 212, 260

interpolation (linear), 210, 212, 234, 260

interrupt processing, *see* aborting

inverse fast Fourier transforms, *see ifft* and *icfft*

inverse function (computing), 82

inverse (matrix), 173, 176, 179

inverse (MCAD) functions, 38, 258

invoking MathCAD, 2, 181, 251, 252, 274

in-region subcommands, 17, 249, 250

interation, 141, 144

JUMP (switch) subcommand ({F8} key), 248, 272

JUSTIFY text subcommand ($\langle$Ctrl$\rangle$N key), 249, 268, 272

Kirchoff's laws, 127, 180

Kronecker delta function (δ_{ij}), 173, 176, 179, 261, 267

Laplace transform, 154

last function (for vectors), 76, 261

least squares fit, 210, 214

length function (for vectors), 261

length (see Dimension)

less-than condition, 40, 226, 257

Levi-Civita density (ε_{ijk}), 173, 177, 179, 261, 267

LIM (expanded) memory, 274, 285

limitations of the student edition of MathCAD, 284, 285

linear interpolation, 210, 212, 234, 260

linear regression, 31, 209, 210, 260

LINELENGTH subcommand, 250, 272

lines (inserting and deleting), 18, 255, 271

linterp function, 210, 211, 260

lissajous figure, 110, 112

literal subscripts, 4, 24, 48, 145

ln (*log* base e) function, 35, 258

LOAD command ({F5} key), 6, 247, 255, 270

local-plot-format, 10, 256, 265

local-result-format, 12, 13, 256, 264

local-sketch-format, 240, 241, 256, 266

local-surface-format, 239, 256, 266

log (base 10) function, 39, 258

logic, Boolean, 226

loop iteration, 144

lspline function, 211, 260

Maclaurin series, 87

manual recalculation mode, 9, 254, 271, 274

mapping (conformal), 195

MARGIN subcommand, 250, 272

MARK block subcommand ($\langle$Ctrl$\rangle$Y key), 233, 271

MARK text subcommand ($\langle$Ctrl$\rangle$X key), 249, 268, 272

matrices, 25, 27, 28, 171–191, 235, 241, 244–247, 256, 257, 261, 262, 271

max function (for vectors), 207, 261

maxima–minima problems, 48, 68

mean function, 133, 205, 207, 259

mean-lives of nuclei, 133

memory (available), 253, 270

MENU command ({F10} key), 5, 255

menus (commands from), 270–272

message line, 3

messages error list, 275

min function (for vectors), 37, 261

Minerr function, 213, 262

mod (modular division) function, 39, 41, 44, 226, 261

modulation, 219

modulus of complex number, 130, 181, 194, 217, 221, 237, 261

MOVE subcommand, 248, 271

NANDing, 227

Neumann functions, 164, 165, 259

Newton's law, 34, 106, 187

nonhomogeneous differential equation, 147, 150

non-degenerate matrix, 184

notational subscripts, *see* literal subscripts

NOTing, 227

not-equal-to condition, 226

nuclear decay, 133

NUDGE subcommand ($\langle$Ctrl$\rangle$N key), 268

octal, 13, 229, 263, 264

  see also radix

Ohm's law, 127

ON-LINE help menu subcommand ({F1} key), 18, 253, 254

ORIGIN set command, 25, 171, 205, 209, 218, 223, 226, 234–239, 244, 246, 250–254, 263

ORing, 227, 228

pagebreak, *see* INSERT PAGEBREAK subcommand

PAGELENGTH subcommand, 250, 251, 272

parentheses (see apostrophe key)

partial derivative, 90, 193

PASTE ({F4} key), 6, 17, 18, 233, 248, 249, 255, 271

Pearson's *r*-factor, 31, 210, 260

percent suffix, 14, 263

periodic functions, 44, 157, 159, 215

PgDn/PgUp key commands, 248, 269

phi for Heaviside function (⟨Alt⟩H key), 42

pi for π (⟨Alt⟩P key), 14, 263, 267

piecewise functions, 42, 157, 215

pipe (¦ key) for absolute value, 257

placeholder, 3

plot (generating with @ symbol), 8, 9, 256, 257

PLOTFORMAT menu {Esc} command, 10, 14, 251, 254, 273

   see also FORMAT and GLOBAL menus

polar coordinates, 79, 80

polynomial sketching, 63, 65

precision displayed, 13, 14, 264

   see also FORMAT result menus

prime symbol (using Backquote key), 15, 45

PRINT subcommand (⟨Ctrl⟩O key), *see* printing a document

printing a document, 5, 250, 251, 254, 268, 270

PRNCOLWIDTH set command, 244–246, 251, 263

PRNPRECISION set command, 244–246, 251, 263

PROCESS subcommand, 209, 244, 254, 271

projectile motion of, 102, 104

pspline function, 211, 212, 260

pull-down menus, 5, 10, 13, 14, 239, 240, 264, 265

pulse waveform, 42, 155

question mark (?) key (for differentiation), 15, 45, 257

QuickBASIC programs, 144, 242, 247

QUIT subcommand (⟨Ctrl⟩Q key), 268, 270

quote key (see double-quote)

radians, 9, 32, 33, 38, 102, 130, 201, 242, 244, 258

radix, 13, 14, 229, 264

   see also FORMAT result menus

random number generator, *see rnd* function

RANDOMIZE subcommand, 41, 271

range variable definition, 8, 26–30, 55–57, 75, 76, 257

ranges, 38, 53, 136, 231

READ function, 247, 262

READPRN function, 244, 252, 262

recalculating document, *see* CALCULATE subcommand

recursion, 73, 74, 75, 76, 142, 144

REDRAW subcommand (⟨Ctrl⟩R key), 5, 18, 268

regression (linear), 31, 209, 210, 260

related rates, 66

relational conditions, 23, 40, 108, 153, 214, 226, 257

relational equals (⟨Alt⟩= key), 23, 108, 214, 226, 257

REPLACE subcommand (⟨Ctrl⟩{F6} key), 249, 255, 271

RESET subcommand, 251, 270

residues, 198

retrace screen, *see* REDRAW subcommand

revert 13, 14, 264

   see also Format menus

rnd (random number generator) function, 39, 41, 207, 220, 261

root function, 20, 49, 65, 71, 185, 262

rows function (for matrices), 261

rsort (matrix row sort) function, 234, 262

Runge-Kutta-Nyström method, 143, 146

sampling waveforms, 217, 220, 223

SAVE subcommand ({F6} key), 5, 248, 255, 270

scalar product, *see* dot product

scroll, 33, 269

scrolling, 269

search (text) subcommand (⟨Ctrl⟩{F5} key, 249, 271

second-order differential equations, 143, 147

secular equation, *see* characteristic equation

seeding random number generator, *see* RANDOMIZE subcommand

seeding recursion, 74, 76, 146

SELECT PRINTER subcommand, 5, 251, 270

self-adjoint, *see* Hermitian

SEPARATE subcommand, 18, 271

sequences, 72

series sums and products, 53, 56, 72, 257

SET {Esc} command, 22, 25, 245, 273

   see also PRNCOLWIDTH, PRNPRECISION ORIGIN, and TOL)

shelling to DOS, *see* DOS subcommand

singular matrix, 173

sin (sine) function, 38, 258

sinh (hyperbolic sine) function, 39, 258
size, *see* Format plot menus
sketch (creating with ⟨Alt⟩% key), 240, 256, 257
SKETCHFORMAT menu {Esc} command, 241, 251, 254, 273
SKIP LINE {Esc} command, 273
SKIP PARAGRAPH {Esc} command, 273
SKIP SENTENCE {Esc} command, 273
SKIP WORD {Esc} command, 273
slope function, 31, 210, 260
solve blocks, *see* Given and Find
sort function (for vectors), 234, 235, 262
spectrum (fast Fourier), 217, 218
splines, 209
square foot (using backslash key), 6, 7, 256
standard deviation, 204, 207, 259
statistical functions, 259
stdev (standard deviation) function, 205, 207, 259
Stefan's law, 121
Stefan-Boltzmann constant, 121, 122
subdivs, *see* FORMAT plot menus
subscripts (generating with left-bracket ([ ) key), 4, 24, 25, 74, 256
suffixes (for numbers), 263
summation (creating with dollar sign ($) key), 54, 257
superscript operation (using ⟨Alt⟩^ key), 177, 186, 235, 257
surface plotting, 235, 256, 257
SURFACEFORMAT menu {Esc} command, 239, 251, 254, 273

table (assigning data in), 26
table (displaying results in), 11
tan (tangent) function, 38, 258
tanh (hyperbolic tangent) function, 39, 258
Taylor series, 87
TEXT command, 248, 249
text editing, 248
text region (creating with double-quote (" key), 17, 256

TEXTBAND subcommand (⟨Ctrl⟩T key), 248, 268, 272
TEXTMARK subcommand (⟨Ctrl⟩X key), 249, 268, 272
TOL (tolerance in numerical computations), 22, 35, 69, 250–252, 263
tr (trace of matrix) function, 10, 14, 77, 81, 173, 176, 178, 261, 265
transpose of matrix (using ⟨Alt⟩! key), 175, 178, 257
trigonometric functions, 38, 258
true (Boolean variable), 40, 226, 227, 229

units (dimensions), 32, 34, 98, 251, 271
until function, 75, 261

var (variance) function, 204, 205, 207, 259
variable names, 4
vector product, *see* cross product
vectorization, 29, 30, 60, 257
vectors, 23–31, 57–60, 205–212, 218, 234, 244, 246, 259–262
volumes computing, 84

WINDOW command, 248, 250, 272
WINDOW SPLIT subcommand ({F7} key), 247, 248, 255, 272
WINDOW UNSPLIT subcommand (⟨Ctrl⟩{F7} key), 248, 255, 272
wrap equation (⟨Ctrl⟩{Enter} key), 16, 17, 257
wrap text, 248, 249, 272
WRITE function, 247, 262
WRITEPRN function, 244–247, 252, 262, 263

XORing, 227

Young's interference pattern, 116

zero tolerance, 14, 264
    see also GLOBAL FORMAT result menu